BACKGROUND FOR MAN

Readings in Physical Anthropology

BACKGROUND FOR MAN

Readings in Physical Anthropology

Selected by

PHYLLIS DOLHINOW
VINCENT SARICH

University of California, Berkeley

LITTLE, BROWN AND COMPANY   *Boston*

CONTENTS

v

III
HUMAN VARIATION
AND RACE

IV
BEHAVIORAL STUDIES: PRIMATES

V
HUMAN BEHAVIOR: TOOLS AND HUNTING

Introductions to selections 1–13 are by Vincent Sarich; those for selections 14–20 are by Phyllis Dolhinow.

BACKGROUND FOR MAN

Readings in
Physical
Anthropology

I
THE
NATURE
OF THE
EVOLUTIONARY
PROCESS

PHYLLIS DOLHINOW
VINCENT SARICH

1 Physical Anthropology: Theory and Methods

In the science of human evolution (often termed either physical anthropology or human biology), man is considered an integral part of the biological universe. Thus, all students in the biological sciences share an intellectual framework — that body of evolutionary theory deriving from Darwin's epochal work and augmented by many others since his time (including a number of scholars represented in this volume). This framework provides guidelines to analyze the data offered as answers to some very basic questions: What events occurred during the evolution of the human lineage? When did these events happen? What were the causes of the events; and why did they take place? Physical anthropologists seek answers to each of these questions; what, when, and why or how? Eventually they will reach deeper insights into the complex relationships between man's biological heritage and the social aspects of his existence.

It will become evident in this volume that many of the questions asked a hundred years ago are still subjects of intense debate today. For example, what were the characteristics of man's immediate precursors; what is the extent of variability among modern men; and what were the important stages of development in the evolution of human behavior patterns? Not only a persistent residue of unanswered questions, but also many new questions, are constantly being posed as the result of advances in our knowledge. This aspect of the field — that so many basic questions remain unanswered — is at once a weakness and a strength. It is a weakness in that anthropologists have often been delinquent in discarding notions and in refusing to rephrase inquiries in the light of newer, often controversial evidence for alternative hypotheses about human evolution. It is a strength because the field remains in ferment and continues to seek understanding. Because basic problems remain unsolved, ongoing research has immediate relevance to all students, both beginning and advanced.

The history of physical anthropology follows a winding path characterized too often by slow acceptance of new information and discoveries. Tradition

2

has been, at times, a very conservative force acting against the consideration of new ideas. What were regarded as the "facts" of time and change demarcated the confines within which the field was allowed to grow, and the pains of the fit were sometimes excruciating. When it was thought that only a few thousand years were available for all of human evolution, and when only a few fossils had been uncovered, views of the events that took place bore little resemblance to our present understanding of man's history. When the events of evolution were thought to be the results of divine action or the products of catastrophic events, the picture of the past was vastly different from what it is today. For a long time students of human evolution had strong biases about the appearance and behavior of the ancestors of modern man, and, in general, about the magnitude of the differences between modern man and his ancestors. Only a short time ago it was unthinkable that the present dignity of man was possible if his forebears even remotely resembled apes. Obviously, many strong feelings and deeply rooted biases concerning man's history had to be set aside before it was possible to investigate the reality of his past.

The subject of human evolution is fascinating to the only species able to cast an eye upon itself, but being both subject and student often leads to major conflicts where one has obviously no appeal to higher authority. The thought of Burns: "O wad some Power the giftie gie us/ To see ousels as ithers see us!" (so appropriate to a consideration of the individual) has little value when applied to the human species, for no one provides an objective external view. Science is a specifically human creation and those who operate within its boundaries must continually recall that the creation contains within it much of the creator. This is of special concern to the anthropologist, who is attempting to develop an understanding of man himself. The nature of this understanding may be of paramount importance in determining the way that supposedly objective data are gathered and analyzed. To minimize the biases that stem from this situation and to increase the probability that the answers obtained bear close relationship to evolutionary reality, the investigator must be careful to apply only those methods that have been demonstrated to have value in the study of evolutionary biology.

Many of the data crucial to the study of human evolution are derived from very specialized disciplines and no scientist can hope to master them all. Yet, to answer the questions that the anthropologist must ask requires the ability to generalize from data provided by specialists — in an age when many other fields are dealing with far more limited problems. The physical anthropologist is, then, in many respects a generalist in an age of specialization. He is not necessarily an expert practitioner in any, much less all, of these specialized disciplines, e.g., paleontology, anatomy, geology, psychology, biochemistry, genetics, systematics, ecology, to name but a few of the more relevant fields. To be a specialist in all these fields is simply not possible today for one human being. It remains for the physical anthropologist to formulate questions in a way that takes advantage of the existing knowledge in many areas. He must find the key to all scientific discovery: asking the right questions of the right sciences. Once the proper questions are asked within the framework of evolutionary theory, then he can begin to see how the data from the more specialized fields are useful in providing understanding. As G. G. Simpson has commented:[1]

> When science was arising, Francis Bacon insisted that all its branches should be incorporated into one body of fundamental knowledge. Bacon placed this in an Aristotelian framework really inappropriate for modern science; he wrote at a time when one mind could grasp the essentials, at least, of all the sciences; and he was not himself a practicing scientist. Of course nowadays, as regards detailed knowledge and adequate research ability, there is no such thing as a general scientist, a general biologist, or even a general entomologist. In the practice and teaching of science, specialization and the accompanying fragmentation of the sciences have become absolutely necessary. Yet this practical necessity has not eliminated the force and value of the conception that the universe and all its individual phenomena form one grand unit and that there is such a thing as science, not just a great number of special and separate sciences.
>
> Bacon further maintained that the unity of nature would be demonstrated and the sciences would be incorporated into one general body by a fundamental doctrine, a *Prima Philosophia*, uniting what is common to all the sciences. Despite the great change in philosophical outlook, that has become a traditional approach to the unification of the sciences. In our own days, Einstein and others have sought unification of scientific concepts in the form of principles of increasing generality. The goal is a connected body of theory that might ultimately be *completely* general in the sense of applying to *all* natural phenomena.
>
> The goal is certainly a worthy one, and the search for it has been fruitful. Nevertheless, the tendency to think of it as *the* goal of science or *the* basis for unification of the sciences has been unfortunate. It is essentially a search for a least common denominator in science. It necessarily and purposely omits much the greatest part of science, hence can only falsify the nature of science and can hardly be the best basis for unifying the sciences. I suggest that both the characterization of science as a whole and the unification of the various sciences can be most meaningfully sought in quite the opposite direction, not through prin-

[1] *This View of Life* (Harcourt, Brace and World, 1965), pp. 95–96.

ciples that apply to all phenomena but through phenomena to which all principles apply. Even in this necessarily summary discussion, I have, I believe, sufficiently indicated what those latter phenomena are: they are the phenomena of life.

And so specialists from very different fields work on myriad aspects of primate biology and behavior, and it is a combination of the results from all these efforts, structured within an evolutionary framework, that will contribute to total understanding.

In contradistinction to the traditional separation and isolation of different academic departments that for so long have kept sources of information apart, constant emphasis in this era is on the integral relationships between all aspects of the study of an organism and its environment. Washburn has stated that "there is a feedback relationship between behavior and its biological base, so that behavior is both a cause of changing gene frequencies and a consequence of changing biology." If this view is accepted, the extent to which the results of investigations of all aspects of the human organism can be combined and related will determine the completeness of our understanding of man. Physical anthropology has developed an essentially new point of view, one that embraces time, structure, and the processes of change.

Determination of the length of time that elapsed during the course of primate evolution was the first major problem to be resolved before any accurate conception of the magnitude and nature of the changes that took place could be formulated. Stratigraphy alone gave few clues to the antiquity of fossil forms, and it was not until modern chemical and radioactive methods of dating were developed that we had a time scale that revealed the millions of years during which the stages of primate development took place. Anthropologists were required to acknowledge that some of the nonhuman primates, and in particular the African apes, were indeed very closely related to man. Still more recently, biochemical studies of the living primates have provided measures, or clocks, by which it becomes possible to estimate the lengths of time that major primate lines have existed. These studies are summarized in this volume.

As soon as experimentation was added to simple description it was possible to begin unraveling the dynamics of evolutionary changes. No amount of measuring and describing could reveal the causes or functions of change, or the relationship of parts to the working of the whole animal. We can see morphological-osteological changes in the fossil record, but only by looking at the structure and behavior of the living is it possible to appreciate the behavioral implications of these changes. The living nonhuman primates are not our ancestors, but they can legitimately provide comparative data to be used in reconstructing more of our history, provided that great caution is exercised in the choice of appropriate comparative forms.

Some lines of investigation produce precise and measurable data as answers to certain questions — such as how long a change has taken to occur. Other questions must be met with data stated in terms of probabilities. The latter approach is required in the attempt to reconstruct behavioral changes that took place in man's history — the patterns of behavior that most likely characterized the different stages of primate evolution. Some estimates are, of course, more valid than others, and with a degree of care each possibility may be given proper weighting for its accuracy.

The major transitions in primate evolution from prosimians to monkeys, to apes, and to man are outlined in this volume. Each grade of development is characterized by a number of morphological features documented in the fossil record and by sets of behavior patterns that must be inferred from the fossils. A picture of each grade is drawn by reconstructing as much as possible of the organism's way of life, beginning with the morphology and the range of movements likely for specific osteological structures, then its probable diet, and finally all available information on its habitat, including climate and associated flora and fauna. Bit by bit every shred of evidence from many sources is collated to reconstruct as much as possible of each major step in primate evolution. The fewer and more fragmented the fossils, the less that can be said. Teeth alone obviously reveal far less than a complete skull, for example, and for many problems a good part of an entire skeleton might be required.

Reconstruction of primate evolution is a slow process at best. If some of its principal investigators had exerted more caution and more patience and had not tended to assign a plethora of new names to each tiny hominid fragment, there would be far less confusion as to degrees of relatedness among fossil forms. But scientists are also human and the temptation always exists to assign special significance to almost everything associated with man, and to see as major those differences, often small, that exist among hominid forms that may be closely related. The standards that apply to taxonomic designations of other mammals have only recently been applied to hominids, and anthropologists are still far from achieving the same degree of objectivity when they regard man and his ancestors.

To conclude in brief, since man is the creator of science, the understanding of man — why he is the way he is and how he got to be that way — depends upon how man gathers and applies the results of his scientific knowledge. Man has a past and that past has shaped him. He needs to understand his past in order to understand himself. It is not too much to assert, we suggest, that this understanding could determine what sort of future man is to have.

GEORGE GAYLORD SIMPSON

*Practically everything George Gaylord Simpson has written
ranks with the best in evolutionary presentation, and we would
particularly recommend to the more general reader a collection
of his essays entitled* This View of Life. *In the selection included
here he ties together the strands of evolutionary events into a
unified process by demonstrating how mutations, the random
production of variation, can be integrated by the various
evolutionary forces into ongoing and meaningful patterns of
change.*

*The essence of the evolutionary process is beautifully
presented by Simpson, but the essential simplicity of that
process has tended to produce a rather shallow criticism:
Evolutionary theory can explain so much in such a facile manner
that it does not really say anything. Modern evolutionary theory
provides a set of rules for playing the game of reconstructing and
understanding the past — the player must appropriately apply
the rules to the particular series of events under consideration.
In his article "In Praise of Waste" Hardin quotes an anonymous
Victorian critic of Darwin: "In the theory with which we have to
deal, Absolute Ignorance is the artificer; so that we may
enunciate as the fundamental principle of the whole system,
that, in order to make a perfect and beautiful machine, it is not
requisite to know how to make it." Hardin notes that though
this critic intended to damn Darwinism beyond hope, he ended
by epitomizing its essence admirably.*

*Evolution is so simple a concept that too many invest it with
some aura of complexity and mysticism hoping thereby to make
it worthy of their intellectual contemplation. Simpson is superb
at applying the simplicity to the solution of what otherwise
appear as very difficult problems. In this, and in his power of
exposition, lie the greatness of the man.*

2   Forces of Evolution and Their Integration

The course of evolution is marked by changes in structures
and functions as these appear in individual organisms. The evolutionary

From George Gaylord Simpson, *The Meaning of Evolution*. Reprinted by permission of
the author and the publisher, Yale University Press. Copyright © 1967 by Yale University.

forces act, of necessity, on individuals, but their effects are not achieved within single individuals. These effects work out within associated groups of individuals, populations, and over the course of successive generations. A key to the process is, then, that evolutionary changes must arise in or must, at least, be transmitted by whatever it is that passes from one generation to the next, by the heredity of the group. The association of individuals into populations that is important in this process must therefore be reproductive association. The group that actually evolves is a group linked together by exchange and transmission of hereditary factors, a population of individuals that interbreed over the course of generations. It is true that the survival of individuals in a community and their success in producing new generations may be strongly affected by nonbreeding members of the community (such as the unsexed workers in insect societies and the older or otherwise nonbreeding members of human society). In the special circumstances of communal life the nonbreeders too may thus have an important role in evolution. It is nevertheless fundamental that evolutionary change consists basically of change in heredity and that this is developed in interbreeding populations.

Heredity is carried by genes, self-reproducing chemical units within the cells of organisms, which are aggregated into groups, chromosomes, that also usually reproduce or reduplicate themselves faithfully whenever one cell divides into two. These chromosomes, with their included genes, are passed on from one generation to the next, usually within specialized germ cells from which individuals of the new generation develop. Their development is controlled or determined by the genes and chromosomes received from parents and under this control it follows a pattern which produces characteristic body forms and physiological systems similar to those of the parents.

Heredity is, on the whole, a conservative factor tending to keep succeeding generations within a common pattern. The acorn produces an oak similar to the tree that produced the acorn, except in unessential details, and the egg produces a chicken essentially like the hen that laid it. We know, nevertheless, that offspring are never *precisely* like their parents, and since evolution is a process of change these differences are of special concern to us here. Such differences may arise in three ways, and in these ways only.

In the first place, the development of the individual is affected not only by the inherited growth determinants but also by the conditions under which growth occurs. Like most of the processes important in evolution, individual development turns out on closer examination to be neither purely autogenous nor purely ectogenous but a combination of the two. No two oak trees, even if grown from twin acorns, have exactly the same size, shape, placing of limbs, number of leaves, etc. Greater or less differences in the environment (for instance in soil or local weather) affect them as they grow, no matter how near each other they may be. Such effects occur to markedly different degrees in different sorts of organisms. When seeds or eggs are simply cast adrift to develop as best they may, their development is strongly affected by the environment. Plants as a whole have much more of such environmentally induced variation than do animals. At the other extreme, probably the most important feature of the mammals is that in them this sort of variation is reduced to a minimum. Development within the nearly uniform environment of the womb followed by maternal care and milk feeding ensures reproduction about as true to type as may be, although of course even here absolute uniformity of the conditions surrounding growth is not obtainable. Crosser changes are still caused by disease and accident, and different activities of the organisms themselves cause change in them, as, for instance, exercise may increase the size of a muscle or lack of use decrease it.

Differences between parents and offspring arising in this way are not hereditary. It was long supposed that they were and a whole theory of evolution, to be mentioned later for its historical interest, was based on this belief; but this has now been disproved beyond reasonable doubt. It is, nevertheless, going too far to suppose that such changes have nothing to do with evolution. They are not themselves changes in heredity such as, in a fundamental sense, constitute evolution, but they may have a decided influence on these hereditary changes. Adaptation to local environment during growth may have definite survival value to the individual and affect its passing on of heredity to future generations. Any individual change not itself hereditary may nevertheless strongly influence the individual's ability or opportunity to reproduce, and in this indirect way will affect the course of evolution of the group as a whole. Individual flexibility or adaptability is also itself an essential characteristic that is heritable and that evolves.

A second and, from an evolutionary point of view, far more important source of differences between parents and offspring is in the mechanism of sexual reproduction, which is not quite, but nearly, universal among both plants and animals. (Even the protozoans, which usually reproduce by simple fission of the whole body, normally undergo from time to time a form of sexual reproduction.) The offspring receive chromosomes, and hence genes that are bundled into chromosomes, from two different sources, usually an equal number from each in corresponding pairs. It is extremely unusual for two individuals to have identical sets of genes, so that the chromosomes received from the two parents in sexual reproduction are practically always different in some respects. The combination of the two sets in the offspring thus differs from that in either parent. There is also involved in this process occasional transfer of genes between the two chromosomes in a pair. When the offspring, in turn, come to reproduce, each passes on to its progeny not simply the set of chromosomes it received from one parent or the other, but a random selection from both sets.

Thus in continued sexual reproduction through the generations the genes and chromosomes are constantly being reshuffled. Even in organisms with relatively simple gene sets and few chromosomes, the number of possible combinations of different genes and dissimilar chromosomes is astronomically large, far larger than the number of individual organisms in the line of successive interbreeding populations. It is rare for any two individuals to have exactly the same sets of these heredity determinants; practically speaking this can happen only when they are identical twins, developed from a single fertilized egg — and such twins, although exactly like each other in heredity, will almost never be exactly like either of their parents. Heredity is essentially conservative in its broad outlines, but this mechanism of shuffling in sexual reproduction makes it almost endlessly varied in detail.

Such changes between parents and offspring are hereditary, subject to continuation of the same sort of shuffling that produces them, and are therefore materials available for basic evolutionary change. Combinations produced in the shuffling process are not necessarily soon lost again by reshuffling. Recombination of genes within single chromosomes is an occasional, not an invariable, process and it is not wholly random. Particular combinations of chromosome pairs, even though produced at random, become more frequent in the population if each sort of chromosome involved becomes more frequent. Identity of all the thousands of genes and of the several or dozens of pairs of chromosomes is exceedingly rare between any two individuals, but similar groupings and identity of certain limited combinations of a few key genes may readily be developed within a large proportion or all of a population.

The role of these changes in evolution is important, but it has limits. New combinations of genes and chromosomes produce new variant sorts of organisms, but no basically new types of organisms can arise and evolutionary change cannot be long sustained, geologically speaking, as long as the genes and chromosome sets remain of the same kinds. Major and long-continued evolutionary changes therefore depend on a third source of difference between parents and offspring: mutations, which are the production of new sorts of genes and chromosome sets. Chromosome mutations may change the number of chromosomes (a change fairly common in plants but much less so in animals) or their form and character, for instance by reduplication of segments, or reversal in their position within the chromosome, or their transfer from one chromosome to another. Such differences may or may not have more far-reaching effects than reshuffling of existing genes and chromosome sets, but they too are limited by the fact that the same sorts of genes, the ultimate determinants as far as we know, continue to appear in them. The most basic changes involved in evolution are gene mutations, the rise of new sorts of genes.

Precisely what happens when a gene mutates is not yet known. For that matter, it is not yet known precisely what a gene is, except that it must be a unit in the chemical make-up of a chromosome and that a mutation must be a change in the structure or composition of that unit. Among the facts of particular evolutionary importance that are known about genes are these: they are inherited as discrete, unblending units but they act in development as interacting and cooperative sets; they do not correspond in a one-to-one relationship with structures of the developed organism but affect or control the growth pattern from which those structures arise; through this growth control single genes may have effects on various different structures and characters (this is called pleiotropism); one gene or several may modify the action of another; and a single character may depend for its development on the presence and interaction of a number of different genes.

Some of the things known about gene mutation and important for study of evolution are these:

Some genes are very stable, some mutate with considerable frequency; it is probable that all can and do mutate in time. Frequency of mutation may be changed by various influences such as the presence of certain other genes or application of heat, radiation, or chemicals; but with some qualifications the nature of the mutation is not determined by such influences. The effect of a single mutation on structural or physiological characters may be almost imperceptible or may result in obvious and radical changes in the whole body. "Large" mutations, those with the greatest effects on the organism, are commonly, but not necessarily, lethal, preventing development of the fertilized egg or bringing early death to the developing individual. Most important of all, from our present point of view, the effects of gene mutations have no evident relationship to the adaptive status, needs, or general way of life of the organism involved. They are in this respect entirely random. This is true, too, of induced mutations; for instance, the effects of those caused by application of heat have no particular relationship to adaptation to temperature of environment. In an organism already well adapted, almost all mutations will be disadvantageous in the previously fixed way of life, simply because in such conditions any random change is likely to be for the worse. The change may, however, or may not, be advantageous in some other way of life which may, or again may not, be accessible to the organism.[1]

One of the frontiers of modern genetical and evolutionary research is

---

[1] The serious enquirer should supplement this minimal presentation of such facts of genetics as are absolutely necessary for understanding of the meaning of evolution by reading some modern treatment of genetics as a whole, such as E. W. Sinnott, and L. C. Dunn, *Principles of Genetics* (3d ed. New York and London: McGraw-Hill, 1939). Th. Dobzhansky's *Genetics and the Origin of Species* (2d ed. New York: Columbia University Press, 1941), which takes for granted knowledge of the elements of genetics, is extremely important. It has had a fundamental influence on current comprehension of evolution and my own understanding and discussion of the subject, throughout this book and otherwise, have drawn heavily on it. Basic principles of heredity and their bearing on the human situation are also summarized in a more popular way in L. C. Dunn and Th. Dobzhansky, *Heredity, Race and Society* (New York: Penguin Books, 1946).

study of the way in which mutations affect different stages in development of the organism and the evolutionary roles of such effects. The different possibilities have been explored in considerable detail and a technical name has been given to each. Some of these names have a certain awesome fascination ("lipopalingenesis," for example) but they need not delay us here. Changes made evident only in later stages of development generally have rather slight effects on final outcome. If they consist essentially of additions at the end of the developmental process, they leave most of that process, as inherited from the ancestry, intact. This sort of change, which is common but far from universal and seldom entirely clear-cut in the evolutionary process, is responsible for the usual very rough approximation of successive ancestral stages in the development of the individual in accordance with the overgeneralized and much abused aphorism of the nineteenth-century evolutionists that "ontogeny repeats phylogeny."

On the other hand, the effects of a mutation may start to operate early in the development of the individual. There is some ground for suspicion, although the point is disputed and cannot be said to be established, that this is the usual course, that mutations ordinarily affect the whole process of development. Their effects may, of course, be more evident in one stage or another. If those effects are slight but cumulative, they may not be noticeable until late stages and may be supposed to be confined to those stages. In any event, if effects are really confined to late stages, their results cannot be very profound, but if they begin to appear early in development the final results may show radical changes from the parental condition, or may again be only slight.[2] A marked alteration of early course of development with consequent still more marked changes in final structure seems to be the usual mechanism for "large" mutations. This in turn provides a possible mechanism for sudden origin of new structural types in evolution. The possibility is evident, but its general significance in evolution is strongly disputed, and especially the question whether this is the way in which basic new types usually arise. This dispute will be mentioned again.

The random nature of changes in heredity must be particularly emphasized. The shuffling of existing stocks of genes in sexual reproduction is, in the main, random. The appearance of chromosome and gene mutations is also largely, although not completely, random and the nature of their effects seems to be altogether random with respect to the needs or adaptation of the organisms and with respect to the direction in which evolution has, in fact, been progressing in the given group. This led some of the earlier students of heredity to think that evolution is really a wholly random

---

[2] The problems and significance of individual development have been discussed from quite different points of view in two previous Terry Lecture volumes: *Order and Life* by J. Needham (New Haven: Yale University Press, 1936); and *Ourselves Unborn*, by G. W. Corner (New Haven: Yale University Press, 1944).

process. "Early" here means only a generation or so ago, for almost all of our real knowledge of how heredity works has been gained in the last fifty years.

In examination of the phenomena of evolution, we have seen that there are indeed elements in these that appear to be erratic and to arise at random. The source of these random effects has now been identified: it is, narrowly, mutation or, more broadly, the largely random operation of the whole mechanism of heredity. We also saw, however, that many of the phenomena of evolution are clearly oriented to some degree. The history of life has not been strictly random or strictly oriented, but an odd mixture of the two, with one predominant here and the other there, but both generally present and almost inextricably combined in the evolution of any particular group. The orienting element was found rather surely to be adaptation, and not such proposed alternatives as innate life tendency or progression toward a destined goal according to plan. Since it has been found that the materials for change are largely random, the question naturally arises as to how evolutionary change can be so extensively nonrandom, how adaptation can orient it.

The mechanism of adaptation is natural selection. The idea of natural selection is very simple, even though its operation is highly complex and may be extremely subtle. Natural selection has this basis: in every population some individuals have more offspring than others. This obvious fact automatically accounts for the possibility of evolutionary change. It has been seen that individuals in any group differ in genetic make-up, hence pass on different heredity to their offspring, and also that mutations occur in a scattered way as such a group reproduces. It may happen, and is indeed the usual thing over small numbers of generations, that the new generation, in spite of its differences between individuals, has about the same average genetic constitution as the parent generation and about the same incidence of mutations, so that no clearly evident change occurs from one generation to the next. It is, however, extremely unlikely that the new generation will have exactly the same genetic make-up as the parental generation. Some individuals do have more offspring than others and their particular genetic characters, which differ to some degree from those of other individuals, will be more frequent in the new generation. The difference may be imperceptibly slight or it may be quite marked, even in production of a single generation.

Even a very slight change will produce evident, eventually large effects if it is cumulative from one generation to the next. This results if there is some constant factor such that, on an average, the individuals that do have more offspring in each generation are those tending toward the same hereditary type; in other words, if they are somehow selected for characteristics that have a hereditary basis. In nature the individuals that tend to have more offspring are, as a rule and no matter how slight the difference, either those best integrated with their environment (including the association with their own species) and most successful in it or those best able to begin to exploit an opportunity not available or less so to their neighbors. Thus natural selection usually operates in favor either of increased adaptation to a given way of life, organism-environment integration, or of such change as will bring about adaptation to another, accessible way of life. Natural selection thus orients evolutionary change in the direction of one or another of these two sorts of adaptation. We have seen, in fact, that these are the directions of orientation in evolution, to the extent that such orientation is effective.

Natural selection as it was understood in Darwinian days emphasized "the struggle for existence" and "the survival of the fittest." These concepts had ethical, ideological, and political repercussions which were and continue to be, in some cases, unfortunate, to say the least. Even modern students of evolution have not always fully corrected the misconceptions arising from these slogans. It should now be clear that the process does not depend on "existence" or "survival," certainly not as this applies to individuals and not even in any intensive or explanatory way as it applies to populations or species. It depends on differential reproduction, which is a different matter altogether. It does not favor "the fittest," flatly and just so, unless you care to circle around and define "fittest" as those that do have most offspring. It does favor those that have more offspring. This usually means those best adapted to the conditions in which they find themselves or those best able to meet opportunity or necessity for adaptation to other existing conditions, which may or may not mean that they are "fittest," according to understanding of that word. Moreover the correlation between those having more offspring, and therefore really favored by natural selection, and those best adapted or best adapting to change is neither perfect nor invariable; it is only approximate and usual.

It is, however, the word "struggle" that has led to most serious misunderstanding of the process of natural selection, along with a host of related phrases and ideas, "nature red in fang and claw," "class struggle" as a natural and desirable element in societal evolution, and all the rest. "Struggle" inevitably carries the connotation of direct and conscious combat. Such combat does occur in nature, to be sure, and it may have some connection with differential reproduction. A puma and a deer may struggle, one to kill and the other to avoid being killed. If the puma wins, it eats and presumably may thereby be helped to produce offspring, while the deer dies and will never reproduce again. Two stags may struggle in rivalry for does and the successful combatant may then reproduce while the loser does not. Even such actual struggles may have only slight effects on reproduction, although they will, on an average, tend to exercise some selective influence. The deer most likely to be killed by the puma is too old to reproduce; if the puma does not get the deer, it will eat something else;

the losing stag finds other females, or a third enjoys the does while the combat rages between these two.

To generalize from such incidents that natural selection is over-all and even in a figurative sense the outcome of struggle is quite unjustified under the modern understanding of the process. Struggle is sometimes involved, but it usually is not, and when it is, it may even work against rather than toward natural selection. Advantage in differential reproduction is usually a peaceful process in which the concept of struggle is really irrelevant. It more often involves such things as better integration into the ecological situation, maintenance of a balance of nature, more efficient utilization of available food, better care of the young, elimination of intragroup discords (struggles) that might hamper reproduction, exploitation of environmental possibilities that are not the objects of competition[3] or are less effectively exploited by others.

It is to be emphasized that the group of its own kind among which an animal lives is also a part of its environment, but a special part. There is an intraspecific selection, based on integration and association within the group, as well as extraspecific selection, based on adaptive relationship to the environment as a whole. (The same sort of distinction was made in discussing specialization and competition in relationship to extinction.) Intragroup selection may involve actual struggle, as in the case of the stags fighting for a doe. It may then be deleterious as regards extragroup adaptation and involve selection opposed to extragroup selection. If such is the case, the result, as Haldane has emphasized, may be deleterious for the species as a whole, although even here we may remark that intra- and extragroup struggle commonly produce selection in the same direction. It is to be added that in intragroup selection, also, struggle is not necessarily or even usually of the essence. Precisely the opposite, selection in favor of harmonious or co-operative group association, is certainly common.

It was a crude concept of natural selection to think of it simply as something imposed on the species from the outside. It is not, as in the metaphor often used with reference to Darwinian selection, a sieve through which organisms are sifted, some variations passing (surviving) and some being held back (dying). It is rather a process intricately woven into the whole life of the group, equally present in the life and death of the individuals, in the associative relationships of the population, and in their extraspecific adaptations.

A criticism often leveled against Darwinian natural selection, but no

[3] The word "competition," used in discussion here and previously, may also carry anthropomorphic undertones and then be subject to some of these same objections. It may, however, and in this connection it must, be understood without necessary implication of active competitive behavior. Competition in evolution often or usually is entirely passive; it could conceivably occur without the competing forms ever coming into sight or contact.

longer valid against the modern conception of this process, was that it seemed to be a purely negative factor in evolution and one that could not account for positive aspects in the orientation of evolution. Some role for selection was admitted, as it must be, but it was maintained that this role was merely the elimination of some individuals or types of organisms: the "unfit." Such negative action seemed to have no particular bearing on the origin of new types or on the maintenance of positive adaptive change in evolutionary trends. This negative aspect obviously exists, but it is now evident that selection also has a positive and creative role and that it is indeed the decisive, the orienting, process in continuing adaptation. Part of the difficulty lay again in thinking in terms of struggle and survival, the death of one animal and the triumph of its enemy or rival. The concept of evolution as change in proportions, combinations, and nature of genetic factors in populations is of more recent development and this entails consequences not yet, it would seem, fully understood by the remaining critics of natural selection as the guiding force in evolution.

Selection is not primarily a process of elimination. It is a process of differential reproduction and this involves complex and delicate interplay with those genetic factors in populations that are the substantial basis of evolutionary continuity and change. In terms of single, arising mutations, those that are unfavorable will be eliminated by selection, as far as its force is effective. (The theory does not demand and the facts do not indicate that selection is always effective, or that at its most effective it can eliminate all unfavorable mutations immediately.) Those that are favorable will, however, tend under the influence of selection to spread through the population increasingly in successive generations. This, in itself, is a positive evolutionary change which is due to natural selection.

Further, the characteristics of an organism as an integrated whole depend not on the action of one gene or another but on the whole interacting set of genes. Some combinations produce poorly integrated organisms, others well-integrated ones. There are, moreover, myriads of different possible combinations even within one population that are all capable of producing workable integration but that produce each a different variant in type. As has been mentioned, the possible number of such combinations vastly exceeds the whole number of individual organisms that can ever exist within a given population or species. Only a fraction of the possible combinations is actually realized in a concrete, existing organism. The chances of such realization for any particular combinations depend on the frequencies in the parental population of the genes involved in the combination. These frequencies, in turn, are to considerable extent if not absolutely determined by the action of natural selection. Selection thus plays an essential part in determining what combinations of genes will be incorporated in individual organisms and so in the actual origin of new variant sorts of organisms. In this role, selection may surely be said to be a creative factor in evolution. Still further, once such favorable or adaptive combinations have arisen, selection tends to hold them together, to keep them from being shuffled apart again in the random processes of heredity in reproduction, and tends to promote their spread through the population.[4]

The way in which selection and the other factors and forces of evolution interact within a population has been worked out in a brilliant series of studies by R. A. Fisher, J. B. S. Haldane, Sewall Wright, and others.[5] It is these studies, more than anything else, that have made possible the synthesis of generations of observations and experiments in a wide variety of fields into a coherent and comprehensive modern theory of evolution. For the reader who may have browsed widely in the literature of evolution and who may have become bewildered by continuing divergences of opinion, here is a touchstone: I think it fair to say that no discussion of evolutionary theory need now be taken seriously if it does not reflect knowledge of these studies and does not take them strongly into account.

The evolutionary materials involved in this complex process are the genetical systems existing in the population and the mutations arising in these. The interacting forces producing evolutionary change from these materials are their shuffling in the process of reproduction, the incidence of mutations (their nature and rate), and natural selection.

The genetical systems existing in a population determine (in further interaction with the environment in each individual case) the nature of the organisms comprising that population. The variety of these systems — and they always are more or less varied — determines the variability of the population. This has extreme importance for evolution, because it is directly on or through this variability that natural selection operates. Limited variability offers correspondingly limited chance of rapid change or of local adaptation to particular conditions, but on the other hand in a population that is well adapted it holds a larger proportion of the population at an optimum, the best adaptive type under existing conditions. Wide variability offers the possibility of rapid (but not indefinitely continued) evolutionary change, quick adjustment to environmental changes, and local adaptation to special conditions within the wider range of the whole population. But it

[4] This creative aspect of selection has been discussed somewhat more fully in G. G. Simpson, "The Problem of Plan and Purpose in Nature," *Sci. Monthly*, 64 (1947), pp. 481–495.

[5] R. A. Fisher, *The Genetical Theory of Natural Selection* (Oxford: Clarendon Press, 1930); J. B. S. Haldane, *The Causes of Evolution* (New York and London: Harper, 1932); S. Wright, "Statistical Genetics and Evolution," *Bull. Amer. Math. Soc.*, 48 (1942), pp. 223–246. These authors and others have written numerous other studies on aspects of this subject. The cited paper by Wright is only one in a long sequence of short contributions made over a period of about twenty years which unfortunately have not been gathered into a comprehensive publication by their author.

means that some proportion, perhaps a considerable proportion, of the population will deviate markedly from the optimum condition, will not be as well adapted as they might be. As in so many evolutionary phenomena there is here a complex interplay, a balancing of opposed advantages and of other factors.

Another important fact to be mentioned only in passing in this necessarily brief review of a very complicated subject is the existence in populations of hidden variability, which can be evoked under the influence of selection or in other ways. This involves the usual presence in populations of genes (especially the recessives of the geneticists) whose action is prevented or overlain in the presence of other genes (especially the dominant alleles of the geneticists) which may be more common in the population. If the general proportion of genes with hidden effects rises in the population, they will more often occur in pairs in the same individual (which is then recessive homozygous in genetical terms) rather than in combination with their concealing equivalent genes (in heterozygous combination), and their effect will then appear.

In a population indefinitely large, breeding wholly at random, not affected by selection, the proportions of the various existing sorts of genes and chromosomes will tend toward definite fixed ratios. When this equilibrium is reached, change in genetic ratios and consequently evolutionary change will cease. The population will still vary, but the variability will be constant in nature and extent. This condition does not occur and evolutionary change does ensue because populations are of limited size, because they do not breed entirely at random, because new sorts of genes and chromosomes arise by mutation, and because selection does act on the population.

The outcome of the shuffling process and the effectiveness, absolute and relative, of mutation and selection are largely dependent on the size and breeding structure of the population. Almost any variation in genetic system and almost any mutation will be affected to some extent by selection, even though the effect may be exceedingly slight. It is rare for such random variations and mutations to have no selective advantage or disadvantage whatsoever. Whatever the influence of selection may be, there is always some chance that these random changes will become established in a certain proportion of the population or even that they will spread to the whole population in succeeding generations. This is one reason why evolution is not completely adaptive and does show random influences. Other reasons are that selection can act only on variations that do occur, which arise at random and are not necessarily or usually the best possible from the point of view of adaptation, and that a given mutation, for instance, commonly has multiple effects some of which are adaptive and others nonadaptive or inadaptive.

Selection almost always has some effect on the fixation or elimination of favorable or unfavorable random changes. The chances of fixation in a population of given size and structure are proportional to intensity of selection for or against, although the chances are very rarely quite 100 per cent or 0. For a given intensity of selection, these chances tend to vary with size of the breeding population. The exact relationships are, again, rather complicated, but the general tendency is for selection to be more effective the larger the population. In large interbreeding populations the chances of spread of a variation purely at random become very slight: favorable selection, even if very slight in degree, will usually ensure such spread and unfavorable selection will usually prevent it. Evolution in large populations is dominated by selection, tends to be closely proportional to the intensity of selection, and tends to have only few and extremely slow changes that are not purely and directly adaptive. It is just such groups that do show, in their evolutionary records, clear and long-continued trends adaptive in control. It is also such groups, with large and widespread populations, that tend to leave more abundant and more continuous fossil records, which doubtless helps to account for the impression on some paleontologists that evolution usually or always follows well-defined trends.

On the other hand, in small breeding populations the effectiveness of selection may be greatly reduced. The chances of merely random change are correspondingly increased. In very small populations, of only a few dozens or perhaps at most hundreds of individuals, evolutionary change may be mainly at random and the influence of selection may be almost negligible unless the intensity of selection is unusually great. Such random evolution is almost always inadaptive and its usual outcome is extinction.

Continuous and evenly distributed interbreeding within a whole population (say the whole of a given species) is not the rule in nature or in human society and, indeed, is perhaps never fully exemplified. In the usual situation, there are local groups that habitually interbreed, with greater or less inbreeding of their various family strains. (In man, these groups are defined not only by geographic proxmity but also by social and occupational status, intellectual level, and other societal factors such as religion.) Between such groups there is a certain but limited amount of crossbreeding, with consequent flow of genetic factors between groups through the generations. The ideal situation for maintenance of continuously good adaptation, including rapid evolution when adaptive change is possible or necessary, seems to involve a relatively large total population divided into a large number of moderate sized local breeding groups, with some continual gene interchange (crossbreeding) between adjacent groups.

With this understanding of the evolutionary process as it really works in populations of organisms and on the factors that determine their heredity, adaptation ceases to be a miracle, or even a serious problem. It is adaptation that gives an appearance of purposefulness in evolution and in its results in the present world of life. Its explanation was the main stumbling block in acceptance of evolution as a fact, and later in attempts to explain the course of evolution by one theory or another. Failures of earlier materialistic attempts to explain this apparent purposefulness were responsible, in large part, for the conclusions of some students that this betokened purpose, in fact, and of certain among these that the purpose betokened a Purposer. It would be brash, indeed, to claim complete understanding of this extraordinarily intricate process, but it does seem that the problem is now essentially solved and that the mechanism of adaptation is known. It turns out to be basically materialistic, with no sign of purpose as a working variable in life history, and with any possible Purposer pushed back to the incomprehensible position of First Cause.

A constant stumbling block in the way of attempts to understand evolution has been that its processes must explain not only adaptation but also absence of adaptation, the existence and persistence of random as well as of oriented features in evolution. This was, and remains, an unanswered argument against theories demanding the reality of purpose or the existence of a goal in evolution. It equally renders untenable all the other theories that attempted to explain evolution by the dominant or exclusive action of one single principle or another, such as the neo-Darwinian insistence on natural selection as essentially the whole story. Modern understanding of evolution is not as simple as were these various theories, but their simplicity was fictitious. They were bound to be wrong in seeking a simple explanation for something that is, in its nature and its phenomena, so far from simple.

The presence, often simultaneously, of both adaptive and nonadaptive, both apparently purposeful and apparently purposeless, both oriented and random features in evolution has now been sufficiently explained. Nonadaptive and random changes have another possible role in evolution which is important and which has so far been suggested only in passing. They have a bearing on changes in broad types of organization, the appearance of new phyla, classes, or other major groups in the course of the history of life. The process by which such radical events occur in evolution is the subject of one of the most serious remaining disputes among qualified professional students of evolution. The question is whether such major events take place instantaneously, by some process essentially unlike those involved in lesser or more gradual evolutionary change, or whether all of evolution, including these major changes, is explained by the same principles and processes throughout, their results being greater or less according to the time involved, the relative intensity of selection, and other material variables in any given situation.[6]

---

[6] The former opinion is adopted by Schindewolf in his work previously cited, and is also strongly supported by K. Beurlen, *Die stammesgeschichtlichen Grundlagen der*

Possibility for such dispute exists because transitions between major grades of organization are seldom well recorded by fossils. There is in this respect a tendency toward systematic deficiency in the record of the history of life. It is thus possible to claim that such transitions are not recorded because they did not exist, that the changes were not by transition but by sudden leaps in evolution. There is much diversity of opinion as to just how such leaps are supposed to happen. Beurlen, for instance, ascribes them vaguely and vitalistically to an inner urge or will on the part of the organisms concerned. Goldschmidt ascribes them to a sudden over-all remodeling of the genetic system, a "systemic mutation" different in kind from the well-known gene and chromosome mutations of more orthodox genetics. Schindewolf thinks that they are mutations, apparently of the usual sort, but large mutations that markedly change the course of individual development from its early stages and thus produce radically new adult forms.

It is impossible in a brief space, and it is unnecessary for present purposes, to discuss the pros and cons of this argument in detail. Enough has, indeed, already been said to throw some of the more extreme views out of court without further hearing. "A will toward individualization and independence" is a resplendent phrase but one essentially meaningless in the face of actual evolutionary processes as these are now known. "Systemic mutations," which have never been observed and the supposed nature of which has not been concretely described, need not be taken seriously if, as is the case, the phenomena that they were postulated to explain can be explained in terms of known processes and forces.[7] If only ordinary, but "large," mutations are supposed to be involved, then we are back within the framework of the modern materialistic theory, although of course we would still like to know, and will still be constrained to discuss, the relative parts played in evolution by large and small mutations.

Transitional types are not invariably lacking in the record. A multitude of them are known between species, many between genera, a few between classes, but none, it is true, between phyla. Most of the phyla appear toward the beginning of the Paleozoic . . . and the absence of record of prior ancestral types is as hard or as easy to explain whether we suppose that they arose

---

Abstammungslehre (Jena: Gustav Fischer, 1937); and R. Goldschmidt, *The Material Basis of Evolution* (New Haven: Yale University Press, 1940). The subject is particularly well reviewed and the arguments of Schindewolf, Beurlen, Goldschmidt, and others of their school strongly and I think conclusively refuted in Rensch, *op. cit.*

[7] In some of his latest work Goldschmidt has implicitly retreated from his position by suggesting that his theory differs from that of almost all his genetical colleagues as regards only the size of the mutations involved, not their nature. If this emendation be accepted, the difference of opinion, as with Schindewolf's views in contrast with those of most other paleontologists, no longer has any fundamental importance for evolutionary theory, although most of the many and strong objections to his views still stand.

instantaneously or gradually. The record is obviously a sampling only and full of gaps. We would suppose that if all changes were by slow transition we still would find only a small proportion of the transitional types and might find none between the phyla, few in number and with their special conditions of early preservation. On the other hand, if major changes were always instantaneous, obviously we should find no transitional types — and we do find many of them. If we did not happen to have found such types between fishes and amphibians, amphibians and reptiles, reptiles and birds on one hand and mammals on the other, or even between eohippus and the horse, these particular changes would surely be considered instantaneous by students who incline to that view. As H. E. Wood has remarked, the argument from absence of transitional types boils down to the striking fact that such types are always lacking unless they have been found.

As far as analysis has been carried on living forms, distinct populations, with their separate characteristics, do not customarily differ in presence or absence of single mutations but in having different, integrated genetic systems, which may involve differences in dozens, hundreds, or thousands of individual genes. On this point Goldschmidt's analysis seems sound and extremely suggestive, although his conclusion that therefore the difference arises by "systemic mutation" is a non sequitur. A mutation produces discrete differences and to this extent its appearance is an instantaneous and discontinuous evolutionary event, whether its effects be small or large. But it is populations, not individuals, that evolve. For a given mutation, regardless of its "size," to become involved in the origin of a new and especially of a highly distinctive group of animals it must spread through a population and while doing so and thereafter it must become integrated in a new sort of genetic system.[8] It is very nearly impossible to imagine these processes occurring except by transition over a long sequence of generations, and certainly no conclusive, or even really suggestive, opposite example is provided by the paleontological record.

It is evident that these processes, which are normal in evolution, could possibly occur with large mutations as well as small. They are, however, far more likely to occur with small mutations than with large. The chance that a mutation will be favored by selection and the chance that it will or can be integrated into a genetic system as a whole are inversely related to the effect of the mutation on the organism. If this effect is really radical, comparable, say, to the difference between one family and another (*a fortiori*, to that between higher categories) in the recent fauna, the chances that the

[8] This special aspect of evolution is expertly treated in C. D. Darlington, *The Evolution of Genetic Systems* (Cambridge, England: Cambridge University Press, 1939). See also C. H. Waddington, *An Introduction to Modern Genetics* (New York: Macmillan, 1939); and his "Evolution of Developmental Systems," *Nature*, 147 (1941), pp. 108–110.

mutation will really take, so to speak, and lead to an evolutionary progression are so small as to be almost negligible. On the other hand, the cumulative effect of mutations so small as to have almost imperceptible effects, each spread in the population and each successively integrated into the genetic system under the influence of selection, is more than adequate to account for transitions from one structural grade to another in the time that the record shows was expended, or was available, in such cases.

It is thus likely, to say the least, that major as well as minor changes in evolution have occurred gradually and that the same forces are at work in each case. Nevertheless there is a difference and many of the major changes cannot be considered as simply caused by longer continuation of the more usual sorts of minor changes. For one thing, there is excellent evidence that evolution involving major changes often occurs with unusual rapidity, although, as we have seen, there is no good evidence that it ever occurs instantaneously. The rate of evolution of the insectivore forelimb into the bat wing, to give just one striking example, must have been many times more rapid than any evolution of the bat wing after it had arisen. The whole record attests that the origin of a distinctly new adaptive type normally occurs at a much higher rate than subsequent progressive adaptation and diversification within that type. The rapidity of such shifts from one adaptive level or equilibrium to another has suggested the name "quantum evolution," under which I have elsewhere discussed this phenomenon at greater length.[9]

Another peculiarity of such evolutionary events is that they always represent distinct changes in the direction of evolution. Such changes may occur even though the trend is continuously adaptive and its control is by natural selection throughout. Change from browsing to grazing in horses is a clear and fully documented example. The same is probably true of changes more radical in character and usually less well documented. The now fairly well known fish-amphibian transition, for instance, has no probably nonadaptive features as regards the essential changes involved. Yet we sense in many such changes that here the random element in evolution has been involved. The change-over from reptile to mammal, for instance, involved a long and adaptive trend in the reptiles, but at the last, in the switch from one type of ear to the other, for instance, there seems to be a sort of non sequitur or random experimentalism. The broadly opportunistic pattern of nature also suggests something of the same thing.

In such cases and in other instances of rather rapid change, great or small, in adaptive type, it is possible, at least, that random preadaptation has

---

[9] In *Tempo and Mode in Evolution* (New York: Columbia University Press, 1944). The term "quantum" in this connection has been subjected to some criticism and indeed it is not very satisfactory, but no one has yet suggested a better.

occurred. The possibility of this process has long been recognized and many geneticists formerly assigned to it a wide, even an all-embracing importance in evolution, which was almost certainly much overemphasized. By "pre-adaptation" is meant the random origin, by mutation, of characteristics nonadaptive or inadaptive for the ancestral way of life, but adaptive for some other way of life which happens to be available.[10] As a rule the spread, integration, and concomitant utilization of such a change could occur only under the influence of selection, and then this is only a special case of adaptation — adaptation changing its direction — and to call it preadaptation may merely be juggling with words and not establishing a real distinction. It is, however, possible for mutations occasionally to become established without benefit of selection, or even in the face of adverse selection, especially in very small populations. Almost always this would lead to extinction, for the group could not survive long if definitely and contin-uously disadvantageous characters became established. In the odd case permitted by the qualification "almost," however, the characters disadvanta-geous in a current way of life might become advantageous when a change in way of life was possible and occurred. This true preadaptation, although probably extremely rare in evolution, provides a mechanism for sudden and erratic changes in adaptive type. The importance of such an event could be great, even though its occurrence were markedly exceptional. Rise of radically new types of organisms is certainly exceptional.

At the other end of the scale of evolutionary phenomena are the features of deployment of populations, of their adaptations to merely local variations in conditions, and of their splitting into two or more discrete populations when interbreeding ceases between subdivisions of them. Under the name of "speciation," these processes have been more intensively studied than any other aspects of the great subject of evolution, and indeed many students seem to consider "speciation" as practically synonymous with "evolution." This orientation of study has been inevitable and, in large degree, desirable. The fundamental proposition of the doctrine of special creation was the immutability of species, so that the first essential in establishing the truth of evolution was to demonstrate that one species may give rise to another. Hence the title of Darwin's great work on evolution in general, *The Origin of Species*. Variations, heredity, and processes of differentiation within species can be studied experimentally, whereas the larger features of evolution cannot. In practice, field naturalists and zoologists in museums are mainly occupied in distinguishing and examining species and their

---

[10] Interesting discussion and exemplification of this phenomenon, written when it was being given undue importance, will be found in L. Cuénot, *L'Adaptation* (Paris: G. Doin, 1925).

subdivisions, so much more numerous than the broader groups and so much more difficult to recognize.[11] More broadly, in dealing with recent animals, this is the best place to attack problems of evolution, where they begin, within populations and in their readily observed characteristics and activities. Here the basic theories of population genetics, partially summarized above, were worked out. . . .

One thing more may be said . . . about speciation in relationship to the processes of evolution here more extensively or explicitly treated. In Huxley's barrel of life speciation is the final pouring in of water, the filling up of the interstices in the long process of packing every available environment with as much life as it can support. To avoid the danger of analogy, it must, however, be emphasized that speciation was by no means the last thing to occur in evolution. It was equally the first, for it goes on all the time, along with any other evolutionary process that may be under way. It is the basic structure of the web of life, the ever-present detail of the fabric of evolution. It is the source and the fundamental process of diversification in the forms of organisms. Its pattern is that of branching, the separation of one group of organisms from another and the distribution between them of different portions of the stock of hereditary variation.

In the actual process of descent and change in the long history of life, speciation is one of the essential patterns. Along with this, and always embodying this within them, are two other patterns of constant occurrence and major importance. One of these is the pattern of trend, progressive, oriented change under the control of adaptation. The other is the more rapid and sporadic, recurrent rather than continuous, pattern of change in adaptive type, adoption of a new and distinct way of life. In all these interwoven patterns the same evolutionary forces are at work, but they vary endlessly in intensity, in combination, and in result.

[11] An excellent discussion of speciation from this particular point of view, together with copious citations from the enormous recent literature on speciation in general, is E. Mayr's *Systematics and the Origin of Species* (New York: Columbia University Press, 1944).

Mayr views the role of systematics in much the same sense as we view the ideal state of anthropology — as an integrative discipline in an age of specialization. The physical anthropologist is but a systematist particularly concerned with man and the nonhuman primates. Thus the model that we delineate in this book for the study of man is very much a specific application of the general model Mayr develops. That is, we accept that we must work within a dynamic evolutionary context, then try to develop a specific history (see "A Molecular Approach to the Study of Human Origins"), and finally attempt to understand the hows and whys of that history (see "The Study of Human Evolution" and succeeding chapters). This book is, therefore, insofar as we can make it, an exercise in modern systematics as Mayr sees that particularly fertile field.

3 The Role of Systematics in Biology

There are many ways of dealing with the topic. . . . One might give a history of the role which taxonomy has played in the development of biology; or one might concentrate on the present status of systematics in biology; or finally one might attempt, in a timeless and somewhat philosophical way, to delineate the niche which systematics occupies within the total conceptual framework of biology. Further thought makes it evident that the three approaches are interdependent to such a degree that one has to give due consideration to all three of them.

Let me start with the question, what do we mean by "systematics," the role of which I am to describe? To be able to answer this question meaningfully requires an excursion into the history as well as philosophy of biology. The ancient Greeks saw a natural order in the world which, they

Reprinted from *Science*, vol. 159, pp. 595–599, February, 1968. Copyright 1968 by the American Association for the Advancement of Science.

thought, could be demonstrated and classified by certain logical procedures. They tried to discover the true nature of things (their essences) and approached classification with the methods of logic. Indeed, Aristotle, the first great classifier, was also the father of logic. The underlying philosophy, now usually referred to as essentialism (from essence), dominated the thinking of taxonomists up to and including the time of Linnaeus. Taxonomic nomenclature and the so-called typological thinking of taxonomists right up to our day have been permanently affected by the Aristotelian heritage (Hull 1965).

HISTORY OF TAXONOMY

During the early history of biology this was no great handicap. Botany and zoology, to state it in a highly oversimplified manner, arose from the 16th century on as applied sciences, attached to medicine. Botany started as a broadened study of medicinal herbs and early botanical gardens were herb gardens. With but one or two exceptions all the great botanists and herbalists from the 16th to the 18th century (Linnaeus included) were professors of medicine or practicing physicians. Zoology arose in connection with human anatomy and physiology. When botany and zoology became independent sciences, the first concern of the two fields was to bring order into the diversity of nature. Taxonomy was therefore their dominant concern, and indeed in the 18th and early 19th century botany and zoology were virtually coextensive with taxonomy. Moreover, by sheer necessity, taxonomy was essentially the technique of identification.

The middle third of the 19th century was a period of decisive change to which many separate streams of development contributed. Increasing professionalism was one, and increasing specialization was another, to mention just two. Taxonomy itself helped in accelerating the change by introducing several new concepts into biology. The greatest unifying theory in biology, the theory of evolution, was largely a contribution made by the students of diversity, as we might call the taxonomists. It is no coincidence that Darwin wrote his *Origin of Species* after encountering taxonomic problems during the voyage of the *Beagle* and after 8 years of concentrated work on barnacle taxonomy. The comparison of different kinds of organisms is the core of the taxonomic method and leads at the same time to the question how these differences originated. The findings of explorer taxonomists, paleotaxonomists, and comparative anatomists inexorably led to the establishment and the eventual acceptance of the theory of evolution.

One might have expected that the acceptance of evolution would result in a great flowering of taxonomy and its prestige during the last third of the 19th century. This was not the case, in part, one might say, for almost administrative reasons. The most exciting consequences of the findings of systematics were studied in university departments while the very necessary but less exciting operations of descriptive taxonomy, based on collections, were assigned to the museums. Furthermore, most taxonomists were satisfied to use evolutionary concepts for rather practical purposes, such as evidence on which to base inferences on classification. As a consequence, evolutionary biology did not contribute as much to the strengthening of the bridge between taxonomy and other branches of biology as one might have expected. The great contributions to biology made by taxonomists during this period, such as population thinking, the theory of geographic speciation, the biological species concept, and several others that I shall mention presently, were incorporated into biology anonymously and without taxonomy receiving due credit.

Biology is no exception to the well-known phenomenon that in science there is a continuous change of fashions and frontiers. Since the 1870's there has been one breakthrough after another, beginning with the improvements of the microscope and the exciting discoveries of cytology. Perhaps the dominant trend during this period was an increasing interest in biological mechanisms, and in the chemical-physical explanation of biological functions. This led to the flourishing of various branches of physiology, of endocrinology, of genetics, of embryology, of immunology, of neurophysiology, of biochemistry, and of biophysics. Taxonomy, the oldest and most classical branch of biology, inevitably suffered in competition with all these brilliant developments. Whenever there was an interesting new growing point in taxonomy, it quickly made itself independent and left a rather descriptive, static, and sometimes almost clerical residue behind. The older ones among us remember the days when taxonomy was regarded by most biologists as an identification service. Some of the best universities in this country refused to accept Ph.D. theses in the field of taxonomy. The Guggenheim Foundation was the only granting agency that considered taxonomy worthy of support. Under the circumstances it was not surprising that only the most dedicated naturalists would choose taxonomy as their life's work, and we must pay tribute here to some inspired teachers who attracted gifted youngsters into our field.

Even today systematists feel that they are not getting their full share of recognition, of adequate financial support, and of truly superior graduate students, yet one must recognize that the change for the better in the last 20 or 30 years has been quite dramatic. This change had many causes but for some aspects it is not easy to say what is cause and what is effect. Taxonomists played a decisive role in the development of the synthetic theory of evolution, and this is being increasingly recognized by the leaders of biology. Julian Huxley and others have emphasized that taxonomy is indeed a vital branch of biology. Simultaneously we have witnessed a steady improvement in the scientific training of taxonomists. In order to obtain a position it is no longer sufficient that the young taxonomist knows how to describe new species; he is now expected to have acquired an adequate training in, and understanding of, genetics, statistics, animal behavior, biochemistry, and other branches of experimental-functional biology. The bridge between museums and universities is being broadened and strengthened in most places and the strong barriers between a narrowly defined taxonomy and the adjacent branches of biology are being obliterated. This new generation of taxonomists is no longer satisfied to work on preserved specimens. This new breed of naturalist-taxonomists insists on studying taxa as living organisms and pursues such studies in the field and in the experimental laboratory, wherever such studies will be most productive.

The ultimate result of these developments has been the general recognition that the universe of the taxonomist is far greater than was previously envisioned. Taxonomists now take an ever-increasing interest in evolutionary, ecological, and behavioral research, and indeed have assumed leading roles in these fields. Up to recently the terms *taxonomy* and *systematics* were generally considered to be synonymous. In view of the recent developments it seems advantageous to restrict the term taxonomy to the theory and practice of classifying, more narrowly defined, and to make use of the term systematics for the study of organic diversity, more broadly defined. This new viewpoint is represented by Simpson's definition (Simpson 1961): "Systematics is the scientific study of the kinds and diversity of organisms and of any and all relationships among them." In short, *systematics is the study of the diversity of organisms.* . . .

THE POSITION OF SYSTEMATICS IN BIOLOGY

When we look at biology as a whole we see that systematics occupies a unique position. Some years ago I pointed out that there are basically two biologies (Mayr 1961). One deals with functional phenomena and investigates the causality of biological functions and processes; the other one, evolutionary biology, deals with the historical causality of the existing organic world. Functional biology takes much of its technique and *Fragestellung* from physics and chemistry, and is happiest when it can reduce observed biological phenomena to physical-chemical processes. Evolutionary biology, dealing with highly complex systems, operated by historically evolved genetic programs, must pursue a very different strategy of research in order to provide explanations. Its most productive method is the comparative method, for which the taxonomists have laid the foundation. Indeed, I can hardly think of an evolutionary problem that is not posed because of some findings of taxonomy.

One can express these basic concerns also in a somewhat different manner. At one extreme of biology there is a preoccupation with the ultimate building stones and ultimate unit processes that are the common denominators throughout biology. This has largely been the concern of molecular biology from the structure of macromolecules to such functional unit processes as the Krebs cycle. As legitimate as the reductionist methodology is when applied to functional problems, it quickly carries us down to a level where we leave behind most of that which is most typically biological, and we are left with a subject matter that is essentially physical-chemical. This is surely true for the chemistry and physics of the ultimate building stones and unit processes of living organisms. If this were the only level of integration in biology, it would be quite legitimate to combine biology with chemistry or physics.

The other extreme is the preoccupation with that level of biology that deals with whole organisms, with uniqueness, and with systems. It is a matter of historical record that taxonomists are among those biologists who have been most consistently concerned with whole organisms and who have most consistently stressed the organismic, the systems approach to biology.

No one will question the immense importance of molecular phenomena but they are not the only aspect of biology. As Michael Ghiselin has stated it so perceptively, just as architecture is more than the study of building materials, so is biology more than the study of macromolecules. In systematics, in evolutionary biology, and in much of organismic biology, one normally deals with hierarchical levels of biological integration that are many orders of magnitude above the molecular level. Each level has its specific problems and its own appropriate methods and techniques. That there is such a difference in levels of integration is completely taken for granted in the physical sciences. No one would expect the aeronautical engineer to base the design of airplane wings on the study of elementary particles. But a uniqueness of role for each level is even more evident for the different levels of biological integration.

Lest I be misunderstood, there is no conflict between molecular biology and organismic biology (including systematics). But it must be emphasized that each level of integration poses its own specific problems, requires its own methods and techniques, and develops its own theoretical framework and generalizations. This has been clearly recognized and frequently stated by the foremost leaders of molecular biology. Consistent with this is the fact that faculty and curriculum in the areas of systematics, ecology, and evolutionary biology have recently been strengthened in several of the leading American universities, and as a result systematics has now become better integrated into biology than at any other time since the days of Darwin.

The role of systematics should now be quite clear: It is one of the cornerstones of all biology. It is the branch of biology which produces most of our information on the levels of integration, designated as natural populations and higher taxa. It supplies urgently needed facts, but more importantly, it cultivates a way of thinking, a way of approaching biological problems, which is alien to the reductionist, but which is tremendously important for the balance and well-being of biology as a whole.

Let me now turn to some of the concrete contributions made by systematics.

THE CONTRIBUTIONS OF SYSTEMATICS TO BIOLOGY

The magnitude of the contributions made by systematics is not appreciated by many biologists. And yet these achievements are extraordinary indeed, even if we adopt the most narrow definition of taxonomy. They include the description of about one million species of animals and half a million species of higher and lower plants, as well as their arrangement in a system. This classification, much as we continue to modify it in detail, is on the whole amazingly logical, internally consistent and stable. It is an immensely useful system of information storage and retrieval. All the comparative work of morphologists, physiologists, and of phylogenetically inclined molecular biologists would be meaningless if it were not for the existence of the classification.

Taxonomists supply a desperately needed identification service for taxa of ecological significance and for the correct determination of fossil species needed for work in stratigraphy and geological chronology. In all areas of applied biology good taxonomy is indispensable, as in public health in the study of vector-borne diseases and of parasites; in the study of the relatives of cultivated plants and of domestic animals; and in the study of insect pests and their biological control. Much work in conservation, wildlife management, and the study of renewable natural resources of all kinds depends for its effectiveness on the soundness of taxonomic research. The faunas, floras, handbooks, and manuals prepared by taxonomists are indispensable in many branches of biology and also widely used by the general public.

As important as these descriptive and service functions of taxonomy are, they are only part of the contribution of systematics, and to many of us the least important part, even though a prerequisite of all the others. I have pointed out already that the founding of evolutionary biology was the work of taxonomists. They also supplied the solution of many individual evolutionary problems. This includes the role of isolation, the mechanism of speciation, the nature of isolating mechanisms, rates of evolution, trends of evolution, and the problem of the emergence of evolutionary novelties. Taxonomists (including paleontologists) have made more significant contributions to all these topics than have any other kind of biologists.

There is hardly a taxonomic operation during which the systematist does not have to face basic biological questions. In order to assign specimens to species he must study variability and particularly polymorphism, and quite often he has to undertake a rather complete population analysis including the study of life cycles. In the study of polytypic species he concerns himself with geographic variation and its meaning; he studies the adaptation of local populations and tests the validity of climatic rules. When studying the population structure of species, he examines isolates and belts of hybridization. Indeed, taxonomists have developed in the last two generations a veritable "science of the species," as cytology is the science of the cell and histology the science of tissues. At every step he must think about the adaptation of populations, their past history, and the magnitude of dispersal (gene exchange between populations).

Many new concepts arose out of this work of the taxonomist but have since diffused broadly into genetics, ecology, physiology, and other areas of biology. By far the most important of these, as I have often stressed in the past, is population thinking. Biology, as all other sciences, was permeated by typological thinking until late in the 19th century, and is still today. When the learning psychologist speaks of The Rat or The Monkey, or the racist of The Negro, this is typological thinking. The early Mendelians were pure typologists. A mutation changed The Wildtype, and the result was a new type of organism, according to De Vries a new species. I have pointed out elsewhere (Mayr 1963) that taxonomists began as early as the 1840's and the 1850's to collect large series of individuals, population samples as we would now say, and describe the variation of these samples. From this purely pragmatic operation emerged eventually a wholly new way of thinking which replaced typological essentialism. From taxonomy, population thinking spread into adjacent fields and was in part instrumental in the development of population genetics and population cytology. Population thinking has now spread into the behavior field, into physiology, and into ecology. This one conceptual contribution alone has been of such great benefit to vast areas of biology as to justify support for systematics.

As the interests of the systematists broaden, it is becoming more and more true that systematics has become, as stated by Julian Huxley (1940), "one of the focal points of biology." Although he may not be able to solve these problems himself, it is the systematist who frequently poses the problems which are of concern to the population geneticist, the physiologist, the embryologist, and the ecologist. For instance, systematics poses the problems in that area of ecology which deals with the phenomena of diversity, the differences in the richness of faunas and floras in different climatic zones and habitats, and so forth. A succession of prominent taxonomists have been leaders in the study of problems of species competition, niche utilization, and structure of ecosystems.

Environmental physiology owes much to systematics. Zoological systematists like C. L. Gloger, J. A. Allen, and Bernhard Rensch have made major contributions to the discovery of adaptive geographic variation and the establishment of climatic rules. Up to the 1920's it was almost universally believed that geographic differences among populations of a species were nongenetic modifications of the phenotype and of no evolutionary interest. As it was stated, "the type of the species is not affected." It was zoologists with taxonomic interests or training who demonstrated the genetic basis for adaptive differences between geographic races. The stress of unique characteristics of individuals, the recognition of differences between populations, the emphasis on the phenotype as a compromise between multiple selection pressures, all this represents thinking which came straight out of evolutionary systematics but has exercised and is continuing to exercise a profound influence on environmental physiology.

Applying taxonomic principles to the interpretation of man's evolution, as was done by Simpson, Le Gros Clark, Mayr, and Simons, has decisively added to our understanding of man's evolution and of hominid classification. The chaos of 29 generic and more than 100 specific names caused by the earlier typological approach was replaced by a biologically oriented classification in which three genera, *Paranthropus, Australopithecus,* and *Homo* (the latter with two species), are recognized.

Whole branches of biology are unthinkable without systematics. Biological oceanography is one example, and biogeography another. This field has traditionally been the domain of the taxonomists to such a degree that it is unnecessary to stress the contribution of systematics. Cytogenetics and bioacoustics are other areas of biology that derived much of their inspiration from systematics. Systematists have enormously contributed to ethology through their comparative behavior studies, particularly of insects.

There are two reasons why it is necessary to stress these contributions. One is that those who have come into biology from the outside (for example, from physics or chemistry) simply do not know this history. The second reason is that there has been a tendency even among those who know the situation to credit all the neighboring fields, population genetics, ecology, or ethology, even though the advances were made by practicing taxonomists and were made possible only by the experience they had gained as taxonomists. It is totally misleading to limit the labels taxonomy or systematics to the purely clerical, descriptive operations and to give a different label to all the broader findings and concepts that are the direct result of the more elementary operations. Regrettably, even some taxonomists have supported the myth that all the more biologically interesting activities and findings of the taxonomist are not part of taxonomy. In this connection it will be of some importance, in order to clarify the situation, to add a few words on the structure of systematics.

THE STRUCTURE OF SYSTEMATICS

In the earlier part of my discussion I described how systematics, as we now understand it, emerged from essentialism and nominalism (by rejecting these concepts) and became based on the fact of evolution. It began to study organic diversity as the product of evolution. It recognized that every classification is a scientific theory with the properties of any scientific theory: it is explanatory, because it explains the existence of natural groups as the products of common descent; it is predictive, because with high probability it can make predictions as to the pattern of variation of unstudied features of organisms and the placing of newly discovered species. Finally, systematics established many new contacts with other areas of biology by adopting the thesis that the characteristics of the living organism are at least as important for classification as those of preserved specimens.

How did these profound changes in the science of systematics affect its working procedure? In some ways not at all, because the needs for sound classification have not changed. There is still the same need to order the diversity of nature into elementary units, biological species. Sorting variable individuals and populations into species (and naming and describing them) is sometimes referred to as alpha taxonomy. There is still need for some alpha taxonomy even in as mature a branch of systematics as bird taxonomy. New species, new subspecies, and all sorts of new taxa of birds are still being found. We still discover occasionally that a species of the literature is nothing but a variant of another species. In ornithology we still are in need of compilations, checklists, and descriptive works of various sorts that fall under the designation of alpha or beta taxonomy. And yet even in these relatively elementary procedures of taxonomy there is a drastic difference between doing them either in a typological (=essentialist) or in a biological-evolutionary fashion.

The typologist acts as if he were dealing with the "essential natures" of created types. He stresses morphotypes and discontinuities; variation is treated as a necessary evil to be ignored as much as this is possible. The biological systematist knows that he is dealing with samples of variable natural populations; he is interested in the biological meaning of this variation. He knows that he is dealing with living organisms and wants to study all their attributes whether they concern morphology, behavior, ecology, or biochemistry.

An understanding of the biological meaning of variation and of the evolutionary origin of groups of related species is even more important for the second stage of taxonomic activity, the sorting of species into groups of relatives ("taxa") and their arrangement in a hierarchy of higher categories. This activity is what the term classification denotes; it is also referred to as beta taxonomy. No matter how interested a taxonomist is in the evolutionary and ecological aspects of the taxa he studies, he will also devote a major share of his time to alpha and beta taxonomy, not only because so much work still remains to be done, but also because the more interesting biological problems are found only through research in alpha and beta taxonomy.

THE FUTURE OF SYSTEMATICS

I would feel rather pessimistic about the future of taxonomy if it were only an identification service for other branches of biology, as is thought by some of our less imaginative colleagues. But he who realizes that systematics opens one of the most important doors toward understanding life in all of its diversity cannot help but feel optimistic. Environmental biology, behavioral biology, and even molecular biology are all moving in our direction. The most exciting aspect of biology is that, in contradistinction to physics and chemistry, it is not possible to reduce all phenomena to a few general laws. Nothing is as typically biological as the never-ending variety of solutions found by organisms to cope with similar challenges of the environment. Nothing is more intriguing than the study of differences between related organisms and the challenge to explain these differences as the result of natural selection. Even in cases where the ultimate solution may come from genetics or biochemistry, it is the systematist who in almost every case is the one who poses the challenging questions. The opportunities for exciting research are virtually unlimited. This is becoming clearer and more widely appreciated every year.

These opportunities are not without obligations. Let us remember at all times that each and every taxonomist is a spokesman for systematics. He must carry out his activities in such a way as to reflect favorably on his field. Let us remember that taxonomy is not a kind of stamp-collecting but a branch of biology. Let us desist from all practices that are injurious to the prestige of systematics, as, for instance, by indulging in nomenclatural practices that lower the value of scientific nomenclature as an information storage and retrieval system. Finally, let us remember that in virtually every taxonomic finding certain generalizations are implicit that are of value and broad interest to biology as a whole. It will help our relations with other branches of biology if we make these findings known. They are sure to have a minor or major impact well beyond the bounds of systematics.

It is my sincere belief, to summarize my discussion, that systematics is one of the most important and indispensable, one of the most active and exciting, and one of the most rewarding branches of biological science. I know of no other subject that teaches us more about the world we live in than systematics, the study of the diversity of life.

REFERENCES

Hull, D. L.
  1965   *Brit. Phil. Sci.* 15:314; *ibid.* 16:1.
Huxley, J. A.
  1940   *The New Systematics.* Oxford: Clarendon Press.
Mayr, E.
  1961   "Cause and Effect in Biology," *Science* 134:1501.
  1963   *Animal Species and Evolution.* Cambridge, Mass.: Harvard University Press.
Simpson, G. G.
  1961   *Principles of Animal Taxonomy.* New York: Columbia University Press, p. 7.

ALFRED SHERWOOD ROMER

*Just as Simpson and Mayr are preeminent in their areas of
interest (and these are fortunately broad ones) so, too, is Romer
a leading figure in American paleontology. In this summary
article, he briefly traces the course that our ancestors passed
through, beginning at a protovertebrate state and progressing
through to modern man. The earlier history is impeccable to us
(though it might be less so to specialists in those areas); the
specifically primate story is, of course, but an outline that the
rest of this volume seeks to enlarge upon. Romer's treatment
provides a much needed perspective to the student, who might
be too strongly tempted to focus on a very narrow span of time,
when what is required is an expertise which is gained from a
general understanding of the evolutionary process as it has
applied to many well-studied events in vertebrate history, and
which is then applied to certain relatively restricted questions
concerned with humans. One cannot be a student of human
evolution in particular without being a student of evolution in
general. It is this point that the selections from Simpson, Mayr,
and Romer are designed to illustrate.*

4   Major Steps in
Vertebrate Evolution

In studies of animal form or function, there often seems to be
an implication that the form studied was created *de novo* to fill the place
which it occupies in the modern world. This is, of course, not the case.
Every animal or plant living today has thousands of millions of years of
history behind it and has been successively adapted to a long series of varied
modes of existence; the structures and functions acquired by its ancestors as
they passed through various stages have left indelible traces in its organiza-

Reprinted from *Science*, vol. 158, pp. 1629–1637, December 29, 1967. Copyright 1967
by the American Association for the Advancement of Science.

tion. It is my belief that the animals of today can be better understood and more reasonably interpreted if the investigator has an appreciation of their past history.

It is this evolutionary, historical approach, particularly as regards our own kin, the vertebrates, which has been the center of my research interests for half a century, and I propose here to give an outline of the present status of our knowledge of this field. The story is not, of course, fully known, but over the decades we have gained a fairly clear picture of most of its main events. There is general agreement as to the greater part of the evolutionary sequence. However, a number of points are still in dispute. Because space here is too limited for full discussion of them, I have selected, where there are alternatives, that interpretation which seems most reasonable in the light of current evidence.

The evidence in part is, of necessity, deduced from data obtained from the study of living animals. Their structures and functions often furnish suggestions of antecedent stages; the study of development can also give valuable information, for embryonic patterns in general tend to be conservative and to suggest the types of former adults to which these developmental processes once gave rise. But, early in their history, vertebrates acquired bony skeletons; this made it possible for them to be discovered in the fossil record. Particularly during the last half century, detailed studies have given important paleontological data on many crucial points of the evolutionary story which I wish to tell.

It might be assumed that the evolutionary story is a straightforward one, beginning with simplicity and going on to increasing complexity and "advance." Not so; it is highly complex. What an organism becomes is not due purely to its inherent potentialities; its fate is strongly modified by physical and biological factors successively met with in its career. Vertebrate evolution has undergone strange shifts due to conditions at various stages; it is not simply an unfolding of innate potentialities. Those who desire a teleological interpretation argue that the evolutionary developments among the vertebrates are so remarkable that they are inexplicable under ordinary theories of evolution. For example, how can we understand such a major shift as that from fish life in the water to vertebrate life on land unless there is some supernatural, directing force behind it? Those who believe that the changes occurring during this transformation are of no immediate selective value feel that a teleological interpretation is necessary. A typical example of this point of view is du Noüy's popular work (1). After demonstrating to his own satisfaction that no interpretation except a teleological one is possible, du Noüy discusses the future of man on the basis of supernatural direction in his development. However, I have failed to be interested in his discussion of our happy future; his conclusions are unsound, because his premises are faulty. Much of the evolutionary story which he believes to be insoluble except on the basis of design is readily interpretable under current neo-Darwinian theories of evolutionary progression.

Vertebrate history has been, of course, a continuum, a sequence of gradual changes and evolutionary development; but for present purposes we may divide this evolutionary story into about ten or so stages. And, abandoning any pretense of objectivity, let us direct the sequence of events toward the appearance of man.

SESSILE ARM-FEEDERS

I shall not attempt to follow our history down to the protozoan level. At the beginning of Cambrian times, some 500 million years ago, there first appeared in the fossil record a considerable variety of invertebrate metazoan animals — trilobites and other arthropods, lamp shells, molluscs, echinoderms, and so on. But of our own ancestors at this time there are no sure traces; quite certainly the vertebrate ancestors were then soft-bodied creatures, not normally to be found in the fossil record. We are forced to rely on clues obtained from surviving lowly relatives of the vertebrates, often included with them in a major animal group known as the phylum Chordata (or in part separated as a lower but related phylum Hemichordata) (2).

What type of organism should a simply built, early metazoan ancestor of the vertebrates have been? Vertebrates are dominantly active animals, seekers of food, bilaterally built forms, and we would expect the early forms to have been of this nature. But while there are, among the oldest fossils, numerous forms of this sort (notably the abundant trilobites), the evidence suggests that our early origins come from a more lowly level.

Today, and in the early fossil record, we find remains of metazoans of very different build and habits — simple sessile forms which do not seek their food, but wait for food particles to come to them. The body, attached by a stalk to the ocean bottom, consists of little except a digestive tract; above this, arms extend out hopefully, along which ciliated bands catch food particles drifting past in the water and direct them down to a receptive mouth. Animals of this sort include (i) the bryozoans, or moss animalicules; (ii) the lamp shells or brachiopods, in which the ciliated arms are enclosed in a pair of shells; and (iii) the crinoids, primitive echinoderms in which the stalk, body, and arms are encased in rings of armor. And present today, as well, although not seen in the fossil record, is a fourth type of arm-feeder, the pterobranchs, tiny and rare deep-sea forms with a few structures which definitely show their relationship to the vertebrate pedigree.

SESSILE FILTER-FEEDERS

The tiny sessile pterobranchs are a far remove from what we would expect in a vertebrate ancestor in body form or function. A further stage, it would appear, developed among early ancestral forms before we reach anything remotely resembling our expectations of vertebrate ancestors. The ciliated arms of a pterobranch are fairly well adapted to picking up passing food particles and bringing them down to the mouth; but this is not too good an adaptation for actually bringing the particles into the mouth and on the way to digestion. This was accomplished by the development of gill slits — paired openings leading on either side from the throat (pharynx) out to the surface; bands of cilia draw inward a current of water containing food particles; in the pharynx, the food materials are strained out, to be carried down the gut, while the water is passed outward through the gill slits. In larger and later types of chordates, the gills are important, as breathing organs, for the absorption of oxygen; in small early types, however, breathing could be satisfactorily cared for by the skin in general; the primary gill function was as a feeding aid. With the development of the gill current, the "arms" could be — and were — lost; in front of the mouth, there was only a noselike proboscis (already present as a sign of chordate relationship in pterobranchs). A simple pair of gill slits is present in one genus of living pterobranchs, and only an increase in number of slits was necessary to attain this new stage. Departing but little from what we believe to have been the truly primitive filter-feeders are the balanoglossids, or acorn worms, essentially sessile burrowers found in modern seas; their name is derived from the fact that the proboscis nestling into a bandlike neck resembles an acorn in its cup. Filter-feeding has been a successful, if lowly, way of making a living, and a further stage in developing a filtering apparatus occurs in the little tunicates, or sea squirts, rather common in modern seas either as solitary or colonial attached forms or as free-floating types. They carry the filtering apparatus to an extreme; in a typical member of this group, almost the entire animal consists of a barrel-shaped pharynx comprising a complex set of gill filters.

THE VERTEBRATE BODY PATTERN

The tunicates are terminal members of this sequence of particle-gathering sessile types — the end of the line. It would seem that nothing further could well develop in an evolutionary sequence beyond the adult of this stage. Nothing did. But from the larva of a tunicate, or presumably a pretunicate, there arose the body type from which the true vertebrates sprang (Figure 1).

We customarily think of evolutionary series in terms of adult animals;

that change took place by gradual modifications in the structures and functions of mature individuals. But there is another possibility, that of paedomorphosis, emphasized especially by Garstang (3) as responsible for the further advance of the chordate-vertebrate series. Normally only a fully grown animal is capable of reproduction. But if immature forms should become sexually mature and reproduce, what then? It is quite possible that the previous adult stage might completely drop out of the picture, and a new evolutionary development might make its appearance.

In many tunicates, reproduction takes place by budding or by a normal direct development to the adult condition. But there is a different pattern in certain living types. Most tunicates make their livelihood where their parents live or where the local water currents carry them during their development. But some freedom of action has become available to certain tunicates by the introduction into the life cycle of a free-swimming, tadpole-like larva, so that the young have some freedom of choice to move to a favorable area for adult life. In a swollen "head" region, the gill apparatus, which is to constitute the major part of the adult body, develops. Behind, there is a muscular swimming tail, strengthened by a stout but flexible longitudinal cord, the notochord, predecessor of the vertebral column; the activity of the motile tail is supervised by a longitudinal dorsal nerve cord, which in the head region receives sensory information from rudimentary sense organs. The life of the larva is short; it swims about for a few hours or days and then settles down, to be attached to the sea bottom. Tail, notochord, nervous system, and sense organs degenerate and are resorbed, and the creature assumes the adult shape of a tunicate.

In this larva, we see the appearance, in simple form, of the typical body pattern characteristic of vertebrates, and it seems certain that we have here the beginnings of a new evolutionary series, radically different from that of the sessile series of which the adult tunicate is an end form. If, as seems surely to be the case, Paleozoic tadpoles of certain tunicates, or pretunicates, became sexually mature and no longer metamorphosed into sessile adults, a new mode of life opened up. Instead of passively waiting for food to come to it, the animal could go in search of food and could explore new areas or new habitats in which it might exist. *Amphioxus,* familiar to every student of biology, represents in slightly specialized fashion the stage in which sexual maturity of the tadpole has taken place, but not much progress toward higher evolutionary levels has occurred.

FIRST VERTEBRATES: THE OSTRACODERMS

These earliest stages in the vertebrate pedigree occurred, at the latest, in very early Paleozoic times, for in the Ordovician, second of the Paleozoic periods, remains of fossil true vertebrates are present. Such

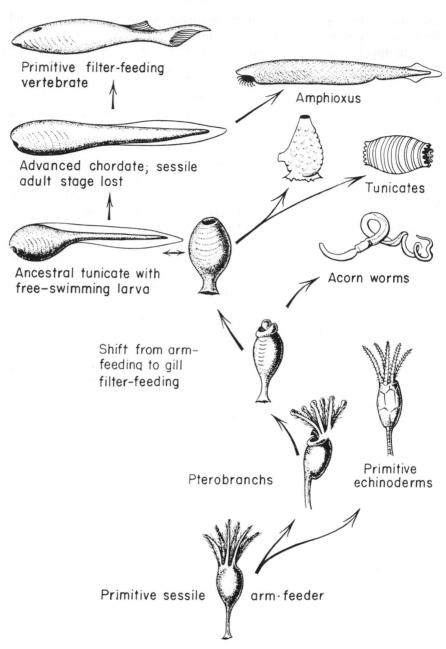

Primitive filter-feeding
vertebrate

Amphioxus

Advanced chordate; sessile
adult stage lost

Tunicates

Ancestral tunicate with
free-swimming larva

Acorn worms

Shift from arm-
feeding to gill
filter-feeding

Pterobranchs

Primitive
echinoderms

Primitive sessile   arm-feeder

FIGURE 1

Diagrammatic family tree suggesting the possible mode of evolution of vertebrates. The echinoderms may have arisen from forms not too dissimilar to the little pterobranchs; the acorn worms may remains become abundant by the end of the following Silurian period, where numerous specimens of varied types of lowly vertebrates termed ostracoderms are found. Our knowledge of them dates from the thorough studies (in the 1920's) of members of the *Cephalaspis* group (4). No one of the late Silurian and early Devonian ostracoderms is to be regarded as a direct ancestor of "higher" vertebrates, but the cephalaspids, best known of ostracoderms, nevertheless show the general structure reasonably to be expected in an ancestral vertebrate. There is an expanded "head" region, exhibiting typical sense organs, and a powerful swimming tail. The "head," when dissected, is seen to be mainly occupied by an enormous gill chamber, terminated anteriorly by a small mouth. We have here, on a higher level, a structure not unlike that present in the tunicate tadpole. The ostracoderm was still a jawless filter-feeder, but it had the great advantage over its tunicate (or pretunicate) ancestor that the large feeding apparatus of the gill basket could be moved about to suitable food localities.

In what environment did the early vertebrates live? We assume that the ocean was the original home of life, and the seas are still the home of a great proportion of all animal types; further, the lower chordates and hemichordates are all marine forms. But many of the finds of early vertebrates are from sediments rather surely laid down in fresh waters, and I came to the conclusion, some decades ago, that early vertebrate evolution took place in lakes and streams rather than in the sea (5). At about the same period, Smith (6) reached a similar conclusion from a comparative study of kidney function. Our conclusions have not gone uncontested (7), and it may be long before definite agreement is reached. But while I must defer further discussion of this question to some future occasion, it still seems clear to me that a freshwater origin fits best into the general picture. With the invasion of the continents by plant life in the Paleozoic, freshwater streams and ponds gave a new area where animals might find food. Few invertebrates have been capable of entering freshwater environments — for successful life inland, the animal must be an active swimmer to avoid being carried back down to the sea. The vertebrates and their advanced chordate ancestors, with the swimming powers given them by their tail development, were one of the few types competent to enter fresh waters and to enjoy them

---

have arisen from pterobranch descendants which had evolved a gill-feeding system but were little more advanced in other regards. Tunicates represent a stage in which, in the adult, the gill apparatus has become highly evolved, but the important point is the development in some tunicates of a free-swimming larva with advanced features of notochord and nerve cord. In further progress to *Amphioxus* and the vertebrates, the old sessile adult stage has been abandoned, and it is the larval type that has initiated the advance. From Romer, *The Vertebrate Story*. Copyright 1959 the University of Chicago.

profitably. Upstream invasion by vertebrates took place rapidly and successfully, so that by the late Silurian and the following Devonian period, fishes
had become prominent dwellers in inland waters.

Because the "lowest" of living vertebrates — lampreys, hagfishes, and
sharks — lack bone and have skeletons of cartilage, and since in the
development of higher vertebrates the skeleton is first formed in cartilage
and is only later replaced by bone, it was long thought that cartilage was the
original skeletal material of vertebrates, and that bone developed only at a
relatively late evolutionary stage. But our present knowledge of the fossil
record shows that the oldest of known vertebrates already had bone, at least
as an external armor. As a consequence, most (but not all) students of the
subject will agree with Stensiö's conclusion that bone developed at the base
of the vertebrate series and that the boneless condition in cyclosomes and
sharks is a secondary, degenerate one; the prominence of cartilage in the
young vertebrate is an embryonic adaptation (8).

Except for improvement of sense organs, the appearance of bone is the
only major advance made by the earliest vertebrates over their higher
chordate ancestors. Why bone? Calcium is physiologically important, and it
has been suggested that its appearance has to do with a functional need.
However, bone, as we see it in the oldest vertebrates, is not simply a calcium
deposit, but an external covering of plates arranged in a complex pattern. It
looks like armor; and very probably it was. In the late Silurian and early
Devonian, we find numerous faunas in which nearly the only animals
present are small armored ostracoderms and eurypterids — a type of predaceous arthropod distantly related to the horseshoe crab of today. The
average eurypterid was much larger than most contemporary vertebrates —
some as much as about 2.5 meters in length, compared with ostracoderms
generally but several centimeters long. It seems clear that the lowly
ostracoderms were their food supply and that the development of bony
armor was an adaptive protective device. In later times, fishes became more
advanced, more skilled in swimming, generally larger, and often predaceous
themselves. Parallel with these advances, eurypterids became rare and
(robbed, it would seem, of their erstwhile prey) extinct before the end of
Paleozoic days (9).

It seems probable, then, that bone first appeared in the form of dermal
armor, laid down in membrane fashion in plates within the skin. In many
ostracoderms, there is no bone except in the surface armor (10). In the
cephalaspids there is some development of internal bone within the head
region, but even here it is of the same "membrane" pattern, laid down in
sheets around the various internal canals and cavities. Only in higher fish
groups, bone development progressed further, to the endochondral stage,
when solid masses of bone are present in internal structure. It seems that,

for the development of a bony skeleton, without which the evolution of the more advanced classes of vertebrates would have been impossible, we must thank the eurypterid enemies of our early ancestors.

The ostracoderms were, in general, small and feeble, doomed to extinction by the end of the Devonian period; they have survived only in the form of the degenerate and specialized lampreys and hagfishes in which the development of a peculiar, rasping, tonguelike structure has enabled them to persist in modest fashion as predators on other fishes. A new era in fish history opened with the development of jaws, formed by enlargement of a pair of skeletal bars which earlier had formed supports for gill slits. Armed with these new structures, fishes were released from the necessity of depending on filter-feeding for a livelihood, and a whole new series of potential modes of life was opened up for them. Early in the Devonian period we find, principally in fresh waters, a varied host of jawed fishes: placoderms, acanthodians, and, most especially, three major groups of advanced bony fishes which played an important role in later vertebrate evolution — the Actinopterygia (or ray-finned fishes), the Dipnoi (or lungfishes), and the Crossopterygii, of little account beyond Paleozoic days, but highly important as the progenitors of land vertebrates.

A persisting major gap in our paleontological record, however, is the almost complete absence of any trace of an earlier jawed fish. Although the common ancestor must have existed well before the Devonian, there is no earlier record of fish of this sort except for a few fragmentary remains of acanthodians in near-shore marine Silurian deposits. Why this gap? To one who believes that these early stages in fish evolution took place in salt water, there is no reasonable answer to this question. But to a believer in freshwater origins, the answer is simple. Earlier than the very late Silurian, continental strata are almost entirely absent from the known geological record. Without question, continental deposits had been formed in the earlier geologic times, but it seems that subsequent erosion has resulted in the destruction of such older beds in which remains of truly ancestral jawed fishes might have been found.

AMPHIBIANS — THE BEGINNINGS OF LAND LIFE

With the radiation of jaw-bearing fishes, vertebrates had obtained a dominant position in life in the water. But a further major advance was presently to come — the conquest of the land, initiated by the amphibians and completed by their reptilian descendants. In recent decades, much of the general picture of this major evolutionary advance has been worked out (Figure 2).

What fish group gave rise to the early four-footed animals, tetrapods,

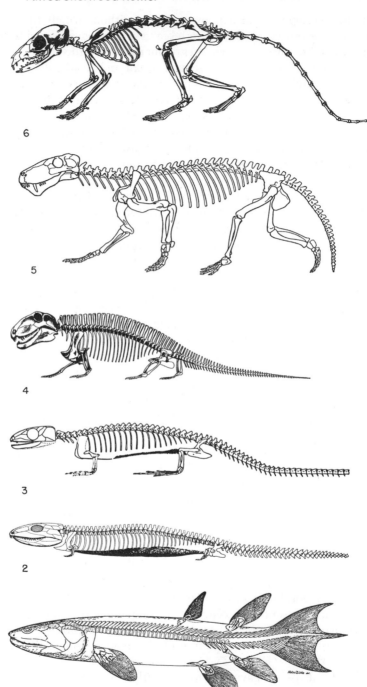

6

5

4

3

2

represented today by the surviving orders of amphibians? Quite surely, all would agree, some type of the higher bony fish of the class Osteichthyes. One may immediately rule out the ray-finned fishes — the actinopterygians — for a variety of reasons; because of various specializations, the lungfishes, despite anatomical and embryological similarities to amphibians, are to be regarded as the "uncles" of the tetrapods rather than as actual ancestors. It has become increasingly certain in recent decades that the ancestors of land vertebrates lay among the Crossopterygii and, particularly, an early central group of crossopterygians, termed the Rhipidistia. The crossopterygians flourished during the Devonian but rapidly declined in numbers, and beyond the Paleozoic they survived only in the form of an aberrant side branch, the coelacanths, of which a single form, *Latimeria*, survives in the Indian Ocean. We know nothing firsthand of the soft anatomy or embryology of rhipidistians, but in regard to the skeleton, the evidence is clear that the older crossopterygians are proper ancestors for the tetrapods. The fin skeleton is of just the type to develop into a land limb, and, in general, a crossopterygian skull can be compared bone for bone not only with amphibians, but also with reptiles, mammals, and man.

The tie-in of crossopterygians with the Amphibia is close, not so much with the living orders as with a great group of forms, the Labyrinthodontia, which began their career at the end of the Devonian, abounded in the Carboniferous and Permian, and survived, before extinction, into the Triassic *(11)*. Over the last half century, a long series of finds has yielded a fairly complete story of the labyrinthodonts. They are of importance in their own right, but one group of them, the anthracosaurs, are especially important in that they show a series of stages leading onward to the reptiles *(12)*.

But whereas we have a fairly clear story of the relationship of the crossopterygians to the labyrinthodonts and through them to the reptiles, the history of the surviving orders of amphibians is still obscure. These consist of (i) the Anura, frogs and toads; (ii) the Urodela, including newts

FIGURE 2

Series of skeletons in approximately true phylogenetic sequence from a rhipidistian crossopterygian to a placental mammal. (1) Crossopterygian *Eusthenopteron*; (2) *Pholidogaster*, an early labyrinthodont tending in a reptilian direction; (3) *Hylonomus*, one of the oldest and most primitive of known reptiles; (4) *Sphenacodon*, a Permian pelycosaur pertaining to the group from which therapsids were derived; (5) *Lycaenops*, a generalized therapsid, with improved four-footed locomotion; (6) The tree shrew *Tupaia*, a generalized placental mammal. [(1) and (6) after Gregory, (3) after Carroll, (4) after Romer and Price, (5) after Colbert] and salamanders; and (iii) the Apoda or Gymnophiona, tropical wormlike forms. The three orders are quite diverse in structure and body form, but recent work suggests that they are, as the Lissamphibia, a phylogenetic unit (13). Possibly related to their ancestry are small Carboniferous and early Permian amphibians known as the Lepospondyli (14); but this does not solve the question, for the pedigree of the lepospondyls themselves is quite uncertain. This is a chapter of vertebrate evolution where further data are needed.

How did the major evolutionary step from water toward and to land take place? Those who favor teleological interpretations insist that some divine or mystical driving force must have underlain this radical shift in habitus and structure since, they say, the development of adaptations fitting the fish descendants for future life on dry land would have had no immediate adaptive value to a water dweller. Here, however, as in other cases, there is no need to call upon the supernatural, for it can be shown that under some special condition such adaptations could have been of immediate selective value. This special condition seems to have been seasonal drought (8). More than half a century ago, Barrell (15) pointed out that the numerous red beds of the late Paleozoic (and Triassic) gave evidence of the widespread prevalence of regions subject to seasonal drought. At certain times of the year (as today in some tropical areas), rainfall would be abundant; at other seasons, the rains would cease, streams slow down, and ponds become stagnant.

There are many structural and functional changes necessary to turn a typical fish into an amphibian and, eventually into a reptile; let us merely take two of the most obvious "improvements" needed — lungs and land limbs. To a fish under normal climatic conditions, gills suffice for breathing purposes. But under drought conditions, with stagnation of waters and low oxygen content, it would be highly advantageous for a fish to be able to come to the surface and avail itself of atmospheric oxygen. Today only five genera of fish have retained true lungs (they live in seasonal drought areas), but our evidence suggests that in the late Paleozoic the great majority of freshwater forms possessed lungs.

But legs? Why should a water dweller have these structures, so essential for land life? The answer seems to be that legs did not evolve as a mystical "preadaptation" for a future life on land, but (seemingly a paradox) as structures which would aid a water-dweller, under drought conditions, to continue his life in his own proper element. In early stages of a severe drought, a fish with lungs would survive stagnant water conditions without trouble. But suppose the drought worsened and the water in a pond dried up completely? An ordinary fish would be literally stuck in the mud and would soon perish unless the rains soon returned. But a form in which there had been some trend for enlargement of fins toward the tetrapod limb condition might be able to crawl up or down a river channel, find a pond with water still present, happily splash in, and resume his normal mode of life. Most fossil amphibians had legs developed to at least a moderate degree. But as far as we can tell, most of them had no yen for life on land; legs were, for the time being, simply an adaptation for bettering the animal's chances for surviving in his proper aqueous environment (16).

THE FIRST REPTILES

Modern reptiles and modern amphibians can be readily told apart. But increased knowledge of the fossil record has brought us to the point where it is almost impossible to tell an advanced fossil amphibian from a primitive reptile on the basis of its skeletal structure. The first reptiles, it now seems clear, were a group of "stem reptiles" (cotylosaurs) known as the Captorhinomorpha, well known in the Permian and now known to have been present far back in Carboniferous times (17). The real distinction, of course, between amphibians and reptiles lies in the mode of reproduction. The typical frogs, toads, or salamanders in our temperate regions gather in the spring in ponds where the eggs are laid and develop, as those of their fish ancestors did, into water-dwelling and water-breathing larvae. Only later, with metamorphosis, lungs develop, and land life becomes possible. In contrast, reptiles are notable in that they lay an amniote type of egg. This is prosaic to us (since it has been retained by the avian descendants of the reptiles), but it is actually the most marvelous "invention" in vertebrate history. This egg can be laid on land; the water stage of development is eliminated. Externally, there is a protective shell; internally, a complex series of membranes protects the growing embryo, and there is an abundant supply of nourishing yolk; a larval stage is eliminated, and the young reptile (or bird) hatches as a miniature replica of the parent, already well adapted to take up a fully terrestrial mode of life.

At what evolutionary stage did this new and revolutionary egg type enter the picture? Certain amphibians of ancient days had well-developed limbs and were apparently ready for a fully terrestrial existence. But they were chained to the water (splendid phrase) by the necessity of the old-fashioned aquatic mode of development. Finally (went the story as it was long told, and as I used to tell it myself), the amniote egg was developed, the chains were broken, and the reptiles burst forth upon the land!

A good story, but, it would now seem, a false one. It is probable that the egg came ashore before the adult was fully ready for land life (18). Study of certain members of the oldest-known reptilian faunas seems to indicate that although they quite surely laid an amniote type of egg, the adults, like their amphibian ancestors, were still amphibious in habits, spending much of their time in the water, with a sustaining diet of fishes. Why, then, a land egg? A review of breeding habits of modern amphibians furnishes a clue. I have mentioned the "typical" mode of reproduction of frogs, toads, and salamanders. But if we survey these types as a whole, we find that the "typical" mode is really exceptional rather than common. Particularly in the tropics, modern amphibians adopt any device possible to avoid laying the eggs in the water. Why? Avoidance of enemies is probably a major objective; to a variety of forms, ranging from insect to other vertebrates, eggs in a pond are a desirable amphibian caviar. But to some degree among modern forms and, I think, to a major extent among the ancestral Paleozoic reptiles, the reason was seasonal drought; if eggs are laid in a pond, drought leads to larval death. Here again, an adaptation which was to be exceedingly useful in terrestrial life appears to have evolved, not with this end in view, but as an immediately useful adaptation to an animal still leading an amphibious life.

MAMMAL-LIKE REPTILES

Once lungs, limbs, and, finally, the amniote egg were developed, full terrestrial existence became possible. The early tetrapods were eaters of animal food; the rise of the insects toward the end of the Carboniferous furnished a basic food supply for early land-dwellers. Soon there was under way a great radiation of reptilian types which were to dominate the world during the Mesozoic era — a radiation leading not merely to the familiar surviving reptilian orders, but also to a host of forms now extinct, such as the great marine reptiles of the Mesozoic, dinosaurs, flying reptiles, and bird ancestors. Curiously, however, the first great development from the primitive reptilian stock was not the one that led to any of these forms, but was the rapid emergence of the Synapsida, a group from which the mammals were destined to evolve. The first synapsids appear in the record almost as early as the first reptiles of any sort, and from the late Carboniferous on through the Permian and into the early Triassic they were the commonest of land animals. From time to time, there sprang from this stock successful, herbivorous, side branches, but the main evolutionary line consisted of forms which were the dominant carnivores, large and small, of late Paleozoic and earliest Mesozoic times. The more primitive representatives of this group were the pelycosaurs, forms to which I have devoted a considerable part of my scientific life (19), and which are best known from the early Permian red beds of Texas. In structure, pelycosaurs had departed little from the most primitive reptiles; they still walked, quite inefficiently, with the sprawled-out pose of the limbs characteristic of all early four-footed animals. During the Permian, there developed from one pelycosaur group a more advanced mammal-like type, that of the therapsids. Here locomotion was greatly improved; the elbows were turned back, the knees forward, the trackway narrowed, the stride increased with resulting greater speed. These therapsids are best known from the Great Karroo deposits of South Africa, from which hosts of therapsids have been described by Broom, Watson, and many other scientists.

Therapsid dominance lasted until the Triassic. But as this period progressed, the therapsids dwindled in numbers and variety, to disappear completely in the Jurassic. The cause of their downfall appears to lie in the rise of a rival reptile group, the archosaurs, or "ruling reptiles." In this reptile subclass, there was a strong trend toward the solution of the problem of efficient locomotion in a fashion different from that adopted by the synapsids. Instead of evolving an improved quadrupedal gait, the front limbs were abandoned in locomotion, and fast bipedal running was attained by elongation and adaptation of the hind legs. This new stance came into being among archosaurs during the Triassic, when early carnivorous archosaurs, known as thecodonts, began a successful competition with the therapsids; by the late Triassic there had evolved carnivorous dinosaurs, which were to dominate the earth during the 100 million years or more which constituted the remainder of the Mesozoic era.

THE RISE OF MAMMALS

The mammal-like reptiles, then, disappeared from the scene, to give way to the dinosaurs, but not without having left behind, as their descendants, the mammals, small early representatives of which, not too far from therapsids in structure, have recently been found in deposits of late Triassic age. These mammalian descendants of the therapsids persisted through the next 100 million years of dinosaurian dominance, but survived only as small and inconspicuous forms. Their history during this long period (20) is sparse and fragmentary; except, perhaps for the late Cretaceous, all known materials (should one treat them so irreverently) would probably little more than fill a derby hat. But this time of tribulation under the constant menace of the dinosaurs was not a wasted one. The first mammals were probably little above the reptilian level; by the close of the Cretaceous, when the dinosaurs became extinct, they had reached a high degree of organization and were competent to take over the rulership of the world.

If we were to attempt to define a mammal briefly, it could perhaps be done in two words — activity and intelligence. We mentioned earlier body improvements in therapsids which made them swift-running quadrupeds; in mammals generally, this four-footed gait is retained and improved. Maintenance of body temperature (toward which end a hairy or furry covering is one adaptation) enables a mammal to be active (quite in contrast to a reptile) at any temperature. Therapsids were active forms, but, as the fossils show, still small-brained, still essentially thoughtless automata. By the end of the Mesozoic, the mammal brain had become highly developed; the cerebral hemispheres were large and complex; learning and training were possible, so that, in a broad sense of the word, intelligence had come into the world. Because the cerebral cortex is a complex organ, as much time as possible should be allowed in the development of the individual so that this important structure may reach its full potentialities before it is put to use. Reproductive improvements in mammals work toward this end. Mammals (except for two archaic types) bear their young alive, and in the higher mammals — generally termed the placentals — there had developed by the end of the Mesozoic a highly efficient nutrient connection, the placenta, between the mother and the fetus within her uterus, so that birth can be delayed until the young reach a much larger size and more mature structure than it was possible for them to do in an egg-laying form. The nursing habit extends further the time before the youngster is forced to live its own life. During this period, the young mammal can be trained and taught; in a sense, we can say that in the nursing habit we see the establishment of the world's first educational institution.

Some of these features, which were to be eventually responsible for mammalian success, were quite surely developed by their therapsid ancestors; most, however, appear to have been brought about as adaptations and advances necessary for the survival of our feeble mammalian ancestors under the reptilian tyranny. As mammals, we owe a debt of gratitude to the dinosaurs for their unintended aid.

LIFE IN THE TREES: PRIMATES

By the close of the Mesozoic and the dawn of Cenozoic times, the evolution of higher mammals had been completed, and there were forms well equipped to take over world dominance from the ruling reptiles. The small ancestral placental types of that day were (as their ancestors had been for innumerable millions of years) potentially carnivores, but we believe that, due to their modest size, they must have contented themselves with insects and grubs as food staples. Forms surviving today with similar diets are considered members of an order Insectivora, of which the shrews are the most characteristic representatives. But while the shrews, in their small size and inconspicuous habits, give us a picture of the life which the early placental mammals must have led under the reign of the dinosaurs, even they have developed certain specializations which remove them from a truly central position in placental evolutionary history. The actual ancestors, of 70 million or so years ago, are extinct; but if we look about us for living forms which appear to be closest to the primitive stock, the choice, I believe, falls on the tree shrews, *Tupaia* and related genera, of the Oriental region. These attractive little animals are often considered as possible ancestors of the primates; but there is little in their structure to prevent them from being considered as playing a still more important role, that of forms approaching most closely the parental stock of all higher mammals.

Once the dinosaurs passed from the scene, the ancestral placental mammals rapidly began a radiation into the varied mammalian types which are with us today — from rats to cats, to bats, to whales, to hoofed mammals of all sorts, and so on. All of these types have had interesting and often spectacular careers in the approximately 70 million years of the Cenozoic Era, the age of mammals. But if we wish (conceitedly) to continue our story in the direction of ourselves, the one mammalian order which comes into focus is that of the Primates, including lemurs, monkeys, apes — and men (Figure 3).

The primates are (with a few exceptions, such as men and baboons) tree-dwellers, and such success as man and his primate relatives have had can be attributed in great measure to features associated with arboreal life (21).

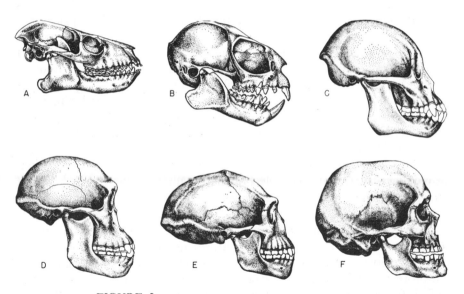

FIGURE 3

Series of skulls of primates, essentially in phylogenetic sequence, showing particularly forward turning of the eyes, reduction of the "nose," and braincase enlargement. (A) Fossil lemur *Notharctus;* (B) Eocene tarsioid *Tetonius* (the dentition is aberrant); (C) Miocene dryopithecine ape "*Proconsul*"; (D) *Australopithecus* of the early Pleistocene; (E) "*Pithecanthropus*" (*Homo erectus*) of the middle Pleistocene; (F) Modern man. [(A) and (B) after Gregory, (C) after Napier and Le Gros Clark, (D) after Robinson, (E) and (F) after McGregor]

Locomotion in the trees, as practiced by primates, demands flexibility and agility, and the primate skeleton is much more generalized in nature than is that of most other mammals. Small tree-dwellers, such as squirrels, may climb trees by digging in their claws; primates, generally of rather larger bulk, have adopted another method — they have developed an opposable thumb and big toe, so that a branch may be grasped. Arboreal life has caused a marked change in the development of sense organs. In most mammals, smell is highly developed, while vision, as far as one can tell, is of a rather fuzzy nature. In the trees, olfaction is unimportant and is greatly reduced (as the snout is) in higher primates. Accurate vision, on the contrary, is essential for safe locomotion in the trees; we find that, in all but the lowest of primates, the eyes, primitively rather laterally directed, are turned forward so that the two fields of vision are identical, and stereoscopic vision, with depth effects and distance judgment, is developed. Further, higher primates have in each retina a central area in which detail is clearly perceived.

The brain of mammals is, in general, highly developed; in primates, its development is of a still higher type than in most other placentals. Locomotor agility in the trees demands a high development of motor centers in the cerebrum, and it is suggestive that the major brain area devoted to the highest mental faculties develops in an area (frontal) alongside the motor centers. Again, the development of good eyesight has rendered possible a far wider knowledge of their environment for primates than for forms which depend upon smell. Also important in primate mentality has been the development of the grasping hand as a sensory aid in the examination of objects. With the potential advantages to be gained from any trend toward increased mental ability, it is not surprising that, in monkeys, apes, and men, selection has resulted in the development of large brains and greatly extended areas of the gray matter of the cerebral cortex.

In early Tertiary times, numerous remains of primitive primates in the lemur stage of primate evolution were present in the fossil beds of both North America and Europe. In the lemurs, which today survive mainly in the protective isolation of Madagascar, primate evolutionary trends have but begun; for example, there is still a large muzzle, and the eyes are directed more laterally than anteriorly. But, early in the fossil record, there are remains of a more advanced primate type, of which the living *Tarsius* of the East Indies is a surviving member. *Tarsius* itself is a somewhat specialized little animal, but shows clearly the advances already present in its early Tertiary relatives. Smell is reduced, and the nose is a mere nubbin; the large eyes are turned straight forward, with the development of stereoscopic vision; the brain is quite large in proportion to body size.

Beyond the *Tarsius* stage, the evolution of higher primates occurred in two separate lines. The next higher level of organization, seen in the monkeys, was attained in one group of tarsioid descendants which migrated to South America and in a second group that developed in Eurasia. In Oligocene rocks of the Egyptian Fayum are found remains (if fragmentary) not only of ancestors of Old World monkeys, but also of small ancestors of the great apes which are man's closest relatives (22).

Of the living great apes, the gibbons and orang presumably split off at an early time. However, in mid-Tertiary rocks, widespread in Eurasia and Africa, there are found remains (mostly fragmentary, unfortunately) of a rather advanced type of great ape. The term *Dryopithecus*, the "oak ape," is generally applied to such remains; an East African member of the series is generally given the special name of *Proconsul*. In members of this group, we are dealing with apes of modest size which are relatively little specialized. As far as we know them, the oak apes appear to be potential ancestors of the chimpanzee, of the gorilla, and, not improbably, of man as well.

DOWN TO EARTH — MAN

Lower primates in general and even such higher apes as the gibbons and orang are definitely tree-dwellers. But the trend was reversed at the top of the primate series. The chimpanzee is less of an arboreal acrobat than the lower great apes, and the mountain gorilla of central Africa has almost completely abandoned tree-dwelling (but is essentially quadrupedal in locomotion on the ground). As yet, we know almost nothing of the late Tertiary history of the specific ancestors of man, but it is suggested, not unreasonably, that his abandonment of the trees may have been associated with reduction, in some of the Old World regions in which his ancestors lived, of a forest covering to a savanna-type of environment, with open areas between the copses; this would have encouraged ground locomotion and introduced prehumans to the possible advantages of terrestrial over arboreal life (23). In recent decades, a part-way step from ape to man has become known with discovery of the australopithecines, whose remains are primarily from South African caves (24). *Australopithecus* and his kin are, unquestionably, morphologically antecedent to man, and with one or two exceptions, all competent investigators in this field now agree that the australopithecines of the early Pleistocene are actual human ancestors. From mid-Pleistocene times, half a million or so years ago, we find remains of forms, such as *Pithecanthropus* and *Sinanthropus*, which are definitely human types, although with brains still well below modern levels and with many primitive features. Later in the Pleistocene, there appear more advanced forms and, toward the end of the Pleistocene Ice Age, some tens of thousands of years back, there appear in Eurasia and Africa representatives of our own species, *Homo sapiens*, fully as advanced as any living race.

SUMMARY

We have come to the end of our story — a long one, covering some half a billion years, it appears. A modern man or other higher vertebrate has traveled far from the simply built insensate type of creature seen in his ultimate metazoan ancestor among the pterobranchs. The course of this evolutionary progression is far from direct and simple, as some might believe to be the case; it is a trail with many twists and turns. Nor is there the slightest reason to attempt a teleological interpretation; there is no trace of design and direction toward an obvious goal. Quite in contrast, it seems clear in many stages of the series that the changes which have taken place are immediately beneficial ones, strongly subject to selection. Obvious, too, is the fact that special environmental factors, biological and physical, have added unexpected quirks to the story. The development of a motile "tadpole" larva at an early chordate stage led to a sharp shift in an evolutionary sequence which otherwise might have simply ended in a sedate filtering form of tunicate type. The development of plant life on the continents opened up to motile chordates a new environment into which few invertebrates could enter and in which the chordates flourished to progress to the vertebrate level. The need for armor as defense against eurypterid enemies appears to have initiated the development of bony

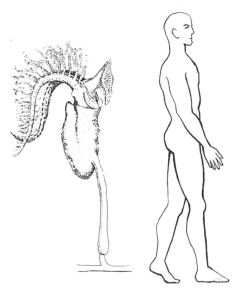

FIGURE 4

Beginning and end of the story. (left) Pterobranch. *Rhabdopleura*, much enlarged, showing the simply built, stalked body, with food-collecting arms above; (right) modern man. [*Rhabdopleura* after Delage and Herouard]

skeletal structures, without which the higher vertebrates could never have developed. The widespread late Paleozoic condition of seasonal drought favored progressive developments which, with the attainment of a reptilian stage, had the happy accidental result of the vertebrate conquest of the land, a conquest aided by the emergence of the insects as a basic food supply. The long period of dinosaur dominance seems to have been responsible for the sharpened wits which made the mammalian descendants of the therapsids competent for terrestrial dominance when the reign of the ruling reptiles ended. The arboreal life of primates was finally abandoned by man, but tree-dwelling had endowed his ancestors with advances in brain, eyes, and hands that were highly advantageous when this relatively feeble creature descended to the ground. It has been a long and tortuous journey; but every stage of it shows its effects in the structures and functions of such an end product as ourselves (Figure 4).

REFERENCES

1. L. du Noüy, *Human Destiny* (New York: New American Library, 1947).
2. An excellent account of prevertebrates is given by C. Dawydoff [in *Traité de Zoologie XI*, P.-P. Grassé, Ed. (1948), p. 367].
3. W. Garstang, *Quart. J. Microscop. Sci.* 72:51 (1928); J. Z. Young, *The Life of Vertebrates* (Oxford, 1950), chap. 3.
4. E. A. Stensiö, *Skr. Svalbard Nordishavet* No. 12 (1927); *The Cephalaspids of Great Britain* (London: British Museum of Natural History, 1932).
5. A. S. Romer, *Amer. Midland Natur.* 16:805 (1935); *Deep-Sea Research* 3 (suppl.), 261 (1955).
6. H. W. Smith, *Quart. Rev. Biol.* 7:1 (1932).
7. For example, R. H. Denison, *Fieldiana Geol.* 11:359 (1956); J. D. Robertson, *Biol. Rev.* 32:156 (1957).
8. A. S. Romer, *Science* 78:114 (1933).
9. ———, *Amer. Natur.* 76:394 (1942).
10. ———, in *Bone Dynamics*, H. M. Frost, ed. (Boston: Little, Brown, 1964), p. 13.
11. ———, *Bull. Mus. Comp. Zool.* 99:1 (1947).
12. ———, *ibid.* 131:129 (1964).
13. T. S. Parsons and E. E. Williams, *Quart. Rev. Biol.* 38:26 (1963).
14. A. S. Romer, *Amer. J. Sci.* 248:628 (1950); D. Baird, *Amer. Zool.* 5:287 (1965).
15. J. Barrell, *J. Geol.* 16:159, 255, 363 (1908); *Bull. Geol. Soc. Amer.* 23:377 (1912).

16. A. S. Romer, *Proc. Amer. Philos. Soc.* 100:157 (1956).
17. R. L. Carroll, *J. Linn. Soc. London Zool.* 45:61 (1964); D. Baird and R. L. Carroll, *Science* 157:56 (1967).
18. A. S. Romer, *Sci. Mon.* 55:57 (1957).
19. —— and L. I. Price, *Geol. Soc. Amer. Spec. Papers* 28, (1940); A. S. Romer, in *International Colloquium on the Evolution of Mammals* (Brussels, 1961), vol. 1, p. 9.
20. Summarized by G. G. Simpson, in *International Colloquium on the Evolution of Mammals* (Brussels, 1961), vol. 1, p. 57.
21. G. Elliot Smith, *The Evolution of Man* (Oxford, 1927); W. E. Le Gros Clark, *The Antecedents of Man: An Introduction to the Evolution of the Primates* (Chicago, 1960).
22. E. L. Simons, *Amer. Mus. Novitates* No. 1976 (1959); *ibid.* No. 2051 (1961); *Postilla* No. 64 (Yale Peabody Museum, 1964).
23. See, for example, G. Heberer, *Die Evolution der Organismen* (Stuttgart: Gustav Fischer Verlag, ed. 2, 1959), pp. 1110–1142.
24. An excellent review of this and later stages in the human story is by W. E. Le Gros Clark [*The Fossil Evidence for Human Evolution* (Chicago: Univ. of Chicago Press, ed. 2, 1964)].

II
PRIMATE
EVOLUTION

VINCENT SARICH

5 A Molecular Approach to the Question of Human Origins

A little more than 100 years ago Thomas Henry Huxley wrote that:

> ... whatever system of organs be studied, the comparison of their modifications in the ape series leads to one and the same result — that the structural differences which separate Man from the Gorilla and Chimpanzee are not so great as those which separate the Gorilla from the lower apes. [Ed. note: by "lower apes" Huxley meant Old World monkeys.]

Time has served to vindicate this early view, even among the general public, for it is the African apes (chimpanzee and gorilla) with whom man most closely identifies upon his visits to zoos. Their basic anatomy and behavior are so strikingly reminiscent of our own that it is difficult to avoid a feeling of close kinship. The translation of this empathy into an evolutionary context explains the similarities as being characters retained from a common ancestor, and the differences as having developed since the time that the lines leading to ourselves and the African apes began their independent development. The nature of this gap, however, Huxley saw as a very important issue:

> It would be no less wrong than absurd to deny the existence of this chasm, but it is at least equally wrong and absurd to exaggerate its magnitude, and, resting on the admitted fact of its existence, refuse to inquire whether it is wide or narrow.

Now, in spite of the vast effort that has been devoted to the study of human evolution since Huxley's time, one can still find no measure of agreement on the size of this chasm. Although most anthropologists generally regard the gorilla and chimpanzee as man's closest living relatives, estimates of the time of divergence of the human lineage from that (or those) leading to the African apes vary widely. In recent years this time has been given to be as short as two to four million years by Washburn in 1965 and as long as twenty-five to thirty million years independently by Leakey,

Simons, and Pilbeam in 1967. These disagreements among people looking at the same data are due in part to the fragmentary nature of the fossil record that consists mainly of teeth and jaws, and in part to the failure of traditional comparative anatomy to develop methods that would lead to agreement, even among anatomists, as to the evolutionary meaning of such data. Even more extreme opinions have been ventured, but this tenfold range of time has to be narrowed appreciably before one can begin any serious investigation of human origins and evolution. A beginning for the human line some three million years ago would almost necessitate an ancestor not unlike the modern pygmy chimpanzee *(Pan paniscus)*, whereas a beginning thirty million years ago would require a derivation from an ancestor that had barely reached the monkey grade of primate evolution. The australopithecines do take the hominid line back to about three million years but the hominid and pongid fossil record beyond this point is a most unsuitable one. The basic question then becomes one of whether the gap between data points is to be no more than one or two million years or about twenty-five million years.

Looking at this situation in early 1965, Allan Wilson (of the Biochemistry Department, University of California, Berkeley) and I decided that the continued analysis of anatomical characters did not appear likely to soon resolve the problem convincingly. As its solution is basic to the whole study of human evolution, we undertook to look more closely at the proteins of man and his primate relatives to see if perhaps biochemistry might succeed in answering Huxley's 100 year old question. Though, as will be seen later, our answer (that man and the African apes derive from a common ancestral species still living in the late Pliocene five million years ago) has not yet proved acceptable to major segments of the anthropological and paleontological community, it is difficult to fault in terms of its own logic. In addition, as will be seen, it has had the far more important virtue of being consistent with the whole body of other molecular evidence obtained subsequent to our original proposal (made in *Science*, 158, 1200–1203, 1967). Finally, this recent date in the late Pliocene can enormously simplify the study of our own evolution.

One should not, however, get the impression that the idea of obtaining evolutionary information from molecules rather than muscles, bones, or teeth was the creation of Sarich and Wilson — it goes back nearly seventy years to an English parasitologist named Nuttall, who wrote in 1902 after a pioneering study in the then nascent science of immunology:

> I do not wish these numbers to be taken as final, nevertheless they show the essential correctness of the previous crude results. To obtain a constant it will be necessary to make repeated tests with the blood of each species with different dilutions and different proportions of antiserum. I am inclined to believe that

with care we shall perhaps be able to "measure species" with this method, for it appears that there are measurable differences in the reactions obtained with related blood, in other words, determine degrees of relationship which we may be able to formulate (British Medical Journal 1:825–827, 1902).

The basis of the molecular approach is, of course, the fact that as organisms evolve, so does their constituent genetic material (DNA) and its functional product (proteins). The peculiar advantage lies in the commonality of DNA and proteins structures in all organisms; i.e., the units (four organic bases for DNA and twenty amino acids for proteins) are identical and it is only the particular sequences in which they are arranged that vary from species to species. Since the units are identical, then, the extent of evolutionary change between a pair of related species is readily quantifiable in a manner common to all extant forms of life.

This evolutionary process is illustrated in Table 1 by a single DNA codon, say GCT (guanine-cytosine-thymine), that instructs the protein synthesizing machinery of the cell to incorporate the amino acid arginine into a developing protein that may have several hundred amino acids in its complete structure, each one of which will be coded for by a sequence of three bases in the DNA. Evolutionary change develops when a mutation occurs and survives the crucible of the selective process (that is, when it is found to be either neutral or advantageous). For example, our GCT codon might mutate to GAT (A for adenine) and we would obtain leucine instead of arginine in the protein. In about 20 per cent of all mutations, because of the redundancy (degeneracy) of the code, a mutation might have no effect on protein structure — GCA, GCT, GCC, and GCG all code for arginine. Thus a mutation from GCT to GCA would affect only the DNA and might well have no functional effects — no matter what the third base in the GC- codon, we always obtain arginine in the protein. The evolutionary process, then, at its most basic level, involves a change (mutation) in the DNA which is incorporated into the ongoing gene pool of the evolving species and which can be reflected by a corresponding change in the amino acid sequence of the particular protein coded for by that gene. Such a process, multiplied millions of times in millions of different populations over hundreds of millions of years has given rise to the bewildering diversity of molecular and morphological structures that we see in today's world.

We might state as a basic rule that such a process will generally have to produce divergence when any two populations become isolated from one another, as a relative rarity of mutations and the finite size of populations make it statistically improbable that identical changes will be available for either natural selection or drift to incorporate into the ongoing gene pools. As long as no interbreeding takes place, then, our two populations will

TABLE 1. THE DNA CODONS AS PRESENTLY KNOWN.
ATT, ATC, AND ACT DO NOT CODE FOR ANY AMINO ACID

Codons	Amino Acid	Codons	Amino Acid	Codons	Amino Acid	Codons	Amino Acid
AAA, AAG	Phenylalanine	AGA, AGG, AGT, AGC	Serine	ATA, ATG	Tyrosine	ACA, ACG	Cysteine
AAT, AAC	Leucine			ATT, ATC	Stop	ACT	Stop
						ACC	Tryptophan
GAA, GAG, GAT, GAC	Leucine	GGA, GGG, GGT, GGC	Proline	GTA, GTG	Histidine	GCA, GCG, GCT, GCC	Arginine
				GTT, GTC	Glutamine		
TAA, TAG, TAT	Isoleucine	TGA, TGG, TGT, TGC	Threonine	TTA, TTG	Asparagine	TCA, TCG	Serine
TAC	Methionine			TTT, TTC	Lysine	TCT, TCC	Arginine
CAA, CAG, CAT, CAC	Valine	CGA, CGG, CGT, CGC	Alanine	CTA, CTG	Aspartic acid	CCA, CCG, CCT, CCC	Glycine
				CTC, CTT	Glutamic acid		

become increasingly different from one another and we may then compare protein structures in the modern representatives as a measure of the differences between the two lines.

Thus, to measure species, in Nuttall's terms, we need only to measure the extent of DNA and/or protein sequence difference between them. Several techniques of measurement are available, none of which is technically simple, but three — DNA hybridization, protein sequencing, and immunology — have been widely used with the results showing a comforting concordance to the student of human evolution. To summarize at the outset, all of the presently available data are inconsistent with any date outside the range of about three–eight million years for the most recent time that a common ancestor of man, chimpanzee, and gorilla could have existed; they indicate a most probable figure in the area of four–five million years, i.e., in the latest Pliocene.

To date by molecules rather than by fossils, a process we have termed an evolutionary or molecular clock, would appear to have been first proposed by Emile Zuckerkandl and Linus Pauling in the early 1960's. Though a number of scientists have discussed this concept since that time, to our knowledge no one had seriously applied it to a specific evolutionary problem prior to the Sarich-Wilson *Science* article already referred to.

That work was based on the study of a single molecule, serum albumin. Questions have been raised about the value of a single locus for probing evolutionary relationships among species containing thousands of loci. The justification lies in the fact that this locus has evolved as a part of the organisms that make up the lineages culminating in those species we see and compare today. Its history is, therefore, necessarily the history of those lineages. In other words, the times of divergence between the various albumin lineages are the same as the times of divergence between the species themselves.

Serum albumins are single polypeptide chains consisting of ca. 570 amino acids and are found in the serum of all tetrapod vertebrates (and probably also in fish). The order of the 570 amino acids (of twenty different kinds) of course varies from species to species and it is this variation that formed the basis for our study. Ideally a comparative study of protein evolution would be carried out by working out the exact sequences of amino acids in a series of primate albumins (or some other appropriate protein). This ideal, however, was not technically feasible for our study because amino acid sequences are not easy to generate; we therefore took a somewhat less precise but far more efficient approach to the evolutionary information contained in these sequences. Instead of working out the sequences, we measured the differences between them by the use of immunological techniques.

Our procedure began by purifying the desired serum albumin from a single primate — for the human sample, I was the source. After purifying my albumin and those of several other primate species, they were injected into a large series of rabbits. When a vertebrate is exposed to a foreign substance, it responds by making antibodies to it. This reaction is the basis of immunizations against disease (e.g., smallpox or polio), rejections in transplants, and allergies. A rabbit does of course contain albumin, but since rabbits and primates shared a common ancestor their respective albumins have been evolving in different directions and so are today very different molecules. Thus a primate albumin is very much a foreign substance to a rabbit. •The antibodies the rabbit produces are themselves proteins and possess reactive ends that "recognize" specific areas (called antigenic sites) on the albumin with which they are injected. These antigenic sites are in no sense well-defined areas intrinsic to the albumin; they are sets of five to eight amino acids which are different from those in the corresponding area on rabbit albumin and which are therefore potentially capable of triggering antibody production in the rabbit. No single rabbit will recognize all possible antigenic sites, nor will each rabbit recognize the same sites. The use of a number of rabbits per primate albumin species, then, provides immunological coverage for a large part of the albumin molecule. This mixture of sera from injected rabbits was our test reagent that was to be reacted with a series of primate albumins. The degree of recognition or cross reaction would then depend on the number of amino acid differences between the homologous albumin (the albumin injected) and the heterologous test albumin. Simplifying the actual situation only slightly, the total reaction would represent the sum of all individual antigenic site-antibody reactions where, if the sites are identical in the homologous and heterologous albumins, one gets a 100 per cent reaction; if the heterologous site has one amino acid difference, one obtains about 50 per cent reaction, and if the heterologous site has two substitutions, there is no reaction. The difference between the homologous and heterologous albumins is calculated on a scale that states that if the homologous and heterologous albumins are immunologically identical, the ID is zero, whereas the weakest cross reactions represent immunological distances of about 200 units. For serum albumins one ID unit is equal to slightly less than one amino acid substitution; i.e., the weakest cross reactions represent about a 30 per cent difference in the two sequences.

These sera from rabbits injected with my own serum albumin and with those of many other primate species were then used to measure differences between many pairs of primate albumins. This process has been repeated for many carnivore, artiodactyl (odd-toed hoofed mammals), perissodactyl (horses, rhinos, tapirs), and other mammalian albumins. The data obtained are almost without exception consistent with the hypothesis that albumin evolution has been the result of a situation where the probability of an amino acid substitution occurring in a given length of time has been the same for *each* albumin lineage throughout its existence. Recent work in our laboratory would suggest that the *same* statistical rate of change applies to amphibian and reptilian albumins as well.

The results of such an evolutionary process can be glimpsed by considering a series of primate albumins: man, chimpanzee, rhesus monkey, and spider monkey. Antisera to all four are available and the following data were obtained (in immunological distances):

Man-chimp	7	Chimp-rhesus monkey	30
Man-rhesus monkey	32	Chimp-spider monkey	56
Man-spider monkey	58	Rhesus monkey-spider monkey	56

If one goes beyond the higher primates (man, apes, and New and Old World monkeys) to the prosimians, the distances jump sharply to 110–140 units, and for those non-primate mammals that show measurable reactions they are greater than 160 units. Even from this limited survey several things are apparent. Clearly the human-chimp difference, relative to the total evolutionary differentiation at the mammalian albumin locus, is a very small one. I might point out here that it is also quite comparable to the distances between the albumins of the following pairs of familiar and closely related species: domestic cat-lion, 7; sheep-goat, 6; dog-fox, 9; horse-donkey, 5; horse-zebra, 8. In addition, we can readily deduce the meaning of this minuscule human-chimp difference by asking whether it might be part of a pattern of less rapid evolution of ape and human albumins relative to the rates seen in other primate lineages. If this were the case, then ape and human albumins would be seen as less changed than, for example, those of the Old World monkeys because of their increased reactivity with antisera to the albumins of the New World monkeys or prosimians. That this is not the case is evident from the fact that human, chimp, and rhesus monkey albumins are almost equally different from that of the spider monkey indicating that since man, chimp, and rhesus monkey last shared a common ancestor, their albumins have undergone very similar amounts of albumin evolution.

One can readily extend this type of analysis into the development of an actual phylogenetic tree for man, chimp, and the two monkey species by using two prosimian albumins, those of lemur and slow loris, as reference points. The following mean distances have been obtained: to man, 123; to chimp, 120; to rhesus monkey, 120; to spider monkey, 121 (see Figure 1). The albumin difference between man and spider monkey is 58 units, therefore $a + c + e + f = 58$. By the same logic $a + c + e + g + h = 123$ and $f + g + h = 121$. Now:

$$a + c + e + g + h = 123$$
$$f + g + h = 121$$

subtracting

$$a + c + e - f = 2$$

however

$$a + c + e + f = 58$$

$$2a + 2c + 2e = 60$$
$$\therefore a + c + e = 30 \text{ and } f = 28$$

Reasoning along similar lines: $a = 4$, $b = 3$, $c = 13$, $d = 15$, $e = 13$. Clearly g and h cannot be calculated unless a non-primate reference point is used. Such a calculation has been done, but it is not necessary to discuss it here.

It is always possible, given the appropriate reference species, to reconstruct the phylogeny of any group of modern species and, of particular importance, calculate the amounts of evolutionary change that took place along those lineages leading to the modern species. To reconstruct the phylogeny of Figure 1, for example, we need only assume that lineage g existed; that is, that man, chimp, rhesus monkey, and spider monkey shared a common ancestor that lived subsequent to the divergence of the lines

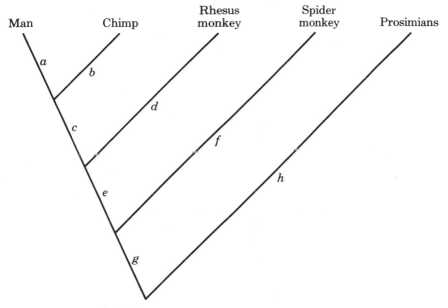

FIGURE 1

A phylogeny of several primate taxa. Each letter indicates the amount of albumin evolution that took place along that lineage. The albumin distance separating any two species is thus the sum of the changes that occurred along the lineages that connect the two species.

leading to lemur and loris. Given that assumption, verifiable by using non-primate albumins as reference points, the internal phylogeny of the higher primates can be developed using only molecular data (Figure 2).

The picture of evolutionary regularity shown by the four primate albumins does not change when the number is increased — the pattern of regularity always remains. This regularity, as discussed above, would appear to have a large random component whose evolutionary outcome is best described in terms of a Poisson distribution. An appropriate homology is the process of radioactive decay. Let us, for example, posit a C^{14} sample that over a period of thirty days provided 1500 decay events. This total of 1500 would not, however, be made up of a set of thirty 50-count days, but of a set of daily counts whose distribution would approximate that given in Figure 3 where the Poisson mean is fifty. The Poisson distribution describes the expected results of a process where the probability of a given individual event remains constant over time and is thus appropriate to the radioactive decay situation — where each C^{14} atom has an equal probability of decaying in a given interval of time. It is also appropriately applied to the process

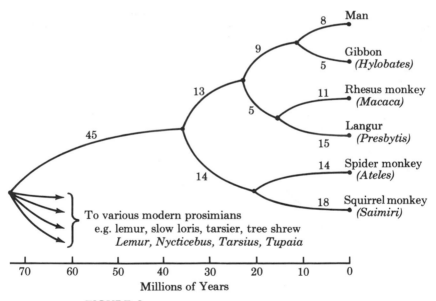

FIGURE 2

A phylogeny of the major higher primate groups. The number on each lineage indicates the amount of albumin evolution (measured immunologically) that took place along it. It is of particular importance to note the large amount of albumin evolutionary history that the higher primates share subsequent to their divergence from any lineage leading to a modern prosimian.

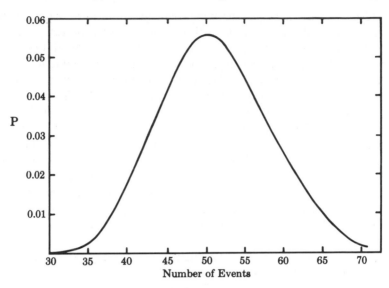

FIGURE 3

A Poisson distribution representing the probability of obtaining a specific number of decay events when the mean is fifty events per day. Note that quite appreciable deviations from the mean are to be expected — and found, as some of the data in Figure 2 indicate.

of protein evolution, not so much because we know a priori the mechanisms of protein evolution, but because evolutionary rate tests (such as that discussed above for human, chimp, rhesus monkey, and spider monkey albumins) consistently give a distribution approximating the Poisson.

One need not explain this phenomenon of regularity to use it, but it does perhaps require some consideration in view of the well-known haphazard nature of the evolutionary process when dealing with anatomical features. A currently feasible explanation has been suggested by Kimura (*Nature 217*, 624–626, 1968) and King and Jukes (*Science 164*, 788–798, 1969) who have pointed out that this regularity could be due to the inexorable fixation of neutral mutations at a low but constant probability in the reality of evolutionary time. Neutral mutations are those "unseen" by the selective process — unseen because they are functionally and therefore selectively equivalent to the original amino acid. As King and Jukes have so elegantly put it:

> Natural selection is the editor, rather than the composer, of the genetic message. One thing the editor does *not* do is to remove changes which it is unable to perceive.

Beyond this quota of surviving neutral mutations, whose evolutionary accretion will follow a statistically determined pattern, will be those substitutions conferring a change in fitness. One might have amino acid changes that increase the fitness in a particular environment; conversely the relative proportion of maladaptive to neutral mutations might be increased in some evolutionarily conservative context. Such positive or negative selection will introduce a nonrandom element that should then be seen as "irregularity." On the basis of the presently available data, both immunological and direct sequence, one suspects that this nonranrom element must be rather minor (though hardly unimportant). Whether or not the neutral mutation model is correct has no bearing on the observed regularity of mammalian albumin evolution. The regularity is there (and not assumed as some of our critics would have it) and its presence allows the use of the primate albumin locus as an evolutionary clock subject to statistical considerations.

A clock must be calibrated in the form of an equation ID $=$ kT where T is the time of divergence between two species and ID is the difference between their albumins in immunological distance units. k must be calculated using a known T corresponding to a measured ID. Once k is set, other times of divergence can be calculated. Since these calculated dates will be relative dates dependent on the accuracy of the assumed calibrating date, one desires a calibrating date subject to as little uncertainty as possible. Looking at the available mammalian data, it appears that the most reasonable equation would be an albumin immunological distance of 100 units set equal to a most probable (in the Poisson sense) time of separation of sixty million years. That is $100 = k$ $(60 \times 10^6$ years) and thus, $k = 1.67$ units per million years of separation or 0.83 units per million years per lineage. Unless the paleontologists are completely wrong in their assessment of all early mammalian history (and whatever our disagreements on the question of human origins this seems very unlikely), this figure is unlikely to require serious adjustment in the future. The picture for primate evolution in general and ape and human evolution in particular derived from this albumin study is given in Figures 2 and 4.

On the specific point of the human–African ape relationship, the albumins of man, chimpanzee, and gorilla stand equidistant from one another with seven units separating any pair of the trio. As there is no indication that the albumins of the apes and man are conservative in their pattern of evolutionary change (that is, they are just as evolved as those of the New and Old World monkeys) a direct application of the albumin clock is indicated. At seven units of albumin immunological distance and 1.67 units of evolution per million years of separation this works out to slightly more than four million years ago as the last time man, chimp, and gorilla shared a common ancestor. The albumin clock also indicates that the Asiatic apes diverged at an appreciably earlier time — the orang at around seven–eight million years and the gibbon at around ten–twelve million.

These dates, particularly for the evolution of the modern apes and man, are, in terms of most current anthropological and paleontological opinion, far too recent. The idea that all the modern apes (chimpanzee, gorilla, orang, gibbon, siamang) share with man a late Miocene to early Pliocene ancestor and that the chimpanzee, gorilla, and man derive from a single species still living in late Pliocene times is disturbing to most students in the field. In view of this and in view of the fact that some degree of statistical and experimental uncertainty exists in our calculations, it is interesting to analyze other genetic data concerning human evolution along the lines given above. Table 2 lists some of these data where comparisons among ape, human, and Old World monkey molecules are available. One notes the interesting fact that the albumin difference seems in no way unique — a result we should have expected from our earlier conclusion that there is a single phylogeny for any group of species and that the phylogeny of a protein locus (or the whole DNA) must be coincident with the phylogeny of the species themselves. Nevertheless, in view of the relative novelty of the molecular approach to evolutionary history, the relative concordance among these various comparisons is comforting.

TABLE 2

Molecule	Human-chimp difference	Human–Old World monkey difference (mean)	Type of comparison
Albumin	7	35	immunological
Hemoglobin	0	15	amino acid sequences
Transferrin	3	30	immunological
Fibrinopeptides	0	7	amino acid sequences
DNA	2.6	10.7	hybridization

It is possible to analyze the hemoglobin data in somewhat greater detail and provide some probability values for our temporal conclusions. As mentioned in Table 2, man and chimpanzee have identical hemoglobins (the gorilla is different from both by two substitutions), whereas the recently sequenced hemoglobin of the rhesus monkey differs from them by about fifteen mutational events. It could be argued that human and chimpanzee hemoglobins are identical because hemoglobin evolution has been slow among the African apes and man. However, if this were the case, then human and chimpanzee hemoglobins should be less different than the hemoglobin of rhesus monkey is from that of some species outside the catarrhines. One such reference point is the horse, from which human, chimpanzee, and rhesus monkey hemoglobins are equally different. Again this result should not be surprising in view of what has already been said concerning the regularity of the protein evolutionary process. Some calculations are also in order. The estimated time of divergence of the apes and Old World monkeys is about twenty-three million years using the albumin data. The average rate of hemoglobin evolution among mammals is about one amino acid substitution per 3.5 million years. Human and rhesus monkey hemoglobins differ by fifteen amino acid substitutions that would correspond to 15×3.5 or 52 million years of evolution apportioned along the two lineages indicating twenty-six million years for the most recent common ancestor of man and rhesus monkey. In view of the small number of changes involved, the concordance of the albumin and hemoglobin dates is heartening.

Now clearly the calculation of an exact time of divergence from the human-chimp-gorilla hemoglobin data is unwarranted for statistical reasons, but these data are obviously compatible with the albumin date of four–five million years. More important, the results are incompatible with the divergence time of twenty–thirty million years that is the general view of most paleontologists and anthropologists today. If we apply the probability model for protein evolution discussed in this article to this case, then we can calculate using the Poisson distribution that there is less than one chance in 10^5 that a sequence difference of zero–two residues could result from a divergence time of thirty million years, and from one chance in 100 to one chance in 1,000 if the date were fifteen million years. Obviously the same probability considerations can be applied to the independently derived albumin date, thus making the combined probability that any date for the hominid-pongid divergence could approach even ten million years vanishingly low. The other protein data given in Table 2, though not subject to as detailed analysis because of the lack of data from the more primitive primates, are entirely consistent with the albumin-hemoglobin date and thoroughly inconsistent with the postulation of any appreciable antiquity for the origin of our lineage.

Added note: After this article was prepared, Dr. David Kohne of the Carnegie Institution kindly provided us with a manuscript on primate DNA evolution. It has been submitted to *Science* (co-authors are J. A. Chiscon and B. H. Hoyer). Their technique depends on the fact that the separated strands of the classic DNA double helix can, under proper conditions, be caused to renature and form the original double helix. Interestingly enough two single stranded DNAs from different species (provided their relationship is sufficiently close) can also form a "hybrid" DNA double helix. Because the DNAs of the two species have been evolving (changing) over the time period since the two species last shared a common ancestor, they will no longer be of perfect complementary fit; e.g., instead of the expected thymine, an adenine on one strand might find itself opposite a cytosine with no resultant bonding. This lack of perfect base pairing in the hybrid DNA will lower the heat stability of the hybrid molecules so that they will fall apart at a temperature lower than that found for the native DNA. For example, whereas the human DNA double helix is 50 per cent separated into its constituent single strands at 82.9°C., the temperature for the human-chimp hybrid is 81.2°C. This decrease of 1.7°C. translates into approximately 2.5 per cent of the nucleotide pairs being mismatched (e.g., adenine-cytosine instead of adenine-thymine). The precise data are shown in Table 3.

TABLE 3

Species compared	DNA[a] difference	DNA time[b] of divergence	Albumin[c] time of divergence
Human-chimp	2.5	5	4
Human-gibbon	6.1	13	11
Human-rhesus monkey	10.3	21	23
Human-capucin monkey	17.4	36	36
Rhesus monkey-green monkey	2.9	6	5

a These numbers represent the calculated percentage of base pair mismatches.
b Calculated using 36 million years for the human-capucin divergence.
c Calculated as discussed above using $k = 1.67$ Immunological distance units/million years and adjusting for any deviations from average amounts of change.

Considering the statistical and experimental uncertainties implicit in the albumin approach, and the relatively untested nature of the DNA approach, I see this agreement as remarkable and, in its way, supportive of both methods and interpretive deductions based on their data.

It is also interesting that the available albumin and fibrinopeptide data make it possible to scale the human-chimpanzee differences against those found in other groups. The human-chimp difference for both these proteins is as already pointed out for the albumins very similar to that found in other undoubtedly closely related pairs of mammalian species: dog-fox, domestic cat–lion, and horse-zebra. All in all, what appeared to be a position out on the end of a long limb taken by Allan Wilson and myself when we first published the albumin conclusions concerning the recency of the hominid-African ape split in 1967 is now beginning to look more and more reasonable as the molecular data accumulate.

It might be instructive to reflect upon what the molecular data and the paleontological times of divergence would lead us to conclude. In the albumin case, using a human-chimp divergence time of twenty million years (Simons and Ettel, *Sci. Am.*, 76–87, Jan. 1970) we should expect about thirty-three ID units of difference. We find seven. In the case of the fibrinopeptides, where the average rate of change is about one substitution per lineage per six million years, we might expect six differences between man and chimpanzee. We find none. For the hemoglobins (α and β chains combined) the average is about one substitution per vertebrate lineage per 3.5 million years (Kimura, 1969). Between man and chimp we might then expect ten differences. We find none. We have already shown that this lack of evolutionary change in the albumins [for the original paper see *Proc. Nat. Acad. Science*, 58, 142–148 (1967)] and hemoglobins [see *PNAS*, 63, 1088–1093 (1969)] cannot be due to retarded evolution in the chimp and/or human lineages. In view of the generally stochastic nature of protein evolution one might consider that much of the argument here is, in large part, an accident of history. It is entirely possible to imagine a situation where the molecular evidence might have come first and the paleontological and comparative anatomical data at some later time. Suggestions of any appreciable antiquity, then, for the African ape-hominid divergence might be greeted with as much skepticism as have been our protein conclusions. A couple of recent quotes might be appropriate here:

> A scale of relationship can be calculated from the magnitudes of the reactions between antihuman albumin and albumins from many primates. This scale can then be converted into units of time. Using this method, Sarich and Wilson have suggested that hominids and pongids were part of a common population about five million years ago. If Sarich and Wilson had looked more carefully at paleontological investigations, they would have found their suggestion is unwarranted. Their suggestion implies that some as yet undiscovered fossils, representative of a population ancestral to modern man, gorillas, and chimpanzees, will provide the evidence to support their interpretation ... there are some things that cannot be done with molecular data and some things that cannot be done with fossils, and I object to careless assumptions and thoughtless statements about evolutionary processes in

some of the conclusions drawn from the immunological data mentioned.

Unfortunately there is a growing tendency, which I would like to suppress if possible, to view the molecular approach to primate evolutionary studies as a kind of instant phylogeny. No hard work, no tough intellectual arguments. No fuss, no muss, no dishpan hands. Just throw some proteins into a laboratory apparatus, shake them up, and bingo! — we have an answer to questions that have puzzled us for at least three generations. [John Buettner-Janusch, *Transactions New York Academy of Science* 32, 132–133 (1969)]

If the immunological dates of divergence devised by Sarich are correct, then paleontologists have not yet found a single fossil related to the ancestry of any living primate[1] and the whole host of species which they have found are all parallelistic imitations of modern higher primates. I find this impossible to believe. Some fossil primates do exhibit evolution parallel to other forms, as is particularly well demonstrated in the case of the subfossil Malagasy lemurs, but it is not presently acceptable to assume that all the fossil primates resembling modern forms are only parallelisms, that highly arboreal apes wandered hundreds of miles out of Africa across the Pontian steppes of Eurasia in search of tropical rain forests, or that *Australopithecus* sprang full-blown five million years ago, as Minerva did from Jupiter, from the head of a chimpanzee or gorilla. [Elwyn Simons, *Annals New York Academy of Science* 167, 330 (1969).]

Rhetoric aside, all this says is that our conclusions somehow don't agree with the presently more or less accepted interpretations of the higher primate fossil record.

The point is that one has to be very careful in distinguishing between data and interpretation. There are molecular and paleontological and anatomical data, but the data often mean different things to different people and thus there are molecular and paleontological and anatomical interpretations of those data. There is, however, but a single evolutionary history or phylogeny for a group of species — therefore all interpretations of what happened and why and how it happened in the history of that group must use this single phyletic framework. One cannot legitimately use one phylogeny to explain the molecular data, another for the paleontological, and still a third for the anatomical. Conversely, one cannot legitimately derive three or more phylogenies from three such sets of data. We require that the various lines of evidence be used to place more and more marked constraints upon interpretations derived from other areas, and in this

[1] [This is silly, of course — *Australopithecus* is certainly ancestral to *Homo*. V. S.]

cybernetic fashion to more closely approach evolutionary reality. No single way leads to perfection; at present the protein picture lacks something in resolution, the fossil record is necessarily rather incomplete, and the anatomical data are often difficult to interpret. I have already discussed the particular advantages of the protein approach in developing the phyletic picture. As might be expected, then, it is not particularly difficult to interpret the available paleontological and anatomical evidence in terms of the short time scale protein phylogeny [see the following chapter and also O. J. Lewis, *Am. J. Phys. Anthrop.* 30, 251–268 (1969)]. I have yet to see any suggestion as to how a twenty million year date for the origin of the hominid line can possibly be used to explain the molecular evidence. To put it as bluntly as possible, I now feel that the body of molecular evidence on the *Homo-Pan* relationship is sufficiently extensive so that one no longer has the option of considering a fossil specimen older than about eight million years as a hominid *no matter what it looks like.*

If the living apes and man shared a common early Pliocene ancestor (ten–twelve million years ago), and if the African apes and man shared one in the late Pliocene (four–five million years ago), then the use of these dates allows the construction of a picture of ape evolution in general and human evolution in particular that has a certain elegance in its simplicity and utility. Washburn points out in the following article that the evolutionary unity of the modern apes and man is exemplified in certain details of anatomy in the upper part of the body that can all be viewed as parts of a locomotor-feeding adaptation, usually termed brachiation. Some specific aspects of this adaptation that serve to differentiate the living apes and man from their monkey relatives include the wide sternum, long clavicle, the large acromion process, and large deltoid muscle, and the fact that the flexor muscles of the upper limb (those facing forward when one stands with palms facing forward) are large relative to the extensors. The structure of the elbow and forearm allows a full 180° of pronation and supination (i.e., with upper arm immobile, the forearm can rotate through a full 180°). Full extension at the elbow is possible. The forearm bone in line with the little finger (ulna) does not articulate with the wrist bones, thus permitting man (and the apes, of course) to freely abduct and adduct in swinging from a limb and to flip a football fifty yards with a so-called "flick of the wrist." The upper limb and hand are very long in relation to the trunk (man, chimpanzees, and gorillas overlap appreciably in upper-limb/trunk length ratios). The lumbar vertebrae are few, and the lumbar region is short. The trunk is short, wide, and shallow. The preceding is condensed and annotated from another Washburn publication. He then went on to state:

> It seems most improbable that this detailed structural-functional similarity could be due to parallelism . . . parallelism means that animals resemble each other because similar groups have adapted in similar ways but that the lines are genetically

independent. To suggest that man evolved the structure of a brachiator by parallelism and not brachiating is to misunderstand the nature of parallel evolution. (*Classification and Human Evolution*, Aldine, p. 195.)

In addition to these details of post-cranial anatomy is the diagnostic difference between the specialized bilophondont molars of the Old World monkeys and the more primitive ape and human molars. The ape molar cusp pattern is a palaeontologically ancient one going back at least to the latter part of the Oligocene period (twenty-five–thirty million years ago), but the brachiating adaptation would appear not to be demonstrable in the primate fossil record. The Miocene apes, of which a fair number exist in the fossil record, I have therefore termed "dental apes." Unless we are being misled by the fossil record, then, the brachiating adaptation evolved after the time represented in the ape fossil record and before the beginning of the modern ape radiation. The molecular data discussed above place this beginning at ten–twelve million years in the past.

The numerous branches of the widespread group of Miocene apes (dryopithecines) must have therefore left but a single surviving lineage — a lineage that owes its unique evolutionary success to the development of the brachiating adaptation. The modern apes and man, as the living products of the adaptive radiation following this development, show similarities in basic pattern (reflecting the attainment of this new grade of organization), but differences in detail (representing the specific adaptations made along the various line comprising the adaptive radiation). The unity of the modern Hominoidea (apes and man) is thus based on the relatively short period of time during which a major adaptation was being evolved; their diversity is based on the relatively long period of time in which each line has been evolving independently of the others (Figure 4).

Our ancestors were, then, functional monkeys until about ten–fifteen million years ago, and brachiating apes until about 6 million years ago. Then apparently a terrestrial adaptation began. The chimpanzee and gorilla are both significantly terrestrial forms — using knuckle-walking to get along on the ground. In this context it is interesting to note the usual lack of hair on the back of our middle phalanges and speculate that this is an indication of a recent phase of knuckle-walking in our own ancestry. It would certainly be a perfect transition state from full brachiation (of which we are of course still perfectly capable) to a bipedal adaptation — the first indication of which comes with the earliest of the South African australopithecines who probably date to some three million years. One is thus left with from one to three million years of our history that remain undocumented by the fossil record and to which the molecular approach can contribute little. It is during this period that the hominid grade, characterized by the bipedal adaptation and reduction in size of the canine complex, was reached.

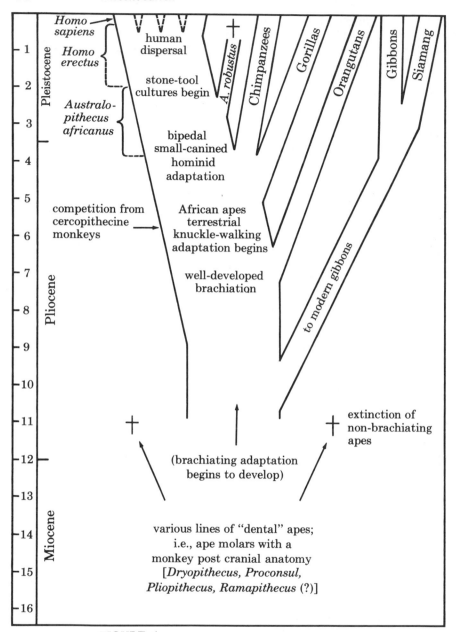

FIGURE 4

A detailed history of recent hominoid evolution. The indicated times of divergence are calculated from the available molecular evidence (albumin, hemoglobin, DNA). The descriptive captions are interpretive attempts to synthesize the biochemical, anatomical, and paleontological evidence.

As indicated in Figure 4, the suggestion is made that the adaptive radiation leading to the African apes and man began as a result of competition in the trees by the evolving cercopithecines (today the macaques, baboons, mangabeys, and guenons). I doubt that it is coincidental that the maximum immunological distances among the albumins of the modern cercopithecines (about eight units) and the differences in their DNAs are practically identical to those within the man-chimp-gorilla triad. This doubt is furthered when the absence of small and truly arboreal apes in Africa is noted. The modern cercopithecines are perhaps the most successful of the modern nonhuman primates and comprise about thirty-five species. The reasons for their recent evolutionary success are not yet clear but there is every reason to think that it was this success that, in effect, chased the African apes out of the trees into varying degrees of terrestrial adaptation made by the common ancestor of man, chimp, and gorilla; and that knuckle-walking represents the "transitional" phase only for man since the chimp and gorilla still operate in the terrestrial locomotor mode abandoned by our ancestors several millions of years ago.

This knuckle-walking transition phase (supported mainly by Washburn) has recently been most strongly contested by Tuttle (*Science 166*, 953–961, 1969):

> In so far as I can discern from dissections of numerous ape and human hands there are no features in the bones, ligaments, or muscles of the latter that give evidence for a history of knuckle-walking in man.

Accepting this assessment, how are we to incorporate it into the model being discussed? The point Tuttle misses, by managing to completely avoid mention of the molecular evidence, is that of time in grade. If knuckle-walking developed in the common ancestor of man and the African apes, then the protein data discussed here suggest that this phase could hardly have begun earlier than about seven million years ago. In view of the australopithecine evidence, the hominid knuckle-walking phase presumably ended no more than two or three million years later. Thus the chimpanzee and gorilla would have been knuckle-walkers some three to five times as long as our ancestors, and in addition, during the time that human ancestors have not been knuckle-walking (and presumably losing the adaptation) the gorilla and chimpanzee have been perfecting theirs. If we ignore these factors — suggested by the molecular data as well as evolutionary logic — then basic disagreement of a pattern familiar to any student of the history of anthropology appears. If, on the other hand, we first develop a phylogenetic framework and then use it, many problems, of which the knuckle-walking contretemps is but one, are resolved.

The reason for knuckle-walking would appear to be a mechanical one representing the most efficient way of transmitting the stresses of forelimb support in an animal where the articulation between the forearm and wrist bones is incomplete, as in the modern apes and ourselves. If we or the apes were to attempt quadrupedal locomotion palms down and wrist hyperextended (palm horizontal and forearm vertical) we would have a distinct tendency to drive the forearm bones right through the wrist — mechanically, a most inefficient situation.

Going back to the cercopithecine-pongid competition in the middle Pliocene tropical forests of Africa, however, it is interesting and more than a little ironic that our potential for eventual success was probably in no small part due to the failure of our ancestors in this competition. They, losing in one niche, exploited a new and open one, and in so doing made man possible.

If one were to ask for the best description that can be made of this species most recently ancestral to the gorilla, chimpanzee, and ourselves, then the most logical answer is that it must have most closely resembled the least specialized of the three. Thus we begin the reconstruction and understanding of our recent history with a form not unlike a small chimpanzee; we move through a phase where the basic hominid grade was reached; and then we draw a fuller picture from the detailed data that the australopithecine fossil record allows. To give an answer to Huxley's 100 year old query it can be concluded that the temporal gap separating man from the African apes is indeed narrow.

In conclusion, it might be appropriate to consider the disagreements between the picture developed in this article and the more traditional ones concerning human origins, and to then suggest how a rapprochement might be effected. What I have attempted here is to provide the DNA and protein data, derive evolutionary conclusions from them, and then, in the light of those conclusions, develop an interpretation of some of the more pertinent anatomical and paleontological data. To the extent that the paleontologists and other physical anthropologists disagree — to the extent that they continue to see discordance where I see concordance — it is up to them to provide some alternative interpretation of the protein data. We are not unaware of this discord but we have also been utterly unable to interpret the protein data in other than the fashion presented here. We are, though, beginning to focus on specific areas of disagreement and as those are ironed out, a closer and closer approach to general agreement concerning the course of early hominid evolution will be made. One trusts that this will not be too long in coming.

(Added note: A recent paper by Read and Lestrel, *Science 168*, 578–580 (1970) has questioned the linearity of the immunological distance-sequence difference function used in this paper. A fuller defense of the particular scale we use is in preparation but involves issues too complex to be properly and lucidly treated here. Basically the problem with the Read-Lestrel accommodation of the albumin immunological and paleontological interpretations of hominid evolution lies in the fact that their proposed model has no predictive value. It would predict that in other protein and DNA comparisons man and chimpanzee would show large differences in the two species and this is simply not the case — as has been pointed out in this chapter. It is also disturbing to note that the Read-Lestrel article, though purporting to be a "critical appraisal" (the title is *Hominid Phylogeny and Immunology: A Critical Appraisal*), does not even mention our 1969 *Proc. Nat. Acad. Sci.* article in which the predictive aspects of the albumin model are tested and found not wanting. The reader, having digested this chapter, should now be capable of providing his own critical appraisal of the Read-Lestrel paper).

SHERWOOD L. WASHBURN

Washburn is one of the most original thinkers in the field of physical anthropology. The following selection is a recent summary of what can now be said concerning the specific course of hominid physical and behavioral evolution. Washburn has long advocated a specifically pongid (brachiating ape) phase of prehominid evolution and has recently added to this a knuckle-walking phase. In all this he is in a distinct minority. He also proposed in print a number of years ago a very recent origin of the Hominidae:

> *From the point of view of behavior, a major question is whether* Australopithecus *represents a stage of long duration, a relatively stable adaptation, or a transitional form evolving rapidly under the new selection pressures which came with the use of tools. My guess is that the second of these alternatives is correct and that tool use caused a rapid change in selection which separated the Hominidae from the Pongidae, possibly entirely within the Pleistocene."* (Classification and Human Evolution *(Aldine: 1963), p. 203.)*

In the preceding chapter Sarich discussed research that demonstrates in striking fashion the essential correctness of Washburn's views in contrast to those that had been (and often still are) held by most anthropologists. As Washburn has pointed out, this work changes the rules of the human evolution game. Where the new rules lead is the rationale of this presentation. We would suggest that Figure 4 of the preceding chapter be substituted in the Washburn chapter for Figure 3 as a more up-to-date assessment. Beyond this we need only to follow a truly original mind as it assesses the path leading to modern man.

6   The Study of Human Evolution

Since the direction of evolution is dominated by selection and the resulting adaptations, it is the behaviors leading to reproductive success that determine the fates of populations.[1] The evolution of a group of

Reprinted with the permission of Condon Lectures Committee, Oregon State System of Higher Education, Eugene, Oregon.
[1] Mayr (1963, p. 1) has given an excellent review of the synthetic theory of evolution.

animals may be viewed as the history of the way selection altered the behavior of populations. For example, the evolution of man may be seen as: (1) the development of kinds of behavior that first distinguished ancestral human populations from populations of apes; (2) the nature of these behaviors that were continuingly successful; and, (3) the results of some millions of years of behavioral success of the human lineage.

If the first question is examined, it is found that contemporary theories offer three quite different answers (Figure 1). According to the first theory, populations in the lineage leading to man became separated more than 30 million years ago in the Oligocene from those leading to the apes. This means that the ancestral form would have been a small, quadrupedal primate (possibly similar to *Aegyptopithecus*, Simons 1965). According to the second theory, man and ape shared a common ancestry into the Miocene, not to become separate lineages until early Miocene (prebrachiating ancestor) or late Miocene (brachiating ancestor). According to the third theory, separation did not occur until the Pliocene and African apes and man are particularly closely related.

Figure 2 makes it clear that each theory suggests a radically different sequence in the evolution of locomotor structures and behaviors. According to the first, nothing is known about human evolution during more than 30 million years, and all the similarities between apes and men have to be accounted for by parallel evolution. According to the second theory, far more of the similarities between men and apes are accounted for by common ancestry and common way of life. According to the third, apes and men shared an arboreal, quadrupedal way of life which evolved during the Miocene into the climbing-feeding way of life termed brachiation. Some apes and men continued to share a ground-living, knuckle-walking adaptation, and from that point in time human ancestors first became behaviorally distinct as bipeds.

In terms of time, the theories are remarkably distinct. The first suggests a separation of the human lineage for more than 30 million years, the second indicates a separation of something on the order of 20 million years, and the third is compatible with a separation of less than 10 million years.

At present there seems to be no doubt that man's closest living relatives

---

The synthetic theory has selected the best aspects from the earlier hypotheses and has combined them in a new and original manner. It attempts to evaluate the respective role of the numerous interacting factors responsible for evolutionary change. In essence it is a two-factor theory, considering the diversity and harmonious adaptation of the organic world as the result of a steady production of variation and of the selective effects of the environment. It is thus basically a synthesis of mutationism and environmentalism.

Mayr stresses the importance of population thinking, of multiple causes, of understanding process and eliminating erroneous theories. Although this paper is principally concerned with the evolution of adaptations, it assumes that the reader will consider these in terms of the synthetic theory — not in Lamarckian, typological, or teleological terms.

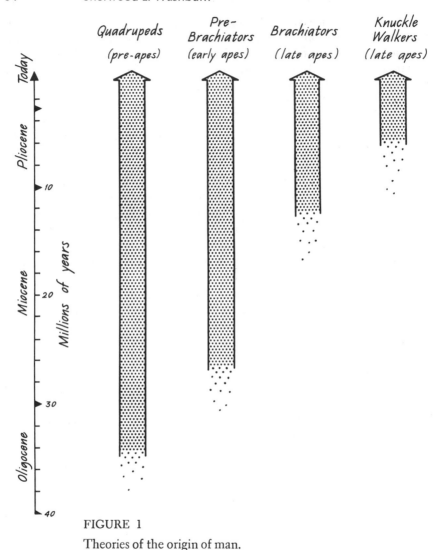

FIGURE 1

Theories of the origin of man.

are the great apes, chimpanzee, gorilla, and orangutan (Simpson 1966). This conclusion is supported by diverse lines of evidence, including the convincing detailed similarity in the chromosomes (Klinger, et al. 1963). The evidence for biochemical similarity has been summarized by Buettner-Janusch (1966), and serological tests suggest that the order of decreasingly close relationship is: man, chimpanzee-gorilla, orangutan, gibbon, Old World monkeys (Goodman 1967; Hafleigh and Williams 1966; Sarich and Wilson 1967 a, b). This evidence indicates that a very early separation of the human lineage is unlikely, and it is most probable that our ancestors were behaviorally apes until late Miocene or early Pliocene. According to Sarich and Wilson (1967b) (Figure 3) the approximate time of the separation of the Hominidae from the Pongidae is on the order of 5 to 10 million years ago, or well within the Pliocene. It is clear that the later the

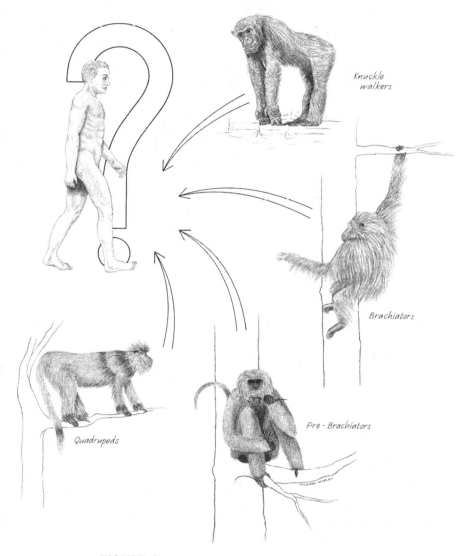

Knuckle walkers

Brachiators

Pre-Brachiators

Quadrupeds

FIGURE 2

Man's closest relatives. According to different theories of human origin man's closest relatives were quadrupedal monkeys, early (pre-brachiating) apes, brachiating apes, or knuckle-walking apes.

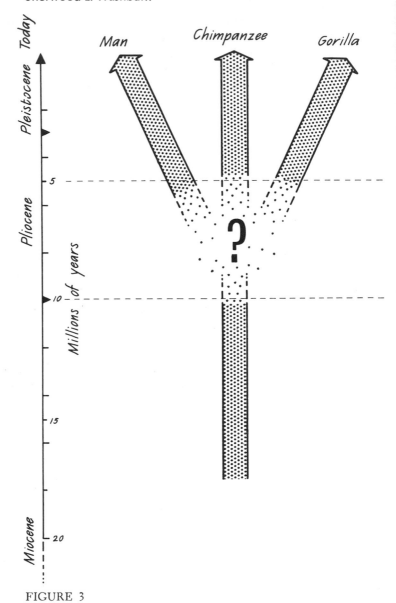

FIGURE 3

Diagram of man's relations to the chimpanzee and gorilla, according to Sarich and Wilson, 1967b.

separation and the closer the relationship between man and the African apes, the more likely it is that our ancestors went through a stage of knuckle-walking. Behavioral stages, arboreal quadruped, prebrachiator, brachiator, knuckle-walker, biped are diagrammed in Figure 2.

These terms attempt to label a stage by using an important locomotor adaptation, but the animals obviously did many other things than just move quadrupedally or brachiate. For example, the knuckle-walking chimpanzee climbs, swings under branches (brachiates), walks bipedally. Ideally, the behavior would be characterized by a profile of all the activities rather than by a single term. It should be stressed that in reality one way of moving (locomotor profile) evolves almost imperceptibly into the next. There are no carefully drawn boundaries in nature, so it is unreasonable to expect every fossil to fit into a definite "stage." Further, contemporary forms have evolved and there is little reason to believe that the actual ancestral forms are identical with any living ones. Obviously, if both skeletons of fossils and data on living forms were available, there would be much less chance of error in the reconstruction, but there are no living prebrachiators with anatomy comparable to the fossils *Proconsul* or *Pliopithecus*. Nor are there fossil brachiators. Apes of the Miocene and early Pliocene are known only from teeth and very small jaw fragments (*Ramapithecus*). Stages were not uniform in length or degree of change and, as Mayr (1963) warns, it is essential to avoid typological thinking. At any time level there were populations containing a high degree of individual variability, and these were combined into many reproductively isolated species. There were many evolutionary lineages, some diverging, some evolving in parallel. The locomotor and behavioral sequence suggested in Figure 2 is only an attempt to view major adaptations which lasted for millions of years.

Keeping these qualifications in mind and remembering the limitations of a very scanty fossil record, I think that the behavioral study of the living forms, the comparative anatomy, and the few available fossils support the following evolutionary sequence of behavioral stages: quadruped, prebrachiator, brachiator, knuckle-walker, biped.

ARMS AND TRUNK

The anatomical evidence of a brachiating behavioral stage in human ancestry is primarily in the trunk and arms of living species. This will be presented first. Then the evolution of bipedalism will be considered and the possibility that a knuckle-walking stage intervened between arboreal ape and a bipedal ground-living stage. Finally, the evolution of the face and brain case will be related to changing locomotor patterns. This order of presentation is the order in which the behavioral complexes occurred and attained approximately their present form, but this is only approximate because there were different rates of evolution even within a single major functional complex. For example, although the arm and trunk appear in most features to have evolved ahead of the pelvis and legs, the foot attained final human form before the hand.

As shown in Figures 4 and 5 the human trunk is similar to that of an ape

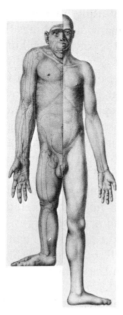

FIGURE 4

Comparison of the proportions of chimpanzees and man. Reproduced from Schultz, A. H., 1956, "Postembryonic Age Changes," *Primatologia*, I. S. Karger, Basel/New York, p. 905, fig. 5.

in length of arm, breadth of trunk and shortness of the lumbar region (Schultz 1936, 1937). More detailed examination shows that the similarity extends to the sternum, length of clavicle, and many details of the bones, joints and muscles. In short, man and apes share major structural features of the trunk and the motions that these make possible such as stretching to the side and hanging comfortably by one arm. The similarity in posture is well shown in Figure 6, which compares a chimpanzee and a human.

The position of the thoracic and abdominal viscera, which are far more alike in man and apes than in long-trunked quadrupedal monkeys is secondarily related to the short, broad trunk (Straus 1936; Washburn 1950).

The shortness of the trunk is, in turn, related to the numbers and kinds of vertebrae. In a quadrupedal monkey, as in small mammals generally, the lumbar region is long, heavily muscled, and important in locomotion. In the apes the intrinsic back muscles are small, the back relatively immobile and the motions between the vertebrae unimportant in locomotion. The reduction in the back muscles is well shown in the gorilla (Gregory 1950, plates 26, 27, 28). The average number of lumbar vertebrae in apes is 4 (Schultz and Straus 1945). In monkeys the usual number of lumbar vertebrae is 7, but the contrast of 4 and 7 gives very little insight into the

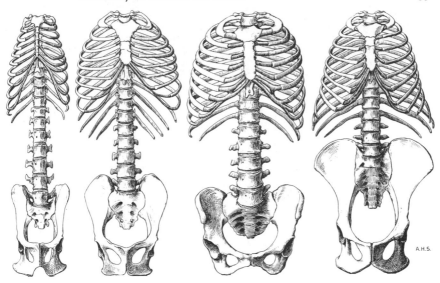

FIGURE 5

Proportions of the trunk skeleton in monkey, ape, and man. Reproduced from Schulz, A. H., 1950, "The Specializations of Man and his Place among the Catarrhine Primates," *Cold Spring Harbor Symposium on Quantitative Biology*, vol. 15, p. 41, fig. 1.

extent of the difference. There are monkeys, gibbons and men with 6 lumbar vertebrae, and these backs are as functionally distinct as the others, in spite of the apparent numerical similarity. Figure 7 shows the comparison of the transitional region between thoracic and lumbar vertebrae in a monkey and a gibbon. It can be seen at once that the last two "thoracic" vertebrae in the monkey look like lumbar vertebrae. They have lumbar type facets, and the transitional vertebrae between the thoracic and lumbar series is number 10 in the monkey and number 12 or 13 in the gibbon. The apparent similarity in the backs is an artifact of the way of counting vertebrae. If all vertebrae with ribs are counted as thoracic, then there appears to be an overlap between ape and monkey and no close correlation of the numbers and form of vertebrae and their function in locomotion. If the vertebrae are divided with reference to motions, facets, morphology, and the accompanying musculature, then the thoracic region is always long in apes and the lumbar region always short and relatively unimportant in locomotion. In quadrupedal monkeys the lumbar region is consistently longer than the thoracic, and it is well muscled and important in locomotion. In passing, it is interesting to note that even such an apparently simple act as counting the number of vertebrae commits the investigator to a theory of what is important, i.e. what is relevant to a particular problem. Dividing the vertebrae solely on the basis of rib

FIGURE 6

Chimpanzee and man.

articulation actually obscures the relationship between the numbers of vertebrae, their functions, and the evolution of the back.

The structures which are most important in differentiating the apes and man from the quadrupedal monkeys are in the shoulder region, including the broad thorax previously mentioned, the sternum, sterno-clavicular joint, the long clavicle, and the shoulder joint proper. It is the long clavicle which keeps the shoulder joint far to the side and it is the stable sterno-clavicular joint which braces the motions of the shoulder. Figure 8 shows the bony anatomy of the shoulder, and the proportions which characterize the Pongidae and Hominidae and separate them from the Cercopithecidae indicated. Brachiators are distinguished from quadrupedal monkeys by their large acromion process, relatively wide and flat glenoid fossa (with a small supraglenoid ossification center and tubercle) and large coracoid process. Also, the brachiator's humerus has a more rounded head with no extension of the articular surface between the tuberosities which are separated by a narrow bicipital groove. These differences in the bones and joints are correlated with many differences in the muscles. For example, pectoralis major arises from the medial third of the clavicle, and the deltoid is large and thick, especially the part rising from the large acromion process. The middle part of trapezius which inserts into the other side of the acromion is also thick, in contrast to the condition in the monkeys in which the trapezius is almost divided into cranial and thoracic portions. These differences are shown in Figure 9. The musculature of apes and men shows many other differences from the conditions in monkeys. For example, in apes and men the primitive serratus anterior becomes divided into a cervical portion (levator scapulae) and a separate thoracic portion. This large muscle acts with trapezius in positioning and fixing the shoulder. The scalene muscles insert only on the first two ribs, instead of interdigitating with serratus as in monkeys. Pectoralis minor gains an insertion on the coracoid process.

All this anatomy makes possible the habitual, powerful use of the arms in motions to the side and above, these are the very actions that characterize ape climbing and feeding. We will return to the meaning of the differences but, to keep perspective, the reason that we find actions, such as those shown in Figure 6, possible and comfortable is that we all have this same anatomical structure. The main functional points can be illustrated using man, chimpanzee, gorilla, orangutan, or gibbon.

The forearm of the apes and man covers a range of approximately 180°

FIGURE 7

Back and side view of the transitional region of the back of the gibbon, *left*, and monkey.

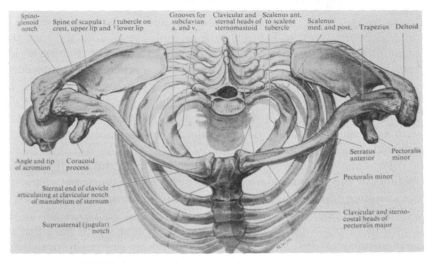

Spino-
glenoid   Spine of scapula :   / tubercle on   Grooves for   Clavicular and   Scalenus ant.
notch   crest, upper lip and ' lower lip   subclavian   sternal heads of to scalene   Scalenus
                                                        a. and v.   sternomastoid   tubercle   med. and post.   Trapezius   Deltoid

Angle and tip   Coracoid   Serratus   Pectoralis
of acromion   process   anterior   minor

                                                                                                  Pectoralis minor
Sternal end of clavicle
articulating at clavicular notch
of manubrium of sternum
                                                                                                  Clavicular and sterno-
                                                                                                  costal heads of
         Suprasternal (jugular)   pectoralis major
               notch

FIGURE 8

Human shoulder and trunk from above. Reproduced by permission
of Faber and Faber Ltd. from Lockhart, R. D., Hamilton, G. F.,
and Fyfe, F. W., 1959, *Anatomy of the Human Body*. London:
Faber and Faber Limited, Philadelphia: J. B. Lippincott Company, p. 77, fig. 155.

rotation, pronation and supination normally permitting powerful flexion in
any natural position. For example, man can chin himself with the palms of
his hands toward himself or facing the bar (Figure 10). In man and apes,
the distal end of the humerus is wide and the part for articulation with the
ulna is separated by a ridge from the round part for articulation with the
radius. Correspondingly, the proximal end of the ulna is wide, so that the
stability of the elbow joint is determined by the fit of the humerus and ulna
and their ligaments, regardless of the position of the radius (that is in any
position of the hand). In monkeys, pronation is the usual position and
approximately 90° of rotation is normal. In quadrupedal monkeys the
proximal ulna is narrow, the proximal radius oval, and both are necessary for
a stable joint. The principal features of the elbow are shown in Figure 11.
(The normal observed range that the animal uses with power should not be
confused with the maximum that can be achieved by manipulation in an
anatomical preparation. The latter sets absolute limits.)

In the wrist of apes and man the ulna does not articulate with the carpal
bones. In monkeys it does and this is part of the structure which permits
less motion between the carpal bones and the bones of the forearm. In man
and apes the hand is given greater freedom in rotation by the form of the
elbow and in side to side motion (abduction and adduction) by the
structure of the joint between the radius, ulna and proximal row of carpals.
The anatomical bases for both actions are shown in Figure 12.

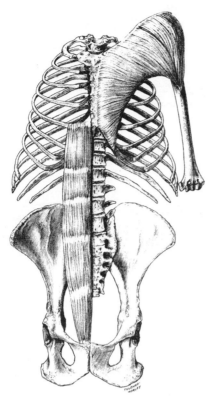

FIGURE 9

Trunk of chimpanzee.

In man, as can be easily demonstrated by feeling one's own wrist, the end of the ulna is maximally in contact with the radius when the hand is partially supinated. When fully pronated, the end of the ulna can be easily felt dorsally. The most stable position of the wrist is in this partially supinated position (in contrast to quadrupedal monkeys in which maximum stability is in full pronation with the ulna articulating with the carpals). This position of partial supination is that taken by the great apes in quadrupedal locomotion. It is particularly clearly seen in the knuckle-walking chimpanzee (Figure 2).

Correlated with the differences in the wrist joint, in monkeys the palm extends up, covering the distal end of the ulna. In apes and man this extension has been lost (Figure 13).

The hand bones found in Bed I, Olduvai Gorge, by Leakey show features which are halfway between those of the contemporary apes and modern man (Napier 1962a). The proximal phalanges have ridges on either side, similar to those of the apes. These bony crests form the attachments of the

Left arm, Lateral view

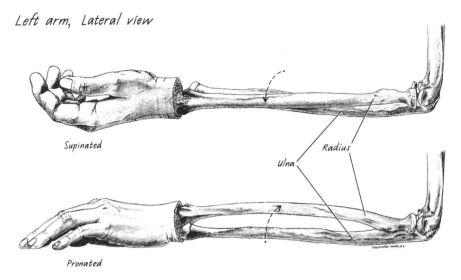

Supinated

Ulna   *Radius*

Pronated

FIGURE 10

Left human forearm, lateral view, in pronation and supination.

capsular ligaments which hold the flexor tendons in place. They are part of the ape anatomy correlated with powerful flexion of the digits. The insertion of the tendons of the superficial flexor tendons are also deeply marked on the middle phalanges. The phalanges are shorter and less curved than those of the contemporary apes, but even in these regards, may differ little from the proportions of the actual ancestral apes. The terminal phalanx of the thumb was larger than the comparable bone of apes but smaller than that of modern man. It suggests a thumb capable of powerful grasping, that is possessing a well-developed flexor pollicis longus muscle as in modern man (Napier 1962b). In short, the hand bones from Olduvai form a link between the anatomy of the human hand and that of the apes. This comparison has been made by Tuttle (1967) who stresses the importance of the adaptation to knuckle-walking in the hands of chimpanzees and gorillas. Although pointing to many resemblances in the hands of man and the members of the genus *Pan*, Tuttle doubts that man passed through a knuckle-walking stage. The difficulty is that some of the anatomical adaptations to knuckle-walking are in the ligaments and are not of a kind which could be determined in fossils, even if the record were far more complete than it is. The major features of hand and wrist which man shares with the apes are evidences of a shared brachiating adaptation rather than the more specialized knuckle-walking adaptations of the African apes.

There are some peculiarities of the human hand which deserve mention in this regard. In addition to the general ape anatomy (form of wrist, development of flexion, loss of sesamoid bones) hair may be lacking on the dorsal surface of the second digits. In addition to the general reduction of hair on the dorsal surfaces of the fingers and toes (a condition which man shares with the chimpanzee), the mid-digital hair is under genetic control. It is far from clear why this particular hair should be subject to special genetic control, unless it is remembered that this is precisely the weight-

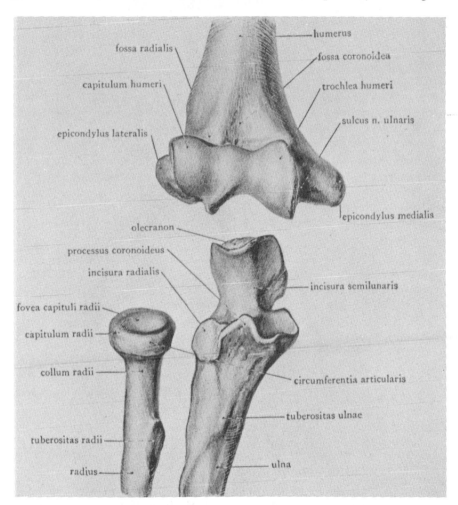

FIGURE 11

Elbow region of man. Reproduced from Warren, John, Green, Robert M., Aitken, H. F., 1930. *Warren's Handbook of Anatomy.* Cambridge, Mass.: Harvard University Press (from original dissections by John Warren, M. D.; drawings by H. F. Aitken), Copyright, 1930, 1958, by the President and the Fellows of Harvard College, p. 164, fig. 154.

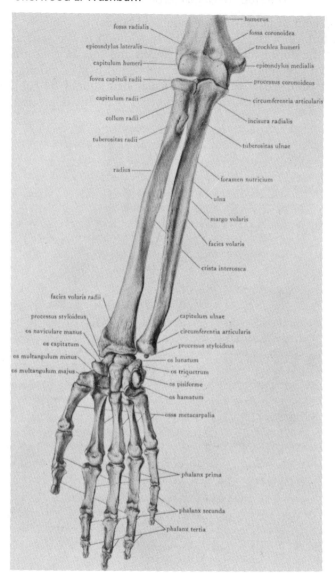

FIGURE 12

Human forearm, wrist and hand. Reproduced from Warren, John, Green, Robert M., Aitken, H. F., 1930, *Warren's Handbook of Anatomy*. Cambridge, Mass.: Harvard University Press (from original dissections by John Warren, M.D.; drawings by H. F. Aitken), Copyright, 1930, 1958, by the President and the Fellows of Harvard College, p. 163, fig. 153.

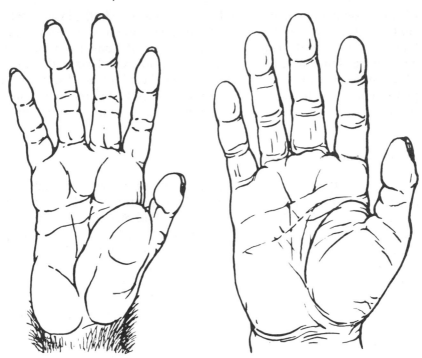

FIGURE 13

Hand of monkey, *Macaca*, *left*, and man, *Homo*, showing differences in extent of ridged skin. Reproduced from Schultz, A. H., 1956, "Postembryonic Age Changes," *Primatologia*, *I*. Basel/New York: S. Karger, p. 916, fig. 7.

bearing surface of the knuckle-walker. In chimpanzee and gorilla the skin on the second phalanx is thickened and hairless (Schultz 1933, 1936; Montagna and Yun 1963; Tuttle 1967). The development of a weight-bearing surface is correlated both with the thickening of the epidermis and with the loss of hair and it may be that the condition of mid-digital hair in man is at least a partial adaptation to knuckle-walking by our remote ancestors.

It is highly unlikely that all these similarities of structure and related function are due to parallel evolution. The similarities are too detailed to make this explanation probable. Further, it must be remembered that the similarities of man and ape are also in other unrelated systems, as noted earlier. It would be more than parallelism if the similarities in the trunk and arms were also accompanied by detailed similarity in chromosomes, immunochemistry, and dentition.

In summary, the structure of the human trunk and arms is remarkably ape-like. It is this anatomical similarity which forms the basis for the actions which are similar in ape and man. Just as the motions in the living creatures are basically similar, so the structures are alike. One way of showing this is that there is little difficulty in using an atlas of human anatomy when dissecting a chimpanzee arm. However, when interest shifts to the legs, the situation is entirely different. There have been major changes in the proportions of the bones, the form of the muscles, and in the functioning of the lower limbs. In contrast to the fundamental similarity of the arms, the structure of the legs in man and apes show differences.

LOWER LIMBS

It is remarkable that the earliest known hominid foot is hardly distinguishable from that of a contemporary man. The foot, found by Leakey in Bed I, Olduvai, may differ from that of a modern man in some minor technical details (Day and Napier 1964), but, as can be seen in Figure 14, the structures are essentially human, rather than ape-like. The great toe is large and a facet between it and the second metatarsal shows that it was not abducted during the life of the individual. The bones are human in form. An arch was present, and there is no indication of the midtarsal bending seen in apes. A talus is known from South Africa, and, before the foot was found, Clark (1947) had predicted that the remainder of the foot would be far more human than ape-like. In my opinion, the order of discovery (skull, 1924; pelvis, 1947; and foot, 1960) exerted a profound effect on the interpretation of the fossils and prevented acceptance of Dart's original claims for over 30 years.[2] If the initial discovery had been the foot, the long controversy over bipedalism might have been avoided, just as the controversy over the use of tools might at least have taken a different form if the initial discovery had been the associations in Bed 1, Olduvai, rather than the specimen from Taung.

The hominid foot (including the Olduvai specimen) shows indications that it has been evolved from the kind of foot seen in the apes, not that of the quadrupedal monkeys (Morton 1935). The essential points are that weight is borne on the great toe and that, in walking or standing, the foot toes out. In monkeys almost no weight is borne on the great toe, and the axis of weight-bearing is through the middle toes, rather than between the first and second toes (Morton 1935). As in the case of the arms, it is easier to see the differences in actions first and then see how they are made possible by the anatomical differences. For example, grasping with the toes is so important in all the nonhuman primates that even a little 12-pound monkey has toes absolutely longer than a 150-pound man. To support even a few pounds by grasping requires length of toes, and describing this in

---

[2] [Ed. note: See Raymond Dart and Dennis Craig, *Adventures with the Missing Link*. (Viking Press, 1961).]

FIGURE 14

Foot bones from Olduvai. Photograph by John R. Napier and L. S. B. Leakey.

terms of percentage of foot length hides the magnitude of the actual difference.

In the nonhuman primates there is a flexibility in the midtarsal region between the talus and calcaneus and the next row of tarsal bones (Clark 1959). For stepping in the human way, this midtarsal bending must be greatly reduced, and the longitudinal arch and associated ligaments perform this function. Once the importance of the rigid tarsal structure for human stepping is appreciated, then the differences in the tarsal region can be understood. The Olduvai foot functioned like that of modern man, and this can be seen in the architecture of the tarsal region. Unfortunately, there are no complete limb bones of *Australopithecus*. The very human character of the foot suggests that the knees must have been close together in walking, and the fragment of the distal femur is compatible with this reconstruction (Clark 1967; Zihlman 1967). The head of the femur in *Australopithecus* was relatively smaller than in the genus *Homo*. The fragments from Bed 1, Olduvai, are from two kinds of *Australopithecus* and from more than one individual. This makes it possible to reconstruct the owner of the foot either with limb proportions much like modern man, or with much more primitive proportions. The foot is very small and the hand large and, if these are combined into one individual, the creature may have looked far more ape-like than in most of the present reconstructions (Howell 1965; Clark 1967). A longer arm with a more ape-like hand may have persisted in a bipedal walker, and the concept of a knuckle-walking transition from ape to man makes this sort of a creature a distinct possibility. However, the fossils are too fragmentary for any definite conclusion on the proportions of arms and legs.

That evolution was progressing at different rates in parts of the same functional complex is shown by the pelvis. The ilium appears to have evolved to human form before the ischium (Zihlman 1967). Starting with behavior will show why this is the case.

Human locomotion is unique in that the trunk is fully erect in bipedal walking and the upper half of the body is minimally involved in locomotion (Zihlman 1967). Neither bipedalism nor length of leg is unique. Birds, some dinosaurs and lizards have evolved bipedal adaptations, showing that merely being bipedal does not free hands for tool using. In fact, bipedalism may actually result in the reduction of the forelimbs. Likewise, the legs of tarsiers and gibbons are as long as those of man relative to the trunk (Schultz 1956), and man's uniqueness is in the pattern of efficient walking (striding, Napier 1967), a concept which must be clearly distinguished from the occasional bipedalism seen in monkeys and apes.

The structural basis for human walking is anatomically complex, and the whole pelvis region was reorganized in evolution. The essential behavioral problem was the evolutionary transfer of the landing and balancing functions of the forelimbs to the hind limbs (Zihlman 1967). In the quadrupedal monkey or knuckle-walking chimpanzee the principal force in locomotion comes from the muscles behind the femur, and, if the main drive is from the right leg, then the animal lands on the left forelimb. In man, as the foot touches the ground, it first must perform the landing-balancing functions of the primitive forelimb, and then give the push resulting in the step (Figure 15).

The changes in the pelvis which make the vertical position possible are shown in Figures 16 and 17. The pelvis of a chimpanzee is compared to that of a man and *Australopithecus*. The main features would be the same if a gorilla, orangutan, or gibbon were substituted for the chimpanzee. The series of reconstructions shows what happens if the transformation is divided into separate events. Shortening of the lower ilium brings the sacrum more behind the pubic bones and creates a complete bony birth canal. With the longer ilium, the fetus is first able to move forward and then backward (Schultz 1949). Shortening does not change the relation of the trunk and legs. If the ilium is bent backward, the trunk is now vertical without a lumbar curve but the sacrum has moved around and blocks the pelvic outlet. Rotation of the sacrum (Figure 17c) opens the pelvic outlet, but now a lumbar curve has to be added to keep the trunk vertical.

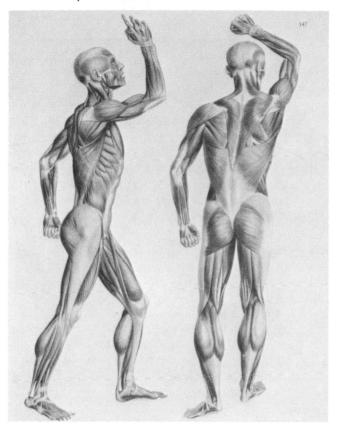

FIGURE 15

Human muscles. Reproduced by permission of Faber and Faber
Ltd. from Lockhart, R. D., Hamilton, G. F., and Fyfe, F. W.,
1959, *Anatomy of the Human Body*. London: Faber and Faber
Limited, Philadelphia: J. B. Lippincott Company, p. 147, figs. 257
and 258.

If only the changes outlined above had taken place, the ilium would lie
behind the hip joint (Figure 17c) and gluteus medius and minimus would
have no power for balancing the pelvis during the step and no power of
internal rotation. Balance and internal rotation are essential in human
locomotion (Zihlman 1967) and these functions are maintained by the
increase in breadth of the ilium (Figure 17d) and the curvature of the crest
of the ilium.

Obviously, the preceding argument is only an attempt to describe major
changes. The actual course of evolution would have involved the
accumulation of small changes over many hundreds of thousands of years,

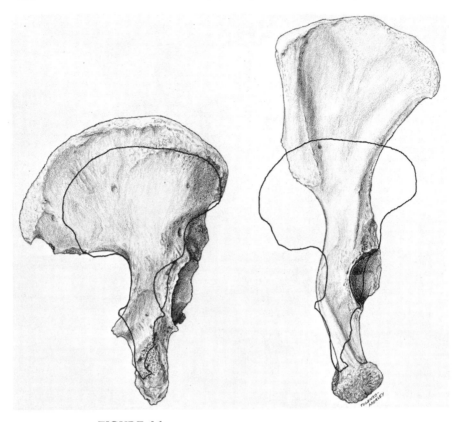

FIGURE 16

Comparison of innominate bones of man, *left*, chimpanzee, *right*, and Australopithecus, *repeated in outline*.

but the fossil record is far too incomplete to yield information on the actual order of the many small transformations.

As can be seen from the preceding discussion the reorganization of the pelvis and associated muscles to make the human kind of bipedal locomotion possible is complex. And the fossil record shows that this reorganization was not complete at the time the foot was practically in its present form. As Zihlman (1967) has shown, in the pelvis of *Australopithecus* there were still ape-like features in the ischium, pubis, and crest of the ilium (Figure 16).

The most probable interpretation of these differences is that *Australopithecus* was capable of the human pattern of locomotion, but was not as efficient bipedally as the subsequent genus *Homo*. The inferences from the bones are supported by other lines of evidence. It seems that

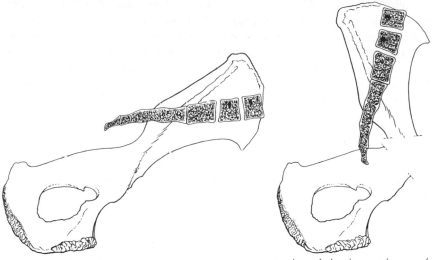

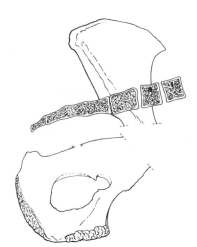

A. *Ape pelvis and sacrum*

B. *Ilium tilted making vertebrae upright*

C. *Ilium shortened and sacrum rotated
to open pelvic canal.*

D. *Lumbar curve added making vertebrae
upright and ilium broadened to
allow attachment of muscles.*

FIGURE 17
Transformation of pelvis.

Australopithecus lived in the savanna, made stone tools, did at least some hunting, and survived in competition with large baboons and a wide variety of other animals. The beginnings of the human way of life appear to have been present, and, judging by the foot, the transitional forms between ape and man must have lived long before. The phylogenetic and behavioral inferences which have been made on the basis of the limb bones may be supported and strengthened by the interpretation of the dentition.

FACE

The dentition supports the notion that *Australopithecus* was a tool-user and had been one for a very long period. The canine teeth of *Australopithecus* are small and very human in form (Robinson 1962). There is no suggestion of the large canine teeth of the male monkeys and apes (Clark 1959).

Field studies show that the canine complex of the males is essential in fighting within the group, between groups, and against predators. The contrast between *Australopithecus* and other nonhuman primates is particularly great if the comparison is made to those living in the savanna. The male canines are particularly large in baboons, absolutely much longer and sharper in a 60-pound baboon than in a 500-pound gorilla. Where escape into trees is limited, the protective function of the large males is maximum. If *Australopithecus* had been adapting to the savanna in the manner of baboons, very large canines would be expected in the males, but the opposite is the case. The reduction of the canines in *Australopithecus* supports the suggestion from other lines of evidence that all members of the genus were tool-users and had been so for a long period of time.

To fight with the teeth involves the canine first lower premolar complex, the jaw muscles, and the neck muscles. Since females also fight with their teeth (although much less effectively), the difference between *Australopithecus* and apes is much greater than the difference between female and male apes. For example, in baboons the length of all three molar teeth in males exceeds that of females by only 3 mm and there is much overlapping. But the temporal muscles in the males are over four times that of the females. My impression is that the neck muscles of the males are equally as much larger. A large part of the temporal muscles (particularly in long-faced forms) arises from the nuchal crest, and it is my opinion that a great deal of similarity between *Australopithecus* and *Homo* is secondary to the differences in the canine complex which involves length of palate, shape of anterior part of palate, nuchal region, position of condyles, and many other features. Just as in the case of the evolution of the ilium, discussed previously, the face is adapting to multiple functions, and head balance is an altogether inadequate way to account for the position of the condyles

(Gibson, in preparation). The structure of the muscles used in fighting with the face is far more important in determining many proportions of the skull than passive balance.

In contrast to the great differences in the canine complex between monkeys and apes on one side and *Australopithecus* and *Homo* on the other, there has not been much evolution in the molar teeth, and the molar teeth of contemporary man may be just as large as those of a chimpanzee. As stressed by Clark (1967), differences between man and ape are primarily in the anterior teeth and in some fossil apes the incisors were small so it is the reduction of the canine complex which is the evolutionarily novel characteristic of the Hominidae. In terms of behavior this means that tools took over functions of the teeth in protection against predators, in fighting within the group and in intergroup fighting. Judging both from the behavior of chimpanzees and from the later archeological record, the stone tools found with *Australopithecus* must have been only a fraction of the objects they actually used.

TOOLS AND BRAIN

To say that *Australopithecus* was a tool-user and maker of stone tools is to regard these creatures as capable of learning beyond the capacities of the contemporary apes in spite of the small size of their brains. Capacities range from approximately 400 to 600 cc, or a little larger if the very fragmentary *Homo habilis* is included. This is not different from the range in gorilla (Tobias 1965). The shaping of stone according to even the simplest plan is beyond the behavior of any ape or monkey. This act seems so simple from a human point of view that it is necessary to keep learning to use tools in evolutionary perspective. Primates have had hands, rather than claw-bearing paws, for something on the order of 50 million years. There are some 40 genera of contemporary primates and millions of individuals. There were vast numbers over the more than 60 million years of the age of the mammals. Primates are digitally dexterous. They groom with precision, they can easily pick up a single grain of rice. But with the exception of the chimpanzee, there is almost no behavior which can be classified as tool-using, and it is only man who makes more than the most minimal improvement in an object he intends to use. The field studies show that the origin of tool-using was not a simple matter, and that, in spite of manual dexterity which would appear to make the discovery of tool-using easy, nonhuman primate intelligence blocked the acquisition of habits which seem easy and almost inevitable from a human point of view.

The minimal tool-use seen in the chimpanzee has apparently not been enough to alter selection pressures on the brain or on the canine complex in any major way. In spite of considerable manipulation of objects, playing with objects, and use of objects in display, the ape brain lacks the features which make complicated, skillful, human tool-making and -using possible. The situation in man is shown in Figures 18 and 19. In Figure 18 the main functional areas are indicated and in Figure 19 a section of the motor area is shown. On the section is the outline of a human figure, distorted to the proportions that the human body is represented on the motor cortex. Obviously, such a figure is a simplification, leaving out supplementary motor areas, the fact that the sensory and motor areas are not sharply distinct, and that much of the cortex is in the fissures and does not show in such a diagram. Nevertheless, the impression is correct that a very large amount of the motor cortex is concerned with hand movements. In a monkey the hand and foot areas are approximately of equal size, and the difference between monkey and man is that the amount of cortex devoted to the hand is large, not that the foot area is small. There is a control on this interpretation because learned hand movements mediated in part by the cortex also involve the cerebellum. The cerebellum of man is approximately three times that of an ape, and the part which is enlarged is that associated with learned hand movements (Cobb 1941). There is no way to study the motor area directly in fossils because all that is preserved is an indication of the size of the whole brain, but the size of the cerebellum can be estimated much more accurately. Figure 20 shows the relation of the brain to the skull, and Figure 21 shows the same view with all the soft

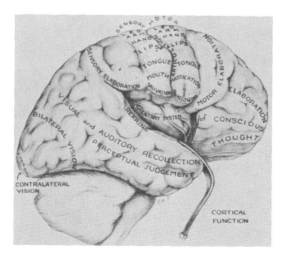

FIGURE 18

Human brain showing the functional areas of the cortex. Reproduced with permission from Penfield, W. and Rasmussen, T., 1957, *The Cerebral Cortex of Man*. Copyright 1950 by The Macmillan Company, p. 206, fig. 110.

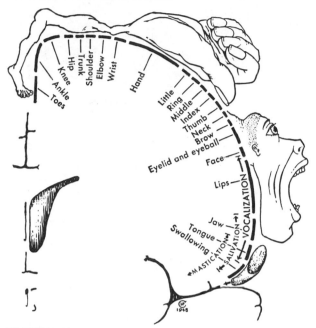

FIGURE 19

Homunculus, showing the way the human figure is distorted in its representation on the cortex. Reproduced with permission from Penfield, W. and Rasmussen, T., 1957, *The Cerebral Cortex of Man.* Copyright 1950 by The Macmillan Company, p. 215, fig. 115.

anatomy removed, indicating the places where the coverings of the cerebellum are attached along the transverse sinus of the petrous temporal bone. From the skull of *Australopithecus* it can be seen that this form did not have the space for either a large cerebellum of the human form or for the large area for motor cortex. As Holloway (1966) has pointed out, size alone is a poor measure of difference in brain function because there was evolution in the size and form of the cells, and, since *Australopithecus* was apparently making stone tools, the behavior of the genus was advanced over that of the contemporary apes. However, simple tools were made for at least a million years and probably at least twice that (Lancaster, 1968b), and this strongly suggests that tool-making and improving was far more difficult for these small-brained forms than for later members of the genus *Homo*. The archeological evidence, comparative anatomical evidence, and the fossil record all give evidence that brains of human size and form evolved long after our ancestors were ground-living, stone-tool-making, savanna-living gatherers and hunters.

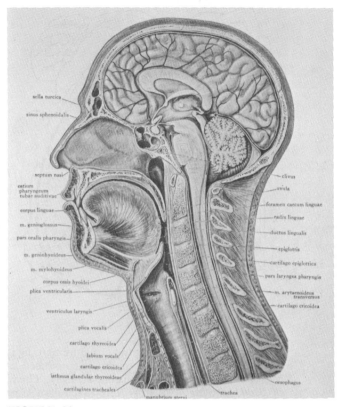

FIGURE 20

Section of human head and neck. Reproduced from Warren, John, Green, Robert M., Aitken, H. F., 1930, *Warren's Handbook of Anatomy*. Cambridge, Mass.: Harvard University Press (from original dissections by John Warren, M.D.; drawings by H. F. Aitken), Copyright, 1930, 1958, by the President and the Fellows of Harvard College, p. 92, fig. 85.

The notion that the evolution of the majority of the unique features of the human brain evolved long after the fundamental patterns of the human way of life agrees with the point of view of Edinger (1948) that the brain tends to follow in evolution, rather than to be the primary creative agent. The main groups of mammals evolved characteristic locomotor and other anatomical patterns before the brains evolved their characteristic forms. To put the matter differently, the success of the new ways of life created new selection pressures which ultimately caused the evolution of new neural structures. In the case of tool-using, the behavioral success of the class of behaviors in the early human lineage led to selection for ease of learning (including interest in objects and exploration), skillful use (including

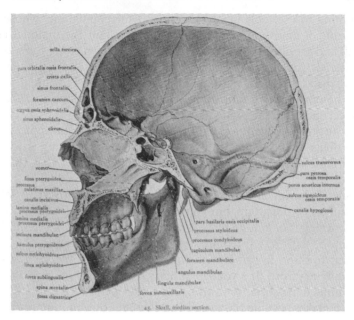

FIGURE 21

Section of human skull. Reproduced from Warren, John, Green, Robert M., Aitken, H. F., 1930, *Warren's Handbook of Anatomy.* Cambridge, Mass.: Harvard University Press (from original dissections by John Warren, M.D.; drawings by H. F. Aitken), Copyright, 1930, 1958, by the President and the Fellows of Harvard College, p. 61, fig. 45.

practice through play), and more complex communication. The relation of tool-using to the evolution of the brain is complex because the behavioral success is of the whole life which the tools made possible. Motor skill as such is only a small part of the evolving behavioral complex, and even the evolution of an apparently simple motor skill (such as throwing) depends on the activity being pleasurable, rewarding, and practiced in play. For example, chimpanzees throwing rocks as a part of agonistic displays consistently miss the creature against which the display is directed (Goodall 1965). They aim, but without skill. In a cage, with nothing to do and the reward of hitting a human, feces-throwing may reach a high level of accuracy. The cage situation determines the conditions of practice and reward, and free-ranging chimpanzees do not find the practice of throwing rewarding. Humans do find practice rewarding, and what evolved was the whole pattern of structure which makes skillful actions both possible and pleasurable.

Normal learning takes place in a social situation (Hall, 1968), and learning to use tools involves selection for populations whose brains were capable of more complex communication about the material environment, skill and social relations. Even the earliest known stone tools are of selected materials (not just the handiest piece of stone) and some were carried for long distances (Hay, personal communication). This implies a knowledge of the environment far beyond that of an ape which picks up any handy object and throws it.

The greatest encouragement for learning skills is the appreciation of other members of the group, and encouragement in learning is so fundamental and basic to human learning that it is easy to forget that this is unique to man. No other primate sits by and applauds success. The infant monkey copies behavior and is restrained by its mother first and later by other members of the group, but conscious social encouragement and facilitation of learning is unique to man. It is my belief that this is essential for learning complex skills which require long practice. For example, the infant human learns to throw in games with encouragement and success is applauded and socially rewarded. If a young chimpanzee throws, it is an isolated event with no immediate social reward or encouragement to repeat, to practice. The brain makes possible the social situation and the communication which lead to the full development of the motor skills.

Obviously, the brain is essential for any act of communication, but apparently very little brain is required in non-linguistic communication systems. The expression of emotions (warning cries, interpersonal signals) is carried on effectively by nonhuman primates, and many other mammals. In contrast, language is directly related to large areas of the brain (Figure 22), and indirectly related to many others. For example, language increases the demand for memory, and this makes possible increased foresight and planning. Language makes possible complex social systems and the social systems require control of emotions, thus affecting the evolution of human emotions (Hamburg 1963). The evolution of language should not be thought of as a separate ability, but as intimately linked through selection with the successful behaviors it makes possible. From an evolutionary point of view, there is no simple relation between language and the brain, but the ability which language makes possible can be easily stated. Language conveys specific information about the environment (Geschwind 1965; Lancaster 1968a). The ability to name is the fundamental distinction between human communication and the communication systems of the nonhuman primates. In nonhuman primates auditory signals are usually accompanied by gestures and, in fact, the nonauditory part of the signal is usually the most important. In nonhuman communication, sounds usually function only to emphasize expression, postures, or other actions, which are communicating emotional state and social intent. Warning cries may distinguish between arboreal and terrestrial predators, with the monkeys

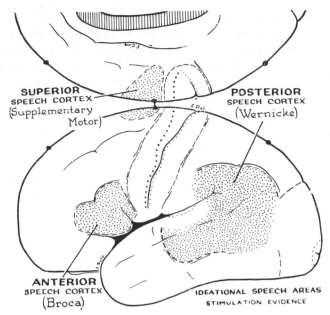

SUPERIOR
SPEECH CORTEX
(Supplementary
Motor)

POSTERIOR
SPEECH CORTEX
(Wernicke)

ANTERIOR
SPEECH CORTEX
(Broca)

IDEATIONAL SPEECH AREAS
STIMULATION EVIDENCE

FIGURE 22

Area of the brain especially connected with speech. Reproduced from Penfield, W. and Roberts, L., 1959, *Speech and Brain Mechanisms*, p. 201, fig. X-4. Copyright © 1969 Princeton University Press.

responding to one cry by dropping to the ground and to the other by climbing into the trees (Struhsaker 1967 a; Altmann 1967). But no distinction can be made between the kinds of terrestrial predators, although this would seem to be of the greatest adaptive value. In language, sounds have specific referents (e.g., lion, leopard), and at present there is no way to determine the time of the beginning of this new communication system which revolutionized man's way of life and became fundamental in every sphere of human activity. However, there are two lines of speculation which may prove to be useful. If the essential adaptive element in language is naming (referring to specific items in the environment), then one may look at the course of human evolution to see what happened in man's relation to the environment. Clearly, the human way was distinct from the ape way because of tools, and these involve interest in the environment in new ways and the communication of new kinds of information. Assuming that *Australopithecus* was prelinguistic, then some millions of years of tool-using may have provided the setting for the evolution of naming. The first importance of the auditory symbols (unique to man) would come with the evolution of stone tools (equally unique to man). This suggestion would account for the slow evolution of the early tools by the lack of a linguistic communication system, and would regard language as the most important adaptation of the genus *Homo*. Obviously, until there is far more agreement as to the nature of language and the relation of language to the brain, evolutionary speculation can only be of a very general nature. The controversies have been ably summarized by Lenneberg (1967), and the evolutionary point of view can add some information. The debate over the nature of the neural structures which make language possible should not confuse the fact that there are new parts of the brain which make language possible. The difference is shown by learning. Apes and monkeys cannot be taught to talk, although they can be conditioned to respond appropriately to sounds. Man learns to talk so easily that a normal person can learn several languages, including thousands of words and their meanings. This human ability is new and the more data that are available on the communication systems of the apes and monkeys, the less they appear to have any beginning of language, of naming specific parts of their environment. For example, chimpanzees manipulate objects, and one can easily imagine how populations of comparable knuckle-walkers over millions of years might evolve the beginnings of far more adaptive patterns of tool-using. But chimpanzees do not have names for a single object. There is no beginning of a naming system whose adaptive success could lead to the evolution of a more complex communication system, and in this sense language represents a more complete break with the past than does tool-using. The essential difference is in the kind and quantity of information that can be transferred by the auditory channel alone. This is minimal in the nonhuman primates, and maximal in the case of man. The difference does not lie in the design features, for Altmann (1967) has demonstrated that monkey communication has all, or almost all, the design features described by Hockett (1960, 1963) for human language. It is the quantity and kind of meaning in the message which is of adaptive value, and the essence of language is the highly useful system of environmental reference (naming) which is of such great practical, adaptive value.

As has been repeatedly emphasized, the cortex of a primitive mammal is largely occupied by primary sensory and motor areas. In man these occupy a relatively small part of the cortex, and the great increase in the size of the human brain over that of an ape is in the association areas, the parts concerned with hand skills, speech, memory, and use of memory (elaboration of conscious thought, planning). The situation is shown in Figure 23. It must be remembered that these are not sharply defined areas, but the effects of electrical stimulation of the cortex, or damage to the cortex, do produce identifiably different results in the various major areas (Penfield and Rasmussen 1957). This complex of evolutionarily new cortex in frontal, parietal, and temporal regions may be thought of as the social brain, the parts making human language skills, and complex social life

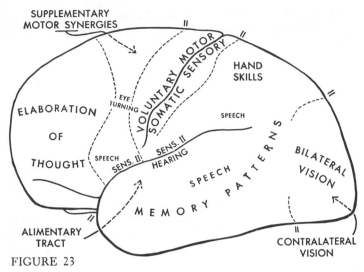

FIGURE 23

Diagram of the functional areas of the human cortex. Reproduced with permission from Penfield, W. and Rasmussen, T., 1957, *The Cerebral Cortex of Man.* Copyright 1950 by The Macmillan Company, p. 221, fig. 117.

possible. Their importance in recent evolution is shown by the increase in size of the corpus callosum, the great connection between the right and left cerebral hemispheres. The importance is also shown in senile atrophy, in which normal social life ceases to be possible.

In summary, some hunting, stone-tool-making, and savanna-living were present for many hundreds of thousands of years prior to the evolution of the genus *Homo* and the brain evolved as a consequence of the adaptive success of the new way of life. The best guess from the archeological record is that this feedback relation between the successful human way of life and the structure of the brain lasted for a very long period of time before the appearance of *Homo sapiens*, of human nature as we know it today. In a single lifetime the abilities of the human brain appear to make possible cultures with all their complexities of social traditions, religions, languages, and arts. But in the perspective of evolution, it is the feedback between successful behaviors and the structures which make them possible that determines evolution.

In the human body today both the record of past events and the biological nature which enter into every human action may be seen. We learn with ease what was important for our ancestors, for it is the basis for those long established learnings which have been incorporated into the biology of the species. Although the evolution of skills, speech, and the social brain has carried us far from the apes, man meets the problems of a technical society with the biology of the hunters of many thousands of years ago.

REFERENCES

Altmann, S. A.
  1967 "The Structure of Primate Social Communication," in *Social Communication Among Primates* (S. A. Altmann, ed.). Chicago: University of Chicago Press.
Buettner-Janusch, J.
  1966 *Origins of Man*. New York: John Wiley and Sons, Inc.
Clark, W. E. L.
  1947 "Observations on the Anatomy of Fossil Australopithecinae," *Journal of Anatomy* 81:300–333.
  1959 *The Antecedents of Man; An Introduction to the Evolution of the Primates*. Chicago: Quadrangle Books.
  1967 *Man-apes or Ape-men? The Story of Discoveries in Africa*. New York: Holt, Rinehart and Winston.
Cobb, S.
  1941 *Foundations of Neuropsychiatry*. Baltimore: The Williams and Wilkins Company.
Day, M. H. and J. R. Napier
  1964 "Fossil Foot Bones," *Nature* 201:967–970.
Edinger, T.
  1948 "Evolution of the Horse Brain," *Memorandum of Geological Society of America* 25:1–777.
Geschwind, N.
  1965 "Disconnexion Syndromes in Animals and Man," *Brain* 88:237–294, 585–642.
Gibson, K.
  In Preparation. *Head Balance*.
Goodall, J.
  1965 "New Discoveries Among Africa's Chimpanzees," *National Geographic* 128:802–831.
Goodman, M.
  1967 "Effects of Evolution on Primate Macromolecules," *Primates* 8:1–22.
Gregory, W. K., ed.
  1950 *The Anatomy of the Gorilla*. New York: Columbia University Press.
Hafleigh, A. S. and C. A. Williams. Jr.
  1966 "Antigenic Correspondence of Serum Albumins Among the Primates," *Science* 151:1530.
Hall, K. R. L.
  1968 "Social Learning in Monkeys," in *Primates: Studies*

in Adaptation and Variability (P. Jay, ed.). New York: Holt, Rinehart, pp. 383–397.

Hamburg, D. A.
 1963 "Emotions in the Perspective of Human Evolution," in *Expression of the Emotions in Man* (P. Knapp, ed.). New York: International Universities Press.

Hockett, C. F.
 1960 "Logical Considerations in the Study of Animal Communication," in *Animal Sounds and Communication* (W. E. Lanyon and W. N. Tavola, eds.). Washington: American Institute of Biological Science.

 1963 "The Problem of Universals in Human Language," in *Universals of Language* (J. H. Greenberg, ed.). Cambridge, Mass.: M.I.T. Press.

Holloway, R. L., Jr.
 1966 "Cranial Capacity, Neural Reorganization, and Hominid Evolution: A Search for More Suitable Parameters," *American Anthropologist* 68:103–121.

Howell, F. C.
 1965 *Early Man.* New York: Time Inc.

Klinger, H. P., J. L. Hamerton, D. Mutton, and E. M. Lang
 1963 "The Chromosomes of the Hominoidea," in *Classification and Human Evolution* (S. L. Washburn, ed.). Viking Fund Publications in Anthropology, No. 37.

Lancaster, J. B.
 1968a "Primate Communication Systems and the Emergence of Human Language," in *Primates: Studies in Adaptation and Variability* (P. Jay, ed.). New York: Holt, Rinehart, pp. 438–457.

 1968b "The Evolution of Tool-using Behavior," *American Anthropologist* 70:56–66 (reprinted as chapter 18, this book).

Lenenberg, E. H.
 1967 *Biological Foundations of Language.* New York: John Wiley and Sons.

Mayr, E.
 1963 *Animal Species and Evolution.* Cambridge, Mass.: Harvard University Press.

Montagna, W. and J. S. Yun
 1963 "The Skin of Primates. XV. The Skin of the Chimpanzee *(Pan Satyrus)*," *American Journal of Physical Anthropology* 21:189–204.

Morton, D. J.
 1935 *The Human Foot.* New York: Columbia University Press.

Napier, J.

1962a "The Evolution of the Human Hand," *Scientific American* 207:56–62.

1962b "Fossil Hand Bones from Olduvai Gorge," *Nature* 196:409–411.

1967 "The Antiquity of Human Walking," *Scientific American* 216:56–66.

Penfield, W. and T. Rasmussen

1957 *The Cerebral Cortex of Man.* New York: The Macmillan Company.

Robinson, J. T.

1962 "The Australopithecines and Their Bearing on the Origin of Man and of Stone Tool Making," in *Ideas on Human Evolution* (W. W. Howells, ed.). Cambridge: Harvard University Press.

Sarich, V. and A. C. Wilson

1967a "Rates of Albumin Evolution in Primates," *Proceedings of the National Academy of Science* 58: 142–148.

1967b "An Immunological Time Scale for Hominid Evolution," *Science* 158:1200–1203.

Schultz, A. H.

1933 "Notes on the Fetus of an Orangutan," *Report of the Laboratory and Museum of Comparative Pathology, Zoological Society Philadelphia* 18:61–79.

1936 "Characters Common to Higher Primates and Characters Specific for Man," *Quarterly Review of Biology* 11:259–283, 425–455.

1937 "Proportions, Variability and Asymmetrics of the Long Bones of the Limbs and Clavicles in Man and Apes," *Human Biology* 9:281–328.

1949 "Sex Differences in the Pelves of Primates," *American Journal of Physical Anthropology* 7:401–424.

1956 "Postembryonic Age Changes," *Primatologia, I.* Basel/ New York: S. Karger.

Schultz, A. H. and W. L. Straus, Jr.

1945 "The Numbers of Vertebrae in Primates," *American Philosophical Society* 89:601–626.

Simons, E. L.

1965 "New Fossil Apes from Egypt and the Initial Differentiation of Hominoidea," *Nature* 205:135–139.

Simpson, G. G.

1966 "The Biological Nature of Man," *Science* 152: 472–478.

Straus, W. L., Jr.

1936 "The Thoracic and Abdominal Viscera of Primates

with Special Reference to the Orangutan," *Proceedings of the American Philosophical Society* 76:1–85.

Struhsaker, T. T.

1967a "Auditory Communication Among Vervet Monkeys *(Cercopithecus aethiops)*," in *Social Communication Among Primates* (S. Altmann, ed.). Chicago and London: The University of Chicago Press.

1967b "Behavior of Vervet Monkeys and Other Cerco-pithecines," *Science* 156:1197–1203.

Tobias, P. V.

1965 "New Discoveries in Tanganyika: Their Bearing on Hominid Evolution," *Current Anthropology* 6:391–411.

Tuttle, R. H.

1967 "Knuckle-walking and the Evolution of Hominoid Hands," *American Journal of Physical Anthropology* 26:171–206.

Washburn, S. L.

1950 "Thoracic Viscera of the Gorilla," in *The Anatomy of the Gorilla* (W. K. Gregory, ed.). New York: Columbia University Press.

Zihlman, A. L.

1967 Human Locomotion: A Reappraisal of the Functional and Anatomical Evidence, unpublished doctoral thesis, University of California, Berkeley.

Much controversy and little agreement have marked the study of our fossil ancestors, mainly because the meager data available were simply not adequate to be threaded into a coherent and unequivocal evolutionary framework, and because the fact that man was studying himself has often hindered rather than helped progress. Objectivity in analyzing ourselves has not been one of our strong points. In recent years, however, the weight of new evidence, especially in providing a temporal context for many pivotal specimens, has begun to force some order into what has often been chaos. We do not pretend that the story is complete or ever will be; nor that the picture presented in this reader has no flaws — it just happens at present to be the simplest one consistent with all the data; but one does sense with some relief the beginnings of clarity.

For the effective study of any living organism, a certain body of information is necessary. Specifically, we want to know the when, what, and why of the particular evolutionary sequence that has led to the organism we see today. Time is always of special importance. It is particularly so for the student of human evolution because of the short span of time he is dealing with, the major evolutionary events and changes that have taken place during that span, and the subsequent necessity for putting those events (what is seen in the fossil and archaeological record) into a proper temporal sequence. We have already seen in the preceding selections the clarity introduced into the study of early hominid evolution by the simple provision of a date for the hominid-pongid divergence even though the actual historical data are extremely scanty. One can do a great deal more with the specifically hominid fossil record — due to the greater amount of data — and thus much more sophisticated questions can be dealt with.

Given a beginning from a form not unlike a small chimpanzee, we face a data gap until we reach the earliest of the South African australopithecines that various lines of evidence suggest date from three million years ago. During this gap the basic adaptations to bipedalism and reduction of the canine complex were accomplished. This phase marked a major grade in the course of primate evolution and logically deserves recognition as a new genus: Australopithecus. The attainment of a new evolutionary grade is often characterized by a subsequent adaptive radiation — representing the exploitation of that grade in diverse ways — and the australopithecines would not appear to constitute an exception. The grade Australopithecus is thus represented by at least two lines (genetically isolated evolutionary lineages) usually given at least specific distinction: A. africanus and A. robustus. It is presumed here that robustus and africanus *share a common ancestor subsequent to the origin of the hominid line; i.e., that their bipedal, small-canined adaptations were not achieved independently, although the time of separation of the two lineages is not presently known.*

The evidence from the various South and East African sites (in particular Sterkfontein, Makapans, Swartkrans, Olduvai, and the Omo area) indicates the coexistence of the two lineages over a minimum of one million years. This presence of two lines allows, and in fact almost requires, two different developments within the grade Australopithecus. Thus the direction of evolutionary change in one lineage need not have any relationship to what happens in the other. We have no reason, then, to be surprised in finding a subsequent major change in grade in one line and not in the other. The various australopithecine data lend themselves to an interpretation of precisely this form. On this hypothesis, favored by both Howell and Robinson, the robustus line remained in the Australopithecus grade throughout its evolutionary history ending in extinction somewhere between 0.5 and 1.0 million years ago. The other lineage developed a truly human cultural adaptation, characterized archaeologically by stone tool cultures and morphologically by an increasing cranial capacity. This latter characteristic was undoubtedly an adaptation to the increasingly complex requirements of human language in an information storage, retrieval, and association sense. The beginnings of this language-mediated cultural adaptation are not yet documented in the archaeological record, but they would appear to postdate the earlier South African material (Sterkfontein and Makapans) and they certainly predate the earliest Olduvai material. Thus the inception of this second major change in the hominid grade can be placed somewhere in the area of two–three million years ago — a period that the immensely rich Omo beds presently being worked by Howell and others should document very nicely. Again a nomenclatural change — this time from Australopithecus to Homo — is indicated. Thus the sympatric existence of Australopithecus (as the robustus line) and Homo, a matter that appears somehow paradoxical to many, is seen as a quite ordinary happenstance.

At this point it is appropriate to consider more seriously the problem of hominid taxonomic nomenclature that has for a long time often confused, rather than illuminated, the study of human evolution. If we accept the historical perspective given in Figure 1, however, it becomes possible to at least appreciate the nature of the problem and thus go a long way toward its solution. In this case the solution is not one that particularly concerns the ICZN (International Code for Zoological Nomenclature) but only one designed to help the student in his study of fossil man.

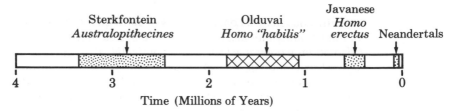

FIGURE 1

Through the accidents of discovery it happens that the first three
major groups of hominid fossils found turned out to be quite
sharply separated from one another in evolutionary time.
Therefore it is not surprising that they should also be quite
distinct from one another in anatomical details as well as in their
archaeological associations. Thus we have the Sterkfontein
material (now universally called Australopithecus africanus),
the Javanese material first found by Dubois in the 1890s and
augmented by the work of von Koenigswald in the 1930s (now
called Homo erectus and dating some two million years later),
and the Neandertal material (usually considered Homo sapiens in
grade whatever line or lines it is placed with) dating from around
100,000 to 40,000 years ago. Without more data we had little
difficulty in seeing three distinct taxa, but as time went on the
gaps in time separating these three groups began to be filled in
with fossil finds. And as we are dealing with an evolutionary
situation it is natural that the morphological gaps separating
these fossils also began to be filled in so that today we have an
almost unbroken record of hominid evolutionary development
reaching from the earliest A. africanus to modern Homo sapiens.
What we call a specific fossil, essentially into which preformed
slot of our thinking we place it, is then very much an artifice often
not related to evolutionary reality. A fossil cranium is found low
in Bed I, Olduvai Gorge, dating from about 1.8 million years. The
indicated cranial capacity is outside the South African africanus
or robustus range, and jaw and teeth material (contemporaneous
but not from the same individual) also suggests a more advanced
(over africanus) form. But given the dating this is precisely what
we might expect. After all, if africanus is ancestral to erectus
there must be populations connecting these two in time —
populations intermediate in morphology between those
exhibited in the temporally disjunct africanus and erectus
material. Thus Leakey and Tobias may wish to call it Homo
habilis, whereas Robinson feels that Homo erectus is a more
appropriate and taxonomically more legitimate term. Whichever
name is used need not distract us from more important matters
— what the material looks like, when it appears, and what it tells

120

us about the course of human evolution. The earliest "habilis" material is advanced in terms of the Sterkfontein australopithecines and primitive in terms of the Javanese erectus material, and thus forms a part of the evolutionary line most of us feel connects the two. The later "habilis" material, that is probably broadly contemporaneous with "Telanthropus," is much nearer classical (i.e., earlier found) erectus in time and thus, not unexpectedly, overlaps it in a number of characteristics.

Whether or not Homo habilis remains in taxonomic circulation is at present a moot point but we should not fall into the trap (probably one that is a quite natural relic of our evolutionary history) of thinking that giving something a name somehow describes and circumscribes it. Taxa that succeed one another in time are not "natural" or objectively delineated units — they are names that man applies to populations (or individuals) in the same presumed line. The source of such distinction is almost always a temporal gap in the fossil record — a gap that further work will often fill in. If one appreciates this general picture and uses it as a sort of intellectual framework, then the details supplied by various lines of evidence can be fitted in as they develop. When they can't, it becomes time to begin altering the framework.

Within the grade Homo, then, as I will expand upon in a later article, one sees a single line within which the language mediated cultural adaptation is developed. The names applied to the various successive populations within that line are open to appreciable debate, as we have already seen. For purely heuristic purposes, one might find it more useful to consider three major cultural stages within the Homo grade: Oldowan times (pre-handaxe), Acheulean times (handaxe), and post-handaxe times. Then we can associate Homo habilis with the first, Homo erectus with the second, and Homo sapiens (including the Neandertals) with the third. As to the general rule of an adaptive radiation following a change in grade — the human dispersal out of Africa during late habilis or early erectus times and the subsequent more or less generically independent development of the various human groups might be considered as such (see "Human Variation in an Evolutionary Context").

In reading the selections by Robinson, Howell, and Mann, if one tries to apply the framework just given to what is being said, the subject of our fossil ancestors should be much clarified.

121

J. T. ROBINSON

This essay possibly too strongly emphasizes the taxonomic aspects of early hominid evolution, but is included to give some flavor of the controversies involved in this field. It is, in addition, a concise and significant statement by one of the major figures involved in the development of the australopithecine evidence. The closing sentence, "The literature abounds with factual error committed primarily because the term australopithecine has been used when in fact one or the other of the two lineages alone is being referred to," is the key to the major significance of Robinson's contribution — the demonstration that the australopithecine grade (in the sense used in the preceding introduction) was composed of two quite distinct lines. Once one is clear on this point, many statements in the literature (some of which are referred to by Robinson) are seen as deliberate obfuscation. One element of caution in the reading of this article — very strong feelings pervade much of the field and so overstatements can be, and are, made. One such overstatement concerns the equivalence of Paranthropus and "Meganthropus" and here Robinson is in distinctly a minority position (and quite justifiably so in our opinion because of the quality of the "Meganthropus" evidence). The other, we feel, is to unduly blur the course of early hominid evolution by proposing the rejection of the name Australopithecus. The justification given — that the "line occupies one adaptive zone" — is flatly contradicted by Robinson's own statements concerning the distinction he proposes between H. transvaalensis and H. sapiens. The discernment of two distinct major stages or grades in hominid evolution is an important advance in our thinking; it would not do to mask this by suggesting that the transvaalensis-sapiens line functioned within a single adaptive zone.

7 Variation and the Taxonomy of the Early Hominids

INTRODUCTION

Taxonomic practice in the field of human paleontology has always tended to be appreciably out of step with general zoological practice. There are a number of reasons for this. An obvious one is the fact that the number of known fossils has been so small, especially in the earlier stages of the development of human paleontology, that much room has existed for genuine major disagreements concerning the systematics of hominids and their close relatives. Probably a much more serious contributing factor has been lack of taxonomic experience. This, in turn, is a consequence of the fact that human paleontologists are usually persons whose training has not been primarily zoological. Usually they are physical anthropologists or persons with medical training whose backgrounds ordinarily do not include formal training in taxonomy. As a further complication, some authors who express opinions on the classification of fossil man have little or no personal experience of any depth with the original material; a situation that is particularly apparent with respect to early hominids.

The consequences of this situation are frequently seen in the relevant literature. For example, the nomenclatural rules governing zoological, hence also hominid, taxonomy are embodied in the International Code of Zoological Nomenclature, but its provisions seem to be poorly known among human paleontologists. For this reason one finds names and their spelling being changed in ways expressly forbidden by the Code. Examples are the changing of *Gigantopithecus* to *Gigantanthropus* and *Giganthropus*; *Australopithecus* to *Australanthropus* or *palaeojavanicus* to *paleojavanicus*. Not only is this contrary to the provisions of the Code and a source of unnecessary confusion, but also it demonstrates lack of understanding concerning the way in which taxonomic affinities are indicated. As the Code makes clear, this is not done by the dictionary meaning of the taxon name itself since the latter is not required to have any meaning; affinities are indicated by the next higher category of the hierarchy to which the taxon is referred. Thus the affinities of a species are indicated by the genus into which it is placed; that of a genus by the family (or subfamily) to which it is referred. Another form of failure to comply with the Code is illustrated by a case to be found in the original taxonomic description of the supposed new taxon *Homo habilis*. This 1964 description contains a direct statement

From *Evolutionary Biology*, volume 1, edited by Th. Dobzhansky, M. K. Hecht, W. C. Steere. Appleton-Century-Crofts. Copyright 1967 by the Meredith Corporation.

to the effect that the new taxon may be the same as another that was described in 1949. According to the Code no taxon that is proposed conditionally after 1960 is valid.

Lack of familiarity with general zoological taxonomic practice on the part of human paleontologists has also led to inadequate treatment of variation, misconceptions about the nature of diagnostic criteria as well as variation within and between taxa at various levels of the hierarchy, especially the species and genus levels. These difficulties have been exaggerated by the fact that the experience of the human paleontologist is usually confined to man and his near relatives and thus his conception of variation may be rather different from that of zoologists working with a greater range of animals.

Fortunately human paleontologists are becoming increasingly aware of these problems and the situation is thus improving, though perhaps too slowly. The present paper is an attempt to make a small contribution to that improvement and is concerned primarily with variation in relation to hominid taxonomy.

SPECIES, FOSSILS, AND LINEAGES

All natural populations are variable. This fact makes it possible for natural selection to work and thus for evolution to occur. However, it also causes endless complication for the taxonomist because this variation has to be analyzed and understood before valid taxonomic conclusions can be drawn.

When dealing with the classification of a heterogeneous collection of living organisms from a single locality, the problem of variation is usually not especially difficult since species that inhabit the same locality normally have no genetic continuity with each other. As a result, intraspecies differences can be distinguished from interspecies differences without serious difficulty.

The problem is not quite so simple when more than one locality is involved. Species variability is then almost always greater and the question of interfertility becomes more problematical. In such circumstances the evaluation of variability for taxonomic purposes can become extremely difficult. This is especially the case if one or more lineages happen to be undergoing speciation and the process is already well advanced.

As is well known, statistical techniques of various levels of sophistication exist that can be used to assist in choosing a path through the complexities of variation in order to reach taxonomic conclusions. These techniques are of great value when used judiciously. However, it does not always seem to be appreciated that, although these techniques can tell one whether or not two samples could have been drawn from the same population, they cannot tell one at what taxonomic level the difference lies in the event that two distinct populations appear to be involved. Nor does it follow, indeed, if a statistically significant difference is found between two populations, that they belong to different taxa. Evaluating the results of statistical analysis in such cases is a problem in biological significance and the statistical techniques do not themselves have biological judgment and are no substitute for biological insight.

I am not here concerned, however, to argue that point but merely to emphasize the fact that although these techniques are invaluable in the analysis of variation, they do not themselves solve the taxonomic problems involved.

As troublesome as taxonomic problems may be in complex extant populations, the difficulties are very seriously magnified in the case of extinct populations as represented by paleontological samples.

In the first place there is the obvious fact that paleontological samples are less complete than modern ones. A fossil seldom represents the whole of the anatomy of the individual from which it came and frequently consists of only a portion of the hard parts of the original animal. A paleontological sample is thus a poorer representation of the population from which it came than is a museum sample of a modern taxon. Furthermore, the possibility usually exists, in the case of the modern sample, to go into the field or into the laboratory to collect information concerning physiology, ecology, and behavior, which can assist in determining affinities. This possibility exists to only a very meager extent with fossils. With luck and care it is possible to learn something about missing soft parts and their function, and some indication may be obtained of ecological and behavioral aspects of the population. But this information is always indirect and incomplete.

In the second place, since the geological record is being dealt with, the taxa concerned are not so restricted in time as are modern taxa. The time dimension is thus more directly and obviously involved in fossil taxa; though it is clear that the time dimension is actually also involved in the case of modern taxa since none consists of a single generation only. Collections of fossils are usually also incomplete in that they represent any lineage only patchily. Paleontological samples thus are inadequate representations of extinct populations both at a single time horizon and in time depth.

The taxonomic difficulties arising from the above properties of the fossil record do not spring from biological characteristics of fossil taxa, but from the fact that one cannot learn as much about a fossil population as one can about a modern one. The difficulty experienced with samples each of which represents a different lineage as compared to modern samples results primarily from the incompleteness of the fossil samples. Since each fossil sample represents a different lineage in this case, there will have been no genetic interchange between them, hence unbridged gaps will have existed between the populations concerned during the time when they represented different lineages.

However, there are also taxonomic difficulties with fossil samples that are not experienced with modern samples and yet do spring from biological properties of paleontological samples. For example, should one be concerned with following a single lineage, or what was a single lineage at one stage, through a substantial segment of time, a situation is met with that is incompatible with the nature of Linnean taxonomy and nomenclature and for which no objective solution exists in terms of that nomenclature. The reason for this, as is well recognized, is simply that one is no longer dealing with discontinuous taxa but with a lineage in which every generation is genetically continuous with both the previous one and the succeeding one.

The consequence of this is clear: whereas in the case of modern populations there is one type of taxonomic distinction only, in the case of paleontological populations there are two quite distinct types. One of these is the same as that in modern populations and concerns the discontinuous, discrete taxa each of which represents a single time-transect of a separate lineage. The second type consists of time stages of a single lineage. Since there is always genetic continuity in time, and since it seems that systemic mutations that at one stroke produce a new and taxonomically distinct form do not appear to be real, there are no discontinuities in a lineage. Consequently there are no natural, sharp initial or terminal boundaries to species, hence to taxa at higher hierarchic levels.

If the lineage concerned is cladogenetic, with speciation occurring at intervals, then the approximate limits of the species are indicated by the points at which branching occurs. However, even here the upper and lower limits of the species will not be sharply defined since one species does not arise sharply from another, even where quantum evolution occurs.

If the lineage concerned is anagenetic, then clearly there is not even the poor definition of species boundaries found in the above case and any taxa set up within a lineage must be quite arbitrary as a consequence.

It is a matter of some importance, therefore, to distinguish between within-lineage (intralineage) variation and between-lineage (interlineage) variation when studying fossil samples.

In the case of paleontological samples, then, one has to cope with the fact that the species is more variable since it has not only the variation characteristic of the biospecies, at one time transect, but also that due to variation from generation to generation in time. That is, the chronospecies is more variable than the biospecies and this fact must be taken into account.

There is the further difficulty, however, that Linnean nomenclature is based on the assumption that the species, and taxa at all other levels of the hierarchy, are discrete, discontinuous entities and this seems never to be true of the chronospecies. So quite apart from incomplete samples and the difficulties involved in arriving at a clear understanding of the biological facts in such a taxonomic situation, there is the further difficulty of having to apply an unsuitable nomenclatural system.

The species is a more useful concept in neozoology than it is in paleozoology. This, however, does not mean that the species is of dubious validity when one is concerned with the *process* of evolution. The causes of evolutionary change actually operate on living populations; that is, the nascent zone of evolution is at the time transect where the future is becoming the past and at this active front the species concept is at its most valid and is adequately defined by the definition of Mayr (1940), which is in common use.[1] The problem with the species concept, hence with taxonomy and nomenclature, comes when the advancing evolutionary front has rolled by and one tries to classify what it has left behind.

When looking at a fossil, then, it should not be seen simply as an isolated thing-in-itself, as human paleontologists often tend to do. If this is done, then the chief concern is to see whether it can be distinguished from other, apparently similar specimens. If so, then it is regarded as belonging to a new taxon. Instead the specimen should be seen as part of a complete individual who was a member of a population that had in principle the same sort of variability and other general characteristics observed in living populations and which existed in some particular environment with which it was very intimately related. Furthermore, it should be seen as part of a time sequence, a lineage, so that its species variation certainly extended both horizontally and vertically.

One further point merits attention here and that is the nature of diagnostic criteria. If one possesses two samples drawn from different populations that are not identical, it is usually possible to distinguish the *samples* statistically — for example, by differences in the means and ranges

---

[1] It seems to me that there is no real difference between the biospecies as defined by Mayr and the evolutionary species as defined by Simpson (1951, 1961) with respect to the difference between a species at one time transect and in time depth. As Simpson has pointed out, his definition is not concerned only with bi-parental organisms as is that of Mayr, and is therefore broader. However, like that of Mayr, it is concerned only with a segment of the species in time since it provides no means of defining the beginning or the end of a species. This, as we have seen, is evidently not possible, except arbitrarily, on any definition. My point here is merely that there appears to be a tendency to think of Mayr's definition as applying to one time horizon and Simpson's as defining the species in time, and this appears to me to be untrue. Since successful interbreeding is involved in Mayr's definition, the time element is also involved here, though it is more overt in Simpson's definition. Both definitions are concerned with discontinuity with other lineages and therefore deal with interlineage differences. Neither deals with the intralineage problem. The definitions seem thus to be essentially equivalent, except for the greater inclusiveness of Simpson's in including uni-parental organisms.

of variation for different measurable characteristics. Such demonstrable differences are not necessarily taxonomic differences, as has already been mentioned. But this means of differentiating samples is of use only *after* the sample has been identified; after the fact has been established that it is a sample. This statistical means of differentiation is useless when one is trying to establish which specimens constitute a sample. If one is sitting at a table on which a large number of unclassified fossil specimens of various sorts are lying, differences that can be demonstrated only by statistical means cannot assist one to sort the specimens into species groups. One needs for this purpose a set of absolute criteria that will allow one to distinguish without fail every single individual of one sort from every single one of another if the groups they represent are to be regarded as good species belonging to different lineages, or to well-separated parts of the same lineage. In the case of fossils the sorting criteria are always morphological, though one may draw conclusions concerning differences that are other than morphological on the basis of further study of a sample once the fact has been established that it is a true and unmixed sample. In samples of extant animals the sorting criteria do not have to be morphological.

It is obvious that many characters will not be diagnostic and will not serve as sorting criteria and if a fragment of fossil does not contain any diagnostic, sorting criteria, it may not be possible to assign the specimen to the correct taxon for lack of suitable information. This is different from the point made above concerning the necessity for sorting criteria to correctly sort every single individual of one taxon from every single individual of another. The latter point applies to the *individual* but not necessarily to every fossil specimen; that is to say, it should be possible to assign every individual to the correct taxon without fail if the taxon is to be demonstrably different at the species level or above. This presents no difficulty in extant forms but obviously paleontological samples are more difficult to deal with since some specimens may not include any of the diagnostic criteria; the more incomplete a specimen is the more likely this is to be the case.

TAXONOMIC CHARACTERS IN EARLY FOSSIL HOMINIDS

Some examples of how variation has been treated in the case of early fossil hominids will now be examined. Since it is currently the center of some controversy, the supposed new species of *Homo, H. "habilis"* (Leakey, Tobias, and Napier, 1964) will be considered first.

One of the characters believed to be diagnostic of the new form is the *length/breadth index* of the teeth, especially the lower premolars and molars. One may use the two premolars and the first molar of the mandibular dentition to check this belief. The published information contains measurements for a single tooth only for each of the second and third molars of *Homo "habilis"* and these differ very slightly or not at all from the corresponding values for *Australopithecus* and *Paranthropus*, hence these have been left out of account here. The relevant information is included in Tables 1 to 3 and is taken from Tobias (1966).

In the case of P_3 the observed range for length falls completely within the ranges for *Australopithecus* and for *Paranthropus*; there is thus no difference here. However, the observed range for breadth does not fall within the corresponding range for either *Australopithecus* or *Paranthropus*, although the gap between the ranges is 0.3 mm only in the case of *Paranthropus* and 0.7 in the case of *Australopithecus*. The breadth of P_3 is thus relatively low in *H. "habilis"* while the length is not. It is therefore to be expected that this will show up as a relatively high length/breadth index as compared to the ranges for the other two forms. This is indeed so, as can be seen from Table 1. Here again the gaps between the ranges are slight; that between the *H. "habilis"* and *Paranthropus* ranges being 0.3 unit only and that in the other case 2.2 units.

Turning to P_4 and Table 2 it is apparent that the observed range for length in *H. "habilis"* falls wholly within that for *Paranthropus* while the observed range for *Australopithecus* falls wholly below those for the above two forms. In the case of the breadth, the pattern for P_3 is repeated; the *H. "habilis"* range falls below those of the other two; again the gaps are small, being 0.2 and 0.6 mm. In the case of the l/b index, the *H. "habilis"* range is again outside that for *Australopithecus* but overlaps to some extent that for *Paranthropus*.

Table 3 shows that the *H. "habilis"* values for M_1 fall within the observed ranges for *Australopithecus*, except for the very slight difference in maximum value of the l/b index. This is also true of the length and breadth ranges for *Paranthropus*, though the l/b index range of the latter is below that for *H. "habilis."*

The above evidence suggests that there is some basis for the conclusion by the authors of *H. "habilis"* that there is a tendency in the latter for the mandibular teeth to be relatively narrow. But it appears that their conclusion that there is "a marked tendency toward buccolingual narrowing and mesiodistal elongation of the teeth, which is especially evident in the lower premolars (where it expresses itself as a marked elongation of the talonid) and in the lower molars. . . ." represents both an overstatement and too broad a generalization on the basis of what is currently known, since it seems that what difference there is is to be found primarily in the lower premolars. It is worth noting also that the "marked elongation" of the talonid referred to does not appear to be unique to *H. "habilis"* since the molarization ratio (ratio of talonid length to length of the rest of the crown; see Robinson, 1956) appears to be of much the same order as that in

TABLE 1. THIRD LOWER PREMOLAR

	N	Length Mean	Length Range	Breadth Mean	Breadth Range	L/B Index Mean	L/B Index Range
Australopithecus	7	10.0	9.0-11.5	12.3	11.0-14.0	81.4	71.4-90.9
Paranthropus	16	9.7	9.2-10.5	11.9	10.6-13.5	81.9	68.1-92.8
Homo "habilis"	3	9.6	9.3- 9.9	9.9	9.3-10.3	96.9	93.1-99.5

TABLE 2. FOURTH LOWER PREMOLAR

	N	Length Mean	Length Range	Breadth Mean	Breadth Range	L/B Index Mean	L/B Index Range
Australopithecus	5	9.6	9.0-10.1	12.3	11.6-14.0	79.2	71.4- 87.1(4[a])
Paranthropus	17	11.3	10.3-14.5	13.2	12.0-15.2	85.7	74.5- 95.6
Homo "habilis"	3	10.6	10.3-11.1	10.9	10.7-11.4	97.2	91.7-103.7

[a] Sample size.

TABLE 3. FIRST LOWER MOLAR

	N	Length Mean	Length Range	Breadth Mean	Breadth Range	L/B Index Mean	L/B Index Range
Australopithecus	10	14.0	12.8-15.1	13.1	11.2-13.9	107.3	100.8-117.0(9[a])
Paranthropus	23	14.8	12.7-16.4	14.0	11.5-15.5	106.1	100.7-110.8
Homo "habilis"	2	14.3	14.3	12.3	12.2-12.4	116.3	115.3-117.2

[a] Sample size.

Australopithecus and in *Paranthropus*, where it ranges from about 1.7 to about 2.3, *Paranthropus* being the more heavily molarized of the two, apparently.

The next step is to determine the significance of the fact that there is the observed moderate degree of narrowing of the mandibular premolars of *H. "habilis."* An obvious difficulty in this connection is the smallness of the sample sizes involved. P_3 and P_4 are each known from three teeth only, derived from *two individuals* only, in the case of *H. "habilis,"*[2] while the samples for *Australopithecus* are only slightly larger.

Those for *Paranthropus* are of reasonable size for fossil hominid samples but even so are much smaller than is desirable. Manifestly, the effect of this is to give an observed range that will differ considerably from the range of variation for the populations from which the samples were drawn, especially in the case of *H. "habilis"* and *Australopithecus*.

In setting up the new taxon, however, the authors have used only the observed ranges (Leakey, Tobias, and Napier, 1964; see also, for example, Tobias, 1966). It is therefore not certain that the nonoverlap of some of the observed ranges for the samples represent true nonoverlap for the populations concerned. Therefore, even though the samples are mostly very small, it is important to use them to estimate the population ranges since this would allow one to assess the probability of the cases of observed nonoverlap in the sample ranges applying also to the population ranges. Since nonoverlap is clearest in the case of the buccolingual breadth dimension, this provides the most suitable test case.

[2] It should be noted that the name *H. "habilis"* is now being used in two quite different ways by its authors. I pointed out (1965) that the Bed I and the Bed II material attributed to this taxon appear to be distinguishable. In conformity with this view, Tobias (e.g., 1966) now uses this taxon as including the Bed I material only from Olduvai and the above sample size is based on this interpretation. Leakey (e.g., 1966), however, still uses it as originally defined, with the exception that he now no longer regards Hominid 16 from FLK II as belonging in this taxon, but to *H. erectus*. Tobias agrees that Hominid 16 does not belong to *H. "habilis,"* but disagrees with placing it in *H. erectus*; he believes it belongs in *Paranthropus* (=*Zinjanthropus*). Needless to say, this difference in usage is confusing. For example, Leakey (1966) attempts to refute my statement that the type mandible of *H. "habilis"* from Bed I has an internal mandibular contour of the sort found in *Australopithecus* and unlike that found in *Homo*, by pointing to the *Homo*-type contour found in a paratype from Bed II. Overlooking for the moment that fact that the contour of the paratype from Bed II throws no light on the nature of that in the type specimen from Bed I, a major point in my 1965 comment on *H. "habilis"* is that the Bed I and Bed II specimens originally attributed to this taxon differ in a number of characters and attention was directed especially to the fact that in this particular character the type mandible resembled *Australopithecus* but the Bed II paratype resembled *Homo*. This does not prove, as Leakey indicates, that *H. "habilis"* has a *Homo*-like contour but, with other evidence, indicates that creating the taxon was unnecessary since the Bed I material can be accommodated without difficulty in *Australopithecus* and the Bed II material in *H. erectus*. Having the taxon *H. "habilis"* is thus an unnecessary confusion, which is now being compounded by its use in two quite different ways by two of the original authors.

TABLE 4. THIRD LOWER PREMOLAR

	N	x	s	s_x	s_x [a]	V	$x \pm 3s$
Australopithecus:							
Length	7	9.96	0.804	0.300	3.0	8.1	7.5-12.4
Breadth	4	12.37	0.723	0.361	2.9	5.8	10.2-14.5
Paranthropus:							
Length	12	9.74	0.378	0.110	1.1	3.9	8.6-10.9
Breadth	11	11.77	0.780	0.235	2.0	6.6	9.4-14.1
Homo "habilis":							
Length	3	9.60	0.300	0.173	1.8	3.1	8.7-10.5
Breadth	3	9.90	0.529	0.305	3.1	5.3	8.3-11.5

N = sample size; x = mean; s = standard deviation; s_x = standard error of the mean; V = coefficient of variation.
[a] Expressed as percent of x.

Estimates for the standard population ranges of P_3 of H. "habilis," *Australopithecus,* and *Paranthropus,* using limits of three times the standard deviation on either side of the mean, are given in Table 4 and shown in Figure 1. Unfortunately, I have had to use even smaller sample sizes — in making these calculations — than are available since I do not have access to the dimensions of all of the teeth on which Tables 1 and 2 are based.

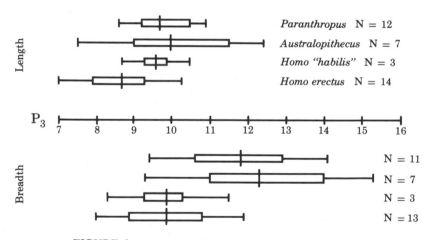

FIGURE 1

Ranges of variation for length and breadth dimensions of the mandibular third premolar in some early hominids. The enclosed space represents the observed range of variation, the central cross line marks the mean, and the total length of each figure indicates the estimated population variation using limits of three times the standard deviation on either side of the mean.

From Figure 1 it is clear that any semblance of nonoverlap has disappeared; in fact, 69 percent of the estimated range of variation for *H. "habilis"* is included within that for *Australopithecus* and 66 percent in the case of *Paranthropus*. Table 4 shows that the standard error of the mean is small in the case of the breadth dimension of all three forms, being well below 5 percent of the mean (*Paranthropus*, 2 percent; *H. "habilis,"* 3.1 percent and *Australopithecus*, 2.9 percent), which suggests that the position of the true population mean has been fixed between fairly narrow limits. The estimated ranges, furthermore, do not represent an excessive amount of variation since the coefficient of variation falls between 5.3 and 6.6, which are normal values for linear dimensions in mammals (Simpson, Roe, and Lewontin, 1960, p. 91). These values are large enough to indicate that the samples are giving a reasonably good impression of the variability of the population for the purposes of the sort of calculation that has been employed here. On the other hand the coefficients of variation here obtained are small enough to indicate that the estimated ranges have not been artificially inflated by mixture in the sample or some other disturbing factor. For these reasons it seems to me that the calculated parameters with respect to P_3 breadth can be accepted as reflecting reasonably accurately those of the population from which the samples came. If this is so, then we must accept that even in the case of the most promising instance of apparent nonoverlap in equivalent ranges of variation in the three forms being compared, there is in fact extensive overlap. The breadth of these teeth cannot thus serve as a diagnostic criterion since it would not be possible to assign all specimens of P_3 to the correct group on this basis.

From Table 4 it is clear that the overlap is much more extensive in the case of the length dimension of P_3 since here the means for the three groups are very similar and the total estimated ranges for *H. "habilis"* and *Paranthropus* are included in that for *Australopithecus*. In this case, however, since the coefficient of variation is only just above three for *H. "habilis"* it is probable that the sample is inadequately representing variation through being made up from two individuals only, even though this does not appear to be true of the breadth dimension sample, which is similarly made up. However, it is quite possible that this value for the coefficient of variation is not significantly too small since the corresponding value for *Paranthropus* ($N = 12$) and for a sample of modern Japanese ($N = 192$) is 3.9 only.

Table 5 compares the coefficient of variation for a number of substantial samples of P_3 of modern man, as well as the much smaller samples of *Homo erectus* (Peking), *Australopithecus*, *H. "habilis,"* and *Paranthropus*. From this table it is evident that there is a great deal of similarity in the values of V without any obviously anomalous values occurring.

From the above considerations it would seem clear that even in the cases

TABLE 5. COEFFICIENT OF VARIATION
OF THIRD LOWER PREMOLAR

| | Length | | Breadth | |
	N	V	N	V
Aleut	158	5.4	135	7.5
Japanese	192	3.9	192	3.5
Javanese	175	7.3	174	8.2
Norwegian Lapps	511	6.8	504	6.2
Pecos Indians	105	4.3	105	5.2
Swedes	306	4.8	—	—
Tristanites	255	6.8	125	6.4
American Whites	172	5.6	—	—
Homo erectus (Peking)	14	6.4	13	6.6
Homo "habilis"	3	3.1	3	5.3
Australopithecus	7	8.1	7	8.1
Paranthropus	12	3.9	11	6.6

of greatest apparent nonoverlap there is actually so much overlap in the estimated population ranges that neither buccolingual breadth nor mesiodistal length are at all diagnostic in the case of the three forms being considered since these characteristics could not successfully be used to sort all specimens into the correct groups.

However, it might be argued that this could be true and yet the shape as reflected by the length/breadth index (L $\times$ 100/B) might be diagnostic. This seems improbable since an index of this sort varies more than do the dimensions upon which it is based (Simpson, Roe, and Lewontin, 1960, p. 15); hence it is to be expected that the index ranges for the populations would overlap even more than do the estimated ranges for length and breadth individually.

From Table 6 it can be seen that the observed range of the l/b index for

TABLE 6. LENGTH/BREADTH INDEX
OF THIRD LOWER PREMOLAR

	N	x	s	$\dfrac{s}{x}$[a]	V	$x \pm 3s$
Paranthropus	12	83.2	4.95	1.7	6.0	68.3- 98.0
Australopithecus	7	81.5	6.86	3.2	8.4	60.9-102.0
Homo "habilis"	3	96.9	3.35	2.0	3.5	86.8-106.9
Homo erectus (Peking)	13	86.3	6.83	2.2	7.9	65.8-106.8

N = sample size; x = mean; s = standard deviation; s_x = standard error of the mean; V = coefficient of variation.
[a] Expressed as percent of x.

Australopithecus is wholly included in that for *Paranthropus*. The small observed range for *H. "habilis"* does not overlap that for either of the other two, although the zones of nonoverlap are small. However, if these figures are used for estimating the population variation it is once again apparent that the respective ranges of variation overlap extensively. This is clear from both Table 6 and Figure 2. The l/b index thus fares no better than do either length or breadth alone; there is so much overlap in the three ranges that this criterion cannot be used diagnostically since the majority of specimens could not be correctly sorted by using it.

If the sample of P_3 of *H. "habilis"* correctly reflects the population characteristics of this form, then it is clear that there is a difference between it and the others with respect to the l/b index since the mean for the former falls quite far from the corresponding values of *Australopithecus* and *Paranthropus*. However, a reason has already been advanced for suspecting that this sample inadequately represents the population, apart from the obvious fact that two individuals only are involved. This is also true of the l/b index since the coefficient of variation for this character falls in the range of 6 to 8 for *Australopithecus*, *Paranthropus*, and *H. erectus* (Peking Man), but is 3.5 only for *H. "habilis,"* suggesting that the sample is too small for estimating the population range adequately. If one assumes that it does adequately represent the population from which the sample came, then it could be argued that this index does indicate a difference between this form and the other two. However, this is not a diagnostic difference by means of which individuals could be correctly sorted, but only a difference demonstrable by statistical means on samples.

Table 7 presents the relevant information with regard to P_4. From this it is clear that in this case the situation is in principle the same as for P_3: extensive overlap of the standard population ranges occurs in all cases.

These considerations seem to suggest, even in the cases of the greatest apparent difference between *H. "habilis," Australopithecus,* and *Paranthropus* with respect to the mandibular dentition, that length and breadth dimensions alone, or combined as the l/b index, are not diagnostic

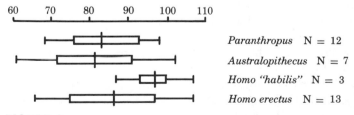

FIGURE 2

Ranges of variation for the length/breadth index for the mandibular third premolar in some early hominids. Conventions as for Figure 1.

TABLE 7. FOURTH LOWER PREMOLAR

	N	x	s	s_x	$\frac{s-^a}{x}$	V	$x \pm 3s$
Australopithecus							
Length	5	9.58	0.54	0.24	2.5	5.6	8.0- 11.2
Breadth	4	12.35	1.12	0.56	4.5	9.1	9.0- 15.7
L/B Index	4	79.20	7.44	3.72	4.7	9.4	56.9-101.5
Paranthropus							
Length	14	10.97	0.63	0.17	1.5	5.7	9.1- 12.8
Breadth	14	13.08	0.72	0.19	1.5	5.5	10.9- 15.3
L/B Index	14	84.34	4.27	1.14	1.4	5.1	71.5- 97.2
Homo "habilis"							
Length	3	10.60	0.45	0.26	2.4	4.2	9.3- 11.9
Breadth	3	10.93	0.45	0.26	2.4	4.1	9.6- 12.3
L/B Index	3	97.23	6.14	3.54	3.6	6.3	78.8-115.7

N = sample size; x = mean; s = standard deviation; s_x = standard error of the mean; V = coefficient of variation.
[a] Expressed as percent of x.

characters by which these forms can be distinguished since their ranges of variation overlap extensively.

Passing now from a consideration of the above characters for the three forms under discussion to a general consideration of the phyletic valence of tooth size and shape in the hominids as a whole, it becomes even more clear that they fail completely as diagnostic criteria. The reason for this is that the population ranges for length and breadth and the l/b index for various modern racial groups of man cover just about the same area as do those of the fossil forms of early hominid. There is almost complete overlap of all the ranges. For example, in the case of the tooth most detailedly examined in the foregoing discussion, P_3, the estimated population range of the l/b index for Peking Man appears to include the estimated ranges of *Paranthropus, H. "habilis,"* and those of a dozen samples of modern man including all the major racial forms as well as almost all of that for *Australopithecus!* The means for the fossil forms, with the exception of *H. "habilis,"* which is almost but not quite included, fall within the range represented by the means of the modern racial groups. This can be seen from Figure 3.

What this means is that the within-species variation, of the l/b index for P_3, within *H. sapiens* is of much the same order and values as the between-genera variation within the hominids. A mixed sample of teeth (P_3) of the various fossil and modern hominids could therefore not be sorted correctly into the proper categories by means of this character. This is

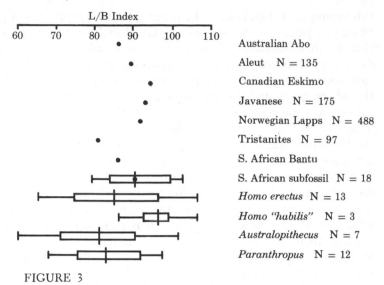

FIGURE 3

Ranges of variation for the length/breadth index for the mandibular third premolar in some hominids. The spots represent the
length/breadth index of the mean dimensions for a series of
samples of modern *Homo sapiens,* for which insufficient data were
available to allow calculation of the sort of information represented in the rest of the diagram. Such data were available for one
sample only (South African subfossil *H. sapiens*), which thus
gives some idea of the type of diagram that might have resulted in
the other cases, had enough information been available. Other
conventions as for Figure 1.

true for demes, species, and genera. This being so, it is obviously not a
diagnostic character in the hominids.

Tobias (1966) has argued that the validity of the l/b index as a diagnostic
criterion in the case of *H. "habilis"* does not depend on whether it can sort
Australopithecus, Paranthropus, and *Homo* successfully, but only on
whether it can distinguish *H. "habilis"* from *Australopithecus africanus.* He
believes that it does successfully separate these two, since the observed
ranges in the two cases do not quite overlap.

This argument, however, is false for two reasons. First, as has been shown
above, taking more careful account of variation demonstrates that
considerable overlap would certainly occur in the ranges concerned if
adequately large samples were available instead of the very small samples
actually available. This criterion therefore does not distinguish the two
groups successfully. Second, there is serious taxonomic confusion underlying

this argument. Tobias believes he is here comparing species, not genera, but he himself places the two species concerned in different genera. This means that the main differences between these two taxa are, in his opinion, the differences between the genera *Homo* and *Australopithecus*. One is concerned with species differences when dealing only with a level below that of the genus, and this means that the species being compared must be within the same genus; if not, then clearly the genus level is also involved. This is clear from the fact that when classifying a species one works down the taxonomic hierarchy to the species level, not up from the latter. The genus has to be decided before it can be decided whether the species being classified is new or an already described one. This is further underlined by the fact that a trivial name can be used many times, although not more than once in any given genus; since no taxon above the species level is valid unless there is an associated species, it is clear that a decision has to be reached about the genus before a trivial name can be decided upon. Whichever way one approaches the matter, it is clear that the generic level takes precedence over the species level and the two must not be confused.

Since Tobias and his coauthors placed the Olduvai material concerned in *Homo*, not *Australopithecus*, and have since defended this judgment as valid, they are thereby maintaining that the differences between their material and that from Sterkfontein, Makapansgat, and Taung lie at the generic level. Whether these authors realize it or not, they are thus using the shape index as a generic diagnostic criterion, and we have already seen that it fails in this capacity.

If it is to be used at the species level, as Tobias believes he is doing, then it must be used to compare *H. "habilis"* with other species of the genus *Homo* only. However, the criterion is so variable, as Figure 3 demonstrates, that it clearly fails at this level also.

There is yet a further point worth mentioning in this regard. I recently (1965) compared published measurements of P_3 in the type mandible of *H. "habilis"* made by Leakey, by Tobias, and by me. These differed sufficiently to yield a range for the l/b index of the tooth on the left side of 93.3 to 116.0! Tobias responded to this comparison as though I had criticized measuring accuracy. However, this was not the point. What did concern me was that if three experienced workers could produce so wide a range of values for the same, identical tooth specimen, then conclusions based on such measurements should allow for the fact that the basic datum is not precise but includes a considerable, wholly spurious range of variation that is not related to the biological variation of the population. This is an additional reason for being suspicious of the reality or meaningfulness of small gaps between observed ranges of variation in this case and in others like it.

This example has been considered in some detail as it illustrates a number of pitfalls consequent upon failure to pay careful attention to evaluating variation in incomplete fossil samples. Furthermore, it involved metrical characters that are somewhat easier to handle than qualitative ones and which are commonly, though in my opinion unjustifiably, regarded as being somehow more scientific and valid than the latter.

Another character that has been advanced as evidence favoring the validity of the proposed taxon *H. "habilis"* is endocranial volume. Tobias (1964) went to a considerable amount of trouble to obtain an estimate of 680 cc from two isolated and incomplete parietal bones of a single individual. Assuming an upper size limit of about 600 cc for *Australopithecus africanus*, on the basis of the scanty evidence available, he concluded that 680 cc is too large for the latter species, thus providing support for the conclusion that a second taxon is present.

Fairly recently I re-examined the evidence for endocranial volume in *A. africanus*, using a sample of six specimens. Two of these provided good estimates since one is a complete skull with braincase empty and intact and the other consists of the greater part of a natural endocranial cast, the missing portion of which can easily be restored from the opposite side. Four other specimens provide less direct estimates, but nevertheless are a firmer basis for estimates than are two parietals alone. This sample gave a mean of 430 cc and an estimated population range of 270 to 580 cc, using limits of three times the standard deviation on either side of the mean. It would seem that the estimates composing the sample are unlikely to have been seriously in error since the standard error of the mean is less than 5 percent of the mean and the coefficient of variation is 11.8 as compared to 11.7 for a sample of 200 specimens of modern man (Ashton and Spence, 1958).

At a glance these results appear to support Tobias' claim. However, two considerations should be taken into account before accepting such a conclusion. In the first place, *A. africanus* is a lineage and our present sample may represent only a small part of its duration in time. Also, as I have suggested on a number of occasions, there is what seems to be good evidence suggesting that it was undergoing brain expansion. If this is so, then we should expect that samples from different time horizons might vary considerably in endocranial volume. Differences in endocranial volume could therefore mislead one into thinking that different lineages were being dealt with when no more than different levels of the same lineage were actually involved. A single, rather indirectly determined, estimate of 680 cc is therefore not very secure evidence that two lineages are involved.

In the second place, the upper limit obtained by me (580 cc) should be treated with caution. It was obtained on the basis of population limits falling three times the standard deviation on either side of the mean. However, using the figures obtained by Ashton and Spence (1958) for modern man on the basis of a sample of 200 individuals and the same population limits, we obtain an estimate of 1,780 cc as an upper limit for the range for modern man. This clearly underestimates the observed range for endocranial volume inasmuch as the observed upper limit is roughly 2,200 cc. This represents an underestimate that is rather more than 30 percent of the mean. Similarly, the above authors provided figures for the gorilla based on a sample of 113 specimens, and three times the standard deviation above the mean also underestimates the observed range, but by a much smaller margin. Using the parameters obtained from the sample by six specimens of *Australopithecus* and using the percentage underestimate referred to above in the case of modern man, an estimate of 700 cc is obtained as the upper limit for the South African population of this form. This clearly is not a secure figure for several reasons. However, it does suggest with considerable force that an endocranial volume of 680 cc is not necessarily outside the possible limits of this taxon as we know it in South Africa. This, coupled with the possibility that the endocranial volume will have differed at different levels in the lineage, suggests to me that the one isolated value of 680 cc from Olduvai is an extremely insecure basis from which to draw support for the idea that the Olduvai form is taxonomically distinct from A. *africanus*.

These examples appear to me to be representative of the best evidence advanced in support of the species H. *"habilis."*[3] Manifestly, these criteria fall short of performing the task they have been set. The combination of lack of diagnostic capacity and taxonomic confusion involving lack of clear distinction between the genus and species levels, is characteristic in general of the original species diagnosis. The latter is much concerned with differentiating, in broad terms, between H. *"habilis"* and *Austalopithecus (sensu lato)*. Such comparisons belong at the generic level since they concern more than one genus and should therefore have been included in the proposed rediagnosis of the genus *Homo*, not in the diagnosis of the new species, which followed it.

The point of importance here is not so much in which part of their discussion the authors should have made the intergeneric comparisons but rather that the manner of handling the problem indicates that they approached the classification of the material concerned without having in mind a clear distinction between the genus and species levels. This, along with the use of observed ranges based on very small samples, resulted in the

[3] It is perhaps worth mentioning here that I use the word *habilis* in quotes to indicate that in my opinion this term is not valid; this for many reasons, but particularly because it never had nomenclatural validity since the original description contained a clear statement that the proposed new taxon could well be the same as an already existing one, that this constitutes conditional proposal, which specifically violates a provision of the International Code of Zoological Nomenclature that was in force at the time the taxon was proposed.

making of taxonomic distinctions that, in my opinion as demonstrated above, are not consistent with the relevant facts at present available.

Both of these seem to have been serious faults of work in human paleontology in general and this example has been used because it is a recent and clear example, which is actively being debated at present in the literature. I particularly wish to make it clear that I am not here setting out to be critical of the *authors* here involved — with all three of whom I have been personally acquainted for many years — but rather to analyze a general problem. Few, if any, human paleontologists have not been guilty in this respect at some time or another. I am certainly no exception, a case in point being Broom's and my creation of a new genus (*"Telanthropus"*) for the small group of specimens from Swartkrans. I believe it is more than justifiable to differentiate this material at the generic level from the other hominid material from the same site (*Paranthropus*), but not from *Homo*. We clearly distinguished the new material from *Paranthropus* but fell into the trap here being discussed by differentiating it taxonomically also from *Homo*. For this reason I subsequently (1961) sank the genus and trans-ferred the included material to *Homo erectus* (though it is interesting to note that the original name frequently recurs in the literature at the present time as though it possessed nomenclatural validity — which it does not!).

Other examples of the inappropriate treatment of variation may be chosen. When the first australopithecine skull was found at Olduvai, the argument was advanced that it represented a new genus, *"Zinjanthropus,"* even though the specimen bore obvious similarity to *Paranthropus* as known from South Africa. From the series of points advanced to support this view (Leakey, 1959) two will be discussed here that seem to me to be representative of the type of diagnostic criterion used and the manner in which diagnosis was approached.

It was suggested that the tympanic plate differed from that of either *Paranthropus* or *Australopithecus* but showed affinities in this respect with *H. erectus* from the Far East. It was stated that this applied to the tympanic plate whether seen in norma lateralis or basalis. The former concerns the shape and structure of the tympanic bone at the end of the auditory meatus. This feature shows great variability in modern man, and its very nature is such that this is just what one might expect. The small series of about eight specimens of *Paranthropus* from Swartkrans and Kromdraai that have the relevant area preserved are also variable, no two being alike. This appears to have been true also of *H. erectus*, judging from the illustrations provided in Weidenreich's monograph on the skull (Weidenreich, 1943). This feature thus has very low phyletic valence since the amount of overlap involved is too great to allow specimens to be sorted into the correct category by this criterion. Some of the variability in the small collection of *Paranthropus*

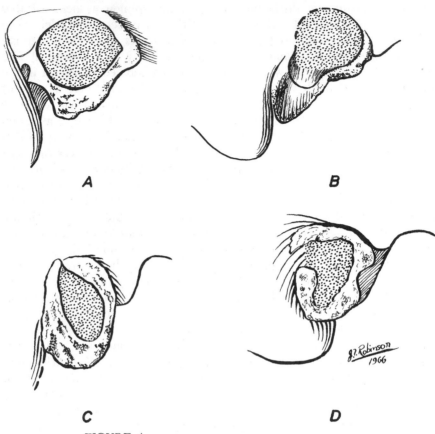

FIGURE 4

The external auditory meatus in four specimens of *Paranthropus* from Swartkrans.

from South Africa, which seems to me to include within its range the Olduvai specimen, can be seen in Figure 4.

The second feature is the shape of the zygomatic process of the maxilla and the adjacent part of the malar, as seen in frontal view. In the taxonomic description this character was not discussed in detail, but Dr. Leakey demonstrated his views in this connection to me on the original specimens. The argument is that the Olduvai specimen has a contour of the cheek region in front view, which forms two sides of an approximately right-angled triangle in passing from the zygoma to the maxilla just above the cheek teeth, while in *Paranthropus* this contour occupies roughly the position of the third side, the hypotenuse, of such a triangle. Here again, the sample of *Paranthropus* from South Africa shows considerable variability, the range including at least one specimen that has an even more right-angled contour than the

Olduvai specimen has and extending up to the diagonal, inverted flying buttress type, which Leakey used as the condition typical of *Paranthropus*. This range thus includes forms in which this feature is similar to that in the Olduvai specimen, as can be seen from Figure 5. This criterion therefore also cannot sort the Olduvai specimen correctly from *Paranthropus* because of overlap.

A number of the listed differentiating characters of the Olduvai form concerned aspects of the single feature that the individual represented by this one skull was a little larger and more muscular than any of the specimens at present known from South Africa. In respect of these points one is thus not dealing with a series of differences, but with one only — greater size. With this is associated greater muscularity, which in turn results in more massive areas of muscular attachment, more obvious crest formation, and so on.

HOMINID TAXONOMY

The number of examples could be multiplied considerably; a few have been chosen from recently created taxa that appear to me characteristic of the sort of taxonomic criterion and approach commonly employed in human paleontology.

Pondering these examples it seems clear that proper attention to variation makes obvious their unsuitability as diagnostic criteria at the generic or the species level. For the most part they are also insignificant characters in the biology of the organisms concerned. Indeed, one is left with the strong impression that most of the characters chosen at one time or another as being of taxonomic importance in hominids are of this sort. I do not here include forms such as *Ramapithecus* or *Oreopithecus*, which have been

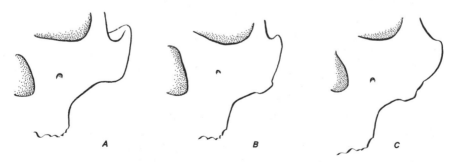

FIGURE 5

Contour of zygomatic process of the maxilla seen in front view. A and B, *Paranthropus* from Swartkrans; C, *Paranthropus* (= "*Zinjanthropus*") from Olduvai. A and B were drawn from the original specimens, C from a photograph. Not accurately to scale.

referred to the Hominidae but which are not generally accepted as belonging there. In the case of *Ramapithecus* the evidence seems to me equivocal and totally inadequate to justify placement in the Hominidae. *Oreopithecus* is better known but the characters it possesses do not appear to be such that they can be included in the Hominidae without considerably altering the character of that group in a way that does not seem biologically meaningful or justified.

The question may be asked whether indeed there are any valid generic distinctions to be made among the known hominids. It was suggested more than a decade ago by Mayr (1950) that all known hominids should be placed in the one genus *Homo*, though he later withdrew this opinion (1963).

Early in this paper it was pointed out that, at least in my opinion, there is a real difference, taxonomically, between species and genera that are in a single phyletic line or lineage as compared to those which each represent a different phyletic line. It seems more profitable, therefore, to approach the taxonomic analysis of fossil hominids as a whole by seeking first to discover whether more than one well-defined phyletic sequence existed.

Different phyletic lines can be detected by virtue of the fact that discontinuities should exist between representatives of different lineages since they are genetically isolated from each other. Such interlineage differences can be accommodated successfully within the Linnean nomenclatural system.

Once analysis for phyletic lines has been completed, then the one or more lineages that have been disclosed can be analyzed taxonomically. In this case the only discontinuities, if any, that exist between taxa will be those resulting from gaps in the fossil record of the lineage. Where the record is reasonably continuous the classification adopted will necessarily be largely subjective.

It should be possible to reach some measure of agreement concerning the number of lineages, but clearly the intralineage classifications will vary greatly with the taxonomic views and inclinations of each person examining the evidence and it will therefore be more difficult to reach agreement in this regard. In my opinion it matters less whether agreement is good or poor in the case of intralineage classification than it does in the case of the number and nature of the lineages represented.

On the surface it would appear likely that Mayr's original view — which was antedated considerably by Weidenreich's opinion that all forms of hominid recognized by him as such (including *Gigantopithecus*) belonged to the species *Homo sapiens* (Weidenreich, 1945) — that all known hominids represent a single lineage and could all be placed in the genus *Homo*, could be more widely supported at present. For example, it is common practice now to place *Paranthropus* in the genus *Australopithecus* (*sensu lato*). Also some genera that were commonly used a decade or more ago, such as "*Sinanthropus*," are now seldom used, being recognized as synonyms of other generic names. *Pithecanthropus* has more recently suffered the same fate, since it is now generally held to be a synonym of the genus *Homo*.

It is usual to retain both *Homo* and *Australopithecus* (*sensu lato*) as valid genera. However, it seems to me quite impossible to make a valid case for separate generic status providing that *Paranthropus* is removed from *Australopithecus*; a case, that is, which will survive the sort of scrutiny that has been given the characters dealt with earlier in this paper. Certainly it is possible to make two groups, for example, by using a character such as the internal mandibular contour (see Robinson, 1966). The two groups obtained in this way coincide very roughly with the present genera *Homo* and *Australopithecus* and approximately the same division will be obtained using other characters such as endocranial volume and some dental characters. However, these characters do not demonstrate two sharply discontinuous groups; the evidence seems rather to demonstrate that these are simply earlier and later stages of a single phyletic sequence. There appears to be no sound evidence of a true dichotomy into distinct lineages.

A single lineage or phyletic sequence need not be, and probably seldom is, a truly single line in a small-scale sense but consists instead of a broad stream containing a number of demes at once so that slightly different changes can be going on at the same time within it, as in the races of man today. But these are very low-level changes that do not allow one to make formal taxonomic distinctions — although they do allow astronauts and neolithic peoples to exist simultaneously.

It might thus seem that there is, indeed, a single lineage only in the hominids. I am by no means persuaded that this is so. If the analytical procedures based on a more realistic appraisal of variation are applied to hominids as a whole, there is much evidence that two validly distinct lineages are present. These are distinct, moreover, on virtually every type of information about fossils that can be mustered. This includes anatomical evidence concerning many parts of the skeleton and some of the soft structures, ecological and behavioral evidence, as well as information concerning coexistence. Furthermore, these characters are not of the sort that have so far been discussed, which, it seems to me, are all characters showing individual variation within a species and consequently cannot serve to distinguish species or genera. For this reason varied and contradictory classifications have been erected by their use, which is another aspect of the tendency to confuse the species and genus levels and intraspecific variation with interspecific variation.

The two phyletic lines that appear to me to be valid are represented by *Paranthropus* on the one hand and *Australopithecus* + *Homo* on the other.

I have discussed elsewhere (Robinson, 1954*a*, *b*, 1961, 1962, 1963) evidence for a real distinction between *Paranthropus* and *Australopithecus* and will not repeat it here in detail. This point of view used not to be accepted at all; instead it was commonly thought that *Paranthropus* represented a later phase of *Australopithecus* even though much evidence contradicted this interpretation. Since about the beginning of the nineteen-sixties evidence has emerged from the Olduvai region that demonstrates that *Paranthropus* coexisted over a long period of time with at least one other lineage, the earlier parts of which bear very close resemblance to *Australopithecus*. As a result there is now a much greater tendency to accept that at least two lineages are involved and that *Australopithecus* and *Paranthropus* do not belong to the same one. However, this has not had much effect on the general view that the two are very closely related, being no more than slight variants of the same theme — for which reason it is held that they are members of the same genus. This is probably in part a reaction against the earlier tendency to multiply taxa unnecessarily. However, there seems to me no greater virtue in lumping together forms that do not belong together than there is in separating into different taxa forms that do belong together.

In support of the idea that *Paranthropus* and *Australopithecus* belong in the same genus one finds statements to the effect that greater differences than are here involved can be found in a single genus of living pongids. I do not believe that such a statement could readily be made by anyone having substantial first-hand acquaintance with the original material. For example, the supra-orbital height index of Clark (1950) makes a distinction between these two that cannot be matched in all the living genera of pongids put together, let alone in any one of them. In fact, all of the genera of pongids and both ceboid and cercopithecoid monkeys that have been investigated in this respect (Ashton and Zuckerman, 1951) have a relatively low index while fossil and modern forms of *Homo* have a relatively high index; *Paranthropus* has an index value, on present evidence, that agrees very closely with the nonhominid primate group, while that of *Australopithecus* falls well above this and in what appears to be the lower end of the *Homo* range, with values close to those for *H. erectus* (see Robinson, 1962). Similarly there are dental differences, such as the size relationship of canine to postcanine teeth, morphology of dm_1, and so on, which are of a nature and magnitude that cannot be matched in a genus of living pongids.

These are not insignificant, low-level differences of the sort already rejected as lacking diagnostic capacity. For example, the dental differences also involved important differences in skull architecture, and this whole complex indicates that the entire masticatory apparatus was differently developed and differently used in the two lineages. Since the masticatory apparatus is primarily concerned with eating, this evidence suggests that there were significant differences in diet between the two. It is worth repeating that this conclusion does not depend on a single character but upon a large character complex involving much of the anatomy of the head. It is supported by quite other lines of evidence: for example, the characteristic and common type of spalling damage to the teeth of *Paranthropus* caused by biting on small, hard particles such as grit, which suggests plant food taken from the soil and improperly cleaned. This type of damage has not been observed in *Australopithecus*, which supports the conclusion that the diet was not the same in the two. This evidence has been misconstrued into differences in wear rate and pattern. (Buettner-Janusch, 1966 — whose discussion of the australopithecines contains many such misstatements about the views of others as well as factual error concerning the specimens.) Also, the evidence concerning climate — which is clearest at present in the case of the South African deposits — indicates that *Paranthropus* did not live in that part of the continent during times when the climate was relatively arid, but *Australopithecus* did. When the climate became appreciably wetter, *Paranthropus* did make its appearance there and remained for a long time. This does not mean, as some authors interpret it to mean, that *Paranthropus* simply was a later development of *Australopithecus*, for which reason it appears later than *Australopithecus* in Southern Africa. The evidence is that *Paranthropus* first appears in Southern Africa about the beginning of the Middle Pleistocene but it had already been in existence further up in Africa for a long time, since it is present early in Bed I at Olduvai in the Lower Pleistocene. Fairly large differences in diet in living pongids and monkeys, which are herbivorous, and in man, who is omnivorous, are accompanied by smaller dental differences than those involved in the case of *Australopithecus* and *Paranthropus*. Clearly, if there was a significant difference in diet, as the evidence suggests, then these two forms necessarily must have had different ecologies and their behavior must have been different. The character complex here being dealt with thus concerns the biology of the organism in a serious and thoroughgoing way and is manifestly of more significance than a difference in cheek contour, for example.

Similarly, the supra-orbital height index is associated with braincase features that reflect aspects of brain nature and development.

The pelvic differences between the two are also not of a minor nature but relate to posture and locomotor habit and the extent to which erect bipedality had been achieved. The indication is that the locomotor habit was rather different in the two since the hamstrings in *Australopithecus* had a relatively short moment arm, of the sort found in modern man, which was associated with a relatively long femur, while *Paranthropus*, also adapted for erect posture, had a long moment arm for the hamstrings. This suggests that the hamstrings in the latter were adapted more for power than speed while the reverse was the case in *Australopithecus*.

The characters here involved are thus intimately related to the entire biology of the organism concerned. Furthermore, all of these characters give the same dichotomy, thus presenting a consistent picture of two different lineages, which differed very significantly with respect to the total adaptive complex involving morphology, ecology, and behavior. Moreover, anyone acquainted with the original material can readily identify specimens as belonging to one or the other lineage on the basis of small parts of the skeleton in isolation. For example, an isolated dm_1 is quite sufficient to indicate which lineage is being dealt with: so is the frontal region, the palate, the pterygoid plate region, the nose, a fragment of mandible with canine and P_3 present, the anterior maxillary alveolar region (even if all the teeth are missing), the top end of the ramus (either the coronoid alone, or the coronoid and sigmoid notch), and the lower half of the innominate bone, to name a few obvious examples. It is also important to note that any piece of the listed material is adequate for the purpose, whether one is comparing *Paranthropus* with representatives of the other lineage at the *Australopithecus* or the *Homo erectus* levels or even with modern man.

It may be argued that insufficient evidence is available at present to be sure that all of these differences are valid because in some cases the series on which they are based are small. This is, of course, a real possibility and certainly much more evidence would be most welcome. But there are two points to notice here. In the first place, better comparisons are available than is suggested by the relatively small amount of australopithecine material available. As a case in point consider dm_1. There are nine specimens known from *Paranthropus* and only four from *Australopithecus*. Although the *Paranthropus* specimens vary quite a bit, they are all clearly and unmistakably of the *Paranthropus* pattern with respect to the features that I have listed as making up that pattern (Robinson, 1956). On the other hand, the *Australopithecus* sample is too small to suggest with any confidence that it is a stable pattern. But this situation is considerably altered by the fact that the pattern found in all of the *Australopithecus* specimens is also the identical pattern found in the few known specimens from fossil forms of *Homo* as well as every specimen of a large number belonging to modern man that I have examined. Or as another example, consider the low cranial vault of *Paranthropus* and the high one of *Australopithecus*. The number of specimens that allow one to determine this character is not very great, being about half a dozen in the case of *Paranthropus* and less than that in the case of *Australopithecus*. These show no tendency to approximate each other with respect to this character, and examination of the most closely related primates shows that the high vaulted type of *Australopithecus* alone is found in hominines, and on the other hand the low vaulted type of *Paranthropus* alone is found in the pongids. Both do not occur in a single genus of higher primates closely related to the early hominids.

The second point to note is that the very fact that the characters concerned are of major importance to the animal and relate to differences of adaptation that are obvious in most cases, means that they are of a sort most unlikely to vary greatly within a species. This is confirmed by the fact that these, or very similar, characters are found to be stable within species or genera of related higher primates. Furthermore each of the two groups of characters forms a consistent adaptational picture that makes good sense in terms of what we know of higher primate evolution. In view of these points, it seems to me very unlikely that more evidence will seriously upset the distinctions made. Indeed, it may be considered experimental verification, in a sense, of these ideas that the new evidence from Olduvai confirms and amplifies them and in no way conflicts with them, even though all of the Olduvai evidence was found after the distinctions had been worked out on the South African material.

My conclusion, therefore, is that these differences reflect a very significant dichotomy within the hominids; one that involves important ecological, behavioral and anatomical differences of the sort commonly found to distinguish genera, rather than two species representing slightly different forms of the same generic adaptation. The genus may be regarded as made up of a group of species of common origin occupying the same adaptive zone that is not shared with other, related genera. Each species utilizes a slightly different aspect of this adaptive zone. My interpretation of the available evidence is that *Paranthropus* and *Australopithecus* were occupying different adaptive zones, not merely slightly different aspects of the same adaptive zone. Furthermore, it is quite legitimate, as Haldane (1956) has pointed out, to take subsequent history into account when classifying. *Paranthropus* became extinct after a long history without achieving anything more than a very primitive level of hominid organization. On the other hand, the other line includes a form that is currently the dominant species on this globe and one representing a major evolutionary development that has added a whole new dimension to evolution which makes possible achievements of which *Paranthropus* was not capable, and this had already been achieved to a significant level when the appreciably more primitive *Paranthropus* became extinct.

The *Australopithecus-Homo* phyletic line developed cultural capacity involving the use and manufacture of tools. This capacity was already achieved to a moderately advanced level by the time *Paranthropus* disappeared from the record and thus this line would be formidable opponents to any other line that was adapting in a similar way. Since there is clear evidence that *Paranthropus* was the less advanced of the two, compared to modern man, the fact that it seems to have coexisted with this other, culture-bearing, line for more than a million years, supports the conclusion that it was appreciably different in the nature of its basic adaptation and was not directly in competition with the *Homo* line. This seems well established since the coexistence does not depend on the East African evidence alone but is well authenticated at Swartkrans and is also known from the other end of the Old World from Sangiran, where *H. erectus* is known from both the Putjangan and Kaboeh beds and so is *Paranthropus* (= "*Meganthropus*"). In the case of Swartkrans the association is between *H. erectus* (= "*Telanthropus*") and *Paranthropus* and is as clear a case of contemporaneity as could be found. The *H. erectus* material was found well down in the deposit with substantial amounts of deposit containing *Paranthropus* both above and below the fairly thick level containing the former. Specimens of the two forms were directly associated; in some cases within inches of each other. The deposit consists of fully consolidated limestone — a solid deposit of rock, that is — which consolidates as it accumulates. Hence younger material cannot get buried into older levels as can happen in unconsolidated deposits. There is no evidence known at present that indicates that the front cave deposit at Swartkrans is of mixed origin or includes breccias of quite different ages (as is the case at Sterkfontein). Even if this were the case at Swartkrans, the unalterable fact is that some of the *H. erectus* material was found cheek by jowl with *Paranthropus* material at the same level. The conclusion that these two forms were contemporaneous at this site does not, therefore, depend on indirect evidence but on substantial evidence of direct association in the same levels of a consolidated deposit in circumstances that leave no reasonable grounds for supposing that this could be accidental association, more than once, at several slightly different levels, of specimens of quite different ages.

Not only is the available evidence consistent with this picture of two lineages adapted to major ecological niches that are significantly different, but also there is a simple and consistent explanation possible for this difference and the reason why the more progressive lineage came into existence and developed the particular cultural features that characterize it.

Such an explanation is that the known desiccation of Africa during the latter part of the Tertiary forced some of the hominids then in existence to change their diet from the basic herbivorous habit to omnivorousness by becoming active predators in order to survive in arid areas. This will have radically altered the selection pattern applying to such demes. Having no natural anatomical weapons or tools, such as large canine teeth, obtaining animal food to supplement their diet of vegetable matter would place a premium on intelligence and skill in the use of natural objects as tools and weapons. This is to say, just those features which are the basic elements of culture would be highly advantageous selectively and the form would be transformed into a more and more efficient hunter as he became better adapted to omnivorous diet in a relatively dry climate.

Those forms, however, which managed to remain in the areas where climatic change did not have so severe an effect, would have continued under essentially the same selection regime as previously and would not have changed. This appears to have been true of the lineage that continued as *Paranthropus* long after the culture-bearing lineage had come into existence. It has been argued that the reduction in canine size of *Paranthropus* means that it was culture-bearing also. This does not necessarily follow since many mammals have not merely reduced but lost their canines altogether, and sometimes all of the upper incisors as well, for reasons that have nothing to do with culture. It may have been primitively culture-bearing, but this will have to be proved on grounds other than reduction of the size of the canines.

CONCLUSION

In the study of any group of organisms, valid taxonomic conclusions that are biologically meaningful cannot be reached without realistic appraisal of population variation being made. This is especially true of extinct forms since the problems involved are more complex than is the case with living forms. For the most part human paleontologists have not handled variation realistically. The reasons for this are complex, but contributory factors appear to be the lack of familiarity with modern taxonomic practice and a tendency not to think in population terms when actually making taxonomic analyses.

It seems to me that human paleontology has been characterized by tendencies to:

1. Overlook population variation and to work primarily with the observed variation of the available samples. Frequently even this is inadequately taken into account.

2. Confuse hierarchic categories of different levels, especially the species and genus levels. Besides not distinguishing properly between these two levels, this involves making no clear distinction between intraspecies and interspecies variation as well as intragenus and intergenus variation.

3. Overlook the fact that species belonging to different lineages differ from each other in a manner different from that in which species of the same lineage differ. This cannot be emphasized too strongly.

The first tendency results in the making of too many taxa; a conspicuous fault of human paleontology. The second and third cause immense confusion in the interpretation of the taxonomic and phylogenetic pictures. This is well illustrated by the present practice of, on the one hand, lumping *Paranthropus* and *Australopithecus* together — which is done virtually without distinction since almost everyone refers to them simply as "the australopithecines" and treats them as though their characteristics were exactly the same, which demonstrably they are not. On the other hand, generic distinction is made between two levels that cannot be distinguished anything like as well as can *Paranthropus* and *Australopithecus*. It seems to me that, for the most part, what is actually intraspecies variation has been mistaken for interspecies or even intergenera variation with unfortunate results.

If variation is properly taken into account and due attention is paid to diagnostic criteria, the obvious conclusion appears to be that the hominids are not a taxonomically diverse group. On the contrary the group seems to have been taxonomically compact with two major lineages only. One is less progressive and comprises the genus *Paranthropus*, which appears to have become extinct in the Middle Pleistocene. The other is a much more progressive line, which at all times after it was recognizably different from the former was adapting to its environment in a manner that involved culture as a very prominent part of the adaptation. This line includes what currently is regarded as *Australopithecus* (*sensu stricto*) and *Homo*. Since it is a line occupying one adaptive zone, I consider it reasonable to use a single generic name for it, and this would have to be *Homo*, according to the Code. Also, being a single lineage, its taxonomy is largely a matter of taste since no completely separate taxa, differentiable by means of properly diagnostic characters, can be found in it. However, since two more or less separate groups can be defined within the lineage, two species could be made without serious difficulty. The first would include the more primitive stage, in which the full characters of the genus were being achieved, in which the brain is relatively small, the primitive type of internal mandibular contour is still present and the cultural level achieved is not especially advanced. This would properly be named *H. transvaalensis*. Some authors have recently suggested something similar to this but refer to the species thus defined as *H. africanus* by simply substituting *Homo* for *Australopithecus*. However, this is not proper since the trivial name *africanus* is preoccupied as far as the genus *Homo* is concerned (having been used by Broom for Boskop Man),[4] hence it may not be used here, and

---

[4] [Boskop Man has nothing to do with the availablility of the trivial name *africanus*, as I was well aware. The above statement that it had was a *lapsus calami* on my part which went unnoticed until after this article had originally appeared in print. Boskop Man was named *Homo capensis* by Broom in 1918. "*Telanthropus*" *capensis* was named

the next senior trivial name, *transvaalensis,* must be used instead, as Mayr realized a long time ago (1950).

The second species, representing the stage in which most of the obvious physical change had already occurred and evolution consisted chiefly of realization of the cultural potential, hence the most obvious change being cultural, would be *H. sapiens,* this name having taxonomic precedence over *H. erectus.* It is obvious, however, that the characters of the one species grade into the other, hence with sufficient material known, some specimens would be difficult to classify. Some workers might prefer to make more species and others may prefer to have only a single species; this is a matter of taste and I have here suggested what appears to me to be most meaningful.

I suggest, therefore, that the time has come to sink the genus *Australopithecus* Dart, 1925 into the synonymy of the genus *Homo* Linnaeus, 1758. On this interpretation the family Hominidae includes the genera *Paranthropus* Broom 1938, and *Homo.* If the above interpretation is correct, then there can hardly be justification for having two subfamilies. There can also be very little justification either for using the term "australopithecine." Although it will be very difficult for a while to get used to not using it, I propose that this term be dropped as not applying to a real category of organisms. This, as I have tried to show, is amply justified on the morphological evidence available. Furthermore, retention of the term simply causes confusion by allowing two very different sorts of organisms to be lumped together as though they were the same. The literature abounds with factual error committed primarily because the term australopithecine has been used when in fact one or the other of the two lineages alone is actually being referred to.

---

by Broom and Robinson in 1949 but sunk into *Homo erectus* by Robinson in 1961. It had been suggested the *H. "habilis"* and *T. capensis* may represent the same species which is distinct from *H. erectus.* In this event *capensis* would have priority over *habilis,* which dates from 1964, but could not be used because of having been preoccupied for *Homo* by Broom's use of it for Boskop Man. In my opinion there is no problem because *T. capensis* and the later *H. "habilis"* material belong in *"Australopithecus" africanus.* The reason which should have been given for *africanus* not being available if *A. africanus* is placed in *Homo* is its use in 1904 by Sergi as *Homo africanus* and in 1937 by von Eickstedt and by Peters as *Homo sapiens africanus* to refer to certain living African peoples. On recently re-investigating this matter, however, I have concluded that Sergi's usage has no standing under the International Code of Zoological Nomenclature. Since the usage of von Eickstedt and of Peters dates from 1937, Dart's use of *Australopithecus africanus* in 1925 has priority. Rather than *Homo transvaalensis,* the new name should be *Homo africanus.* J. T. Robinson, 1970.]

REFERENCES

Ashton, E. H. and T. F. Spence
    1958   "Age Changes in the Cranial Capacity and Foramen Magnum of Hominoids," *Proc. Zool. Soc. London* 130:169.

Ashton, E. H. and S. Zuckerman
    1951   "Some Cranial Indices of *Plesianthropus* and Other Primates," *Amer. J. Phys. Anthrop.* 9:283.

Buettner-Janusch, J.
    1966   *Origins of Man.* New York: John Wiley and Sons.

Clark, W. E. L.
    1950   "New Palaeontological Evidence Bearing on the Evolution of the Hominoidea," *Quart. J. Geol. Soc.* (London) 105:255.

Haldane, J. B. S.
    1956   "Can a Species Concept be Justified?" in *The Species Concept in Palaeontology* (Sylvester-Bradley, ed.). London: The Systematics Association, Publication No. 2, 95.

Leakey, L. S. B.
    1959   "A New Fossil Skull from Olduvai," *Nature* (London) 184:491.
    1966   "*Homo Habilis, Homo Erectus* and the Australopithecines," *Nature* (London) 209:1279.

Leakey, L. S. B., P. V. Tobias, and J. Napier
    1964   "A New Species of the Genus *Homo* from Olduvai Gorge," *Nature* (London) 202:7.

Mayr, E.
    1940   "Speciation Phenomena in Birds," *Amer. Natural.* 74:249.
    1950   "Taxonomic Categories in Fossil Hominids," *Cold Spring Harbor Sympos. Quant. Biol.* 15:109.
    1963   *Animal Species and Evolution.* Cambridge, Mass.: Harvard University Press.

Robinson, J. T.
    1954a   "The Genera and Species of the Australopithecinae," *Amer. J. Phys. Anthrop.* 12:181.
    1954b   "Prehominid Dentition and Hominid Evolution," *Evolution* 8:324.
    1956   "The Dentition of the Australopithecinae," *Mem. Transvaal Mus.,* No. 9.
    1961   "The Australopithecines and Their Bearing on the Origin of Man and of Stone Tool-Making," *S. African J. Sci.* 57:3.
    1962   "The Origin and Adaptive Radiation of the Australopithecines," in *Evolution und Hominisation* (G. Kurth, ed.). Stuttgart: Gustav Fischer Verlag.

1963 "Adaptive Radiation in the Australopithecines and the Origin of Man," in *African Ecology and Human Evolution* (Howell and Bourlière, eds.). Chicago: Aldine Publishing Co.

1965 "*Homo 'Habilis'* and the Australopithecines," *Nature* (London) 205:121.

1966 "The Distinctiveness of *Homo Habilis*," *Nature* (London) 205:953.

Simpson, G. G.

1951 "The Species Concept," *Evolution* 5:285.

1961 *Principles of Animal Taxonomy*. New York: Columbia University Press.

Simpson, G. G., A. Roe, and R. C. Lewontin

1960 *Quantitative Zoology*, 2nd Ed. New York: Harcourt, Brace and Co.

Tobias, P. V.

1964 "The Olduvai Bed I Hominine with Special References to Its Cranial Capacity," *Nature* (London) 202:3.

1966 "The Distinctiveness of *Homo Habilis*," *Nature* (London) 209:953.

Weidenreich, F.

1943 "The Skull of *Sinanthropus Pekinensis*," *Palaeont. Sinica*, No. 127.

1945 "Giant Early Man from Java and South China," *Anthrop. Papers Amer. Mus. Nat. Hist.* 40:1.

F. CLARK HOWELL

The story detailed in Man-Apes or Ape-Men? *is one well worth reading — particularly in conjunction with the more personal* Adventures with the Missing Link *by Dart and Craig (Viking, 1961). What Howell provides is an appropriate evolutionary and temporal framework within which to view the whole of the australopithecine and early* Homo *evidence — a framework which is somewhat obscure in the Clark volume, but which is otherwise a most excellent introduction to the australopithecine story. Howell's framework is then a most economical assessment of the relevance of the fossil hominids to the student of human evolution. One should note that the table included is Howell's summary of Clark's views and the figure represents Howell's view of the situation (one with which we are in essential agreement). The controversy, such as it is, concerns the antiquity of the South African australopithecines and is a relatively minor one in the gradual progress that has been made toward the appreciation of the australopithecines as bridging the gap between terrestrial ape and members of the genus* Homo *— progress to which Clark has made a substantial contribution.*

8 Review of Man-Apes or Ape-Men?

The discovery of the australopithecines and the recognition of their hominid status have been events of profound significance in advancing understanding of the evolution of the Hominidae. Robert Broom's little book, *Finding the Missing Link*, was the first (in '50) popular account by one of the principal participants. Raymond Dart's role was later (in '59) engagingly exposed in a popular, and personal, vein in *Adventures with the Missing Link*, as well as in Robert Ardrey's very successful, and controversial, *African Genesis*. Now, in *Man-Apes or Ape-Men?*, Sir Wilfrid Le Gros

From *American Journal of Physical Anthropology*, Vol. 27, pp. 95–101. Reprinted by permission of the Wistar Institute of Anatomy and Biology, Philadelphia, and the author.

Clark has provided the first overall general appraisal, in semi-technical form, of the structure and phylogenetic significance of these early hominids, and revealed his own role in their study and evaluation.

The discoveries of the australopithecines aroused unusual, and doubtless undue, controversy which persisted intermittently over some 30 years. Sir Wilfrid's aim in this slender volume has been to follow "the sequence of controversies from 1925 to the present time, with the endeavor to resolve conflicting opinions by a review of the nature of the evidence on which they have been based." It is of some historical interest to record that the author was himself once skeptical of the hominid status of *Australopithecus*, and so stated this position in papers published in 1939 and 1940. However, in 1947 he reversed this position, following a personal study of the original specimens then known, and thereafter became a staunch and dogged advocate of the contrary view. There can be no doubt that his comparative studies of the dental, cranial, and postcranial structure in australopithecines and recent apes were of paramount importance in demonstrating the essential resemblance of these creatures ("ape-men") to Hominidae and their fundamental divergence from Pongidae ("man-apes"), whether recent or extinct.

The initial chapters discuss the taxonomic and historical background for an appraisal of the australopithecines. The first chapter defines the higher primates (Hominoidea), the principal distinctions between Pongidae and Hominidae, and briefly outlines the post-australopithecine evolution of Hominidae. The second considers the initial discovery at Taung(s) and the ensuing controversy which followed preliminary publication by Dart in *Nature* of the specimen. The third discusses Broom's first discoveries at Sterkfontein and Kromdraai, their principal publication by him (and Schepers) in 1946, the critical and detailed evaluation of these specimens in 1947 by Le Cros Clark after his first visit to Africa, and the attendant controversy between him and Sir Solly Zuckerman as to the hominid or pongid resemblances displayed by certain features of skull and dentition. The fourth enumerates the subsequent recovery of australopithecine remains in southern Africa (at Sterkfontein and Swartkrans, and at Makapan Limeworks) and, most recently, in eastern Africa (at Olduvai and in the Natron basin). [The author regards the Yayo (Chad basin) and Ubeidiya (Jordan valley) specimens as possibly australopithecine, but *neither* are, and in both instances there is no evidence to support an age earlier, at most, than Lower/Middle Quaternary — as opposed to Basal Quaternary.] Four subsequent chapters treat fairly systematically the australopithecine dentition, skull, pelvis and upper and lower limb morphology and its functional implications. The final two chapters consider the thorny issues of the australopithecine way of life and possible phylogenetic relationships to antecedent hominoids of Tertiary age. There are 95 selected references, an index, and 33 figures in the text. There are also an uncalled for number of typographical errors, often trivial but still annoying.

Sir Wilfrid's principal theses are that (1) australopithecines are hominids, not pongids, (2) that they occupied sub-Saharan Africa between ca. 2.0 and 0.5 million years ago, prior to the differentiation of the genus *Homo*, (3) that there were a number — still unknown — of local populations of australopithecines, variable both in space and through time, within this area of distribution, (4) that taxonomic differentiation, whether spatial or temporal, within the australopithecines was at most at the specific level, with known samples falling within *Australopithecus africanus*, a more gracile form, or *Australopithecus robustus*, a more robust form, and (5) that some australopithecines, notably populations attributed to the gracile form, were directly ancestral to the earliest species, *erectus*, of the genus *Homo* (for the latter he unfortunately persists in using the misleading term pithecanthropines).

Some of these conclusions are reasonable and broadly consistent with the evidence available thus far. These might even be taken as representative of the majority opinion among those concerned with the long term evolution of Hominidae. However, others are less firmly established and the evidence employed to support one interpretation may, in some cases, be interpreted in alternative ways. It would be grossly misleading, in the reviewer's opinion, to treat some of these as other than hypotheses still to be tested against future discoveries and the results of various investigations still in progress.

The controversy over the hominid status of the australopithecines is now surely terminated. The evidence of the postcranial skeleton and the dentition is so conclusive of hominid, as opposed to pongid, affinity that it would be merely ill-informed to seek to maintain a contrary view. Sir Wilfrid's role in elucidating the higher taxonomic affinities of these creatures was almost certainly critical at a time when there was notable opposition, even hostility towards any attribution other than to the Pongidae, or variants thereof. In this respect the author's vigorous and repeated argumentation to demonstrate the hominid status of australopithecines is effort somewhat wasted and, at this time, in the nature of tilting at windmills.

Most well-informed students of the subject would probably agree that the overall structure and grade of organization characteristic of australopithecines is appropriate for a stage in hominid phylogeny antecedent to the genus *Homo*. However, there is still little in the way of consensus as to the actual phylogenetic relationships of australopithecines, as a group, to *Homo*, any more than there is consensus in regard to relationships of individual populations (or taxa) of australopithecines to that genus. A number of workers have also maintained, and some continue to do so, that the temporal relationships between these taxa are either unclear, or such as to rule out such ancestral affinity.

The temporal relationships of the several occurrences of australopithecine fossil remains are not really considered and evaluated in detail by the author. He evidently accepts that all are Quaternary — hence <3.0 million years in age — and that some are Early Quaternary (both gracile and robust forms) whereas others are Middle Quaternary (both gracile and robust forms — the former on the basis of remains once termed *"Telanthropus,"* from Swartkrans, and the latter on the basis of occurrences at Swartkrans, Kromdraai, and Peninj in the Natron basin). However, on his own estimates, this is a truly vast range of Quaternary time — as much as 2.5 million years — some 3 to 5 times the duration of the remainder of the epoch!

It is obviously critical that the temporal positions of the several southern African and eastern African populations be fixed, both provincially and interregionally. The temporal datum is especially significant in regard to the recognizable longevity of the several australopithecine taxa (*only* two species, according to the author), their relationships one to another (whether contemporaneous, wholly or in part, or successive), and their respective relationships with early representatives of the genus *Homo*.

On this latter point the author is not entirely explicit, but presumably he would accept the coexistence of *A. robustus* with *Homo erectus*, on the basis of his statements (p. 49) in regard to the australopithecine remains from Natron, Kromdraai and Swartkrans, and their presumed synchrony with demonstrable occurrences of *Homo erectus* elsewhere in Africa and in Asia. On the other hand he feels that "the precise relationship between the robust australopithecines and the gracile type (which in my view includes the smaller-toothed Sterkfontein fossils, as well as *Telanthropus* and *Homo habilis*), still awaits solution. They may well have been living together sympatrically (and in amicable, or at least unhostile, association) in exactly the same regions where their remains have been found" (p. 48). In fact Sir Wilfrid would evidently have this sympatric relationship one of extremely long duration, approximating 1.5 million years, if the diagram (Figure 1) does justice to his views.

To the reviewer this interpretation appears to accord well neither with the available data nor with expectations from evolutionary theory. Sir Wilfrid states (p. 47) that "it is difficult to suppose that australopithecines and more advanced hominids (presumed to be representatives of the genus *Homo*) existed side by side in the same environment one and three quarter million years ago, and still continued to live side by side about half a million years ago (as some have supposed to be the case in South Africa). Surely, in the course of more than a million years, the australopithecines would have been altogether wiped out to extinction by the predation of much more advanced and skillful hominids if the latter really had occupied the same habitat over this prolonged period of time." (To the reviewer's knowledge this claim has not actually been put forth in this form; certainly it does not

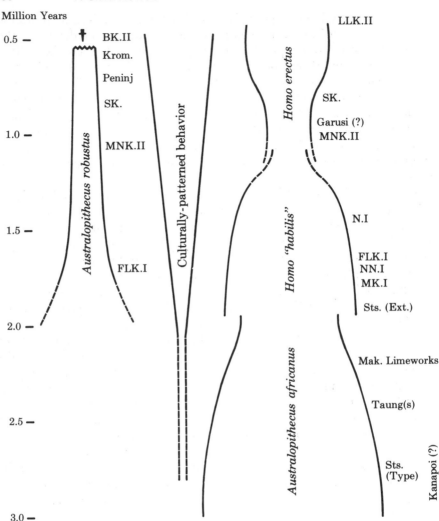

FIGURE 1

conform with Robinson's views, with the reviewer's views, and agrees only partially with the published views of Tobias.) However, if attention is given to Table 1, Sir Wilfrid would evidently have us believe that two taxa of australopithecines occupied the same open grassland or wooded savanna habitat over a known period of some 1.5 million years, until the almost spontaneous advent of *Homo erectus*, derived probably from "the earlier, more gracile, form of the australopithecines, that is *Australopithecus africanus*," whereas *Australopithecus robustus*, "the robust type represented an aberrant sideline of evolution that became extinct" (p. 31).

There can be little doubt now of the substantial range in time of the

TABLE 1

Million years	A. africanus	A. robustus
.5		Kromdraai
		Peninj
	Swartkrans	Swartkrans
	Garusi(?)	
1.0		
	Sterkfontein $\left\{\begin{array}{l}\text{extension site}\\ \text{type site}\end{array}\right.$	
1.5		
	Olduvai (MK.I, N.N.I.)	Olduvai FLK.I.)
2.0		

robust australopithecine, *Australopithecus robustus* or *(Paranthropus) robustus*. This is well demonstrated by the occurrences brought to light in the Olduvai and Natron basins. Also the comparative faunal evidence is consistent with an age for this taxon in southern Africa equivalent to, or somewhat older than, its *latest* known occurrence in eastern Africa. An absolute estimate of such an age should reasonably fall between 0.5 and 0.7 million years.

However, it is also quite clear that an early species of *Homo*, very likely *Homo erectus*, is represented in the fossil record by that time. This is well attested at Olduvai, in the sediments of lower Bed II, where skeletal parts of hominids no. 13 and no. 14 have been recovered from site MNK. II. On the evidence of the dentition, jaw structure, and cranial morphology there is little question that these should be attributed to *Homo*, and not to *Australopithecus*. Moreover this lineage has its roots still farther back in time, perhaps close to (or even in excess of) 1.0 million years, to judge from lamentably smashed, but restorable remains of Olduvai hominid 16 (from locality FLK. II. It is interesting, and reassuring, that here the Olduvai evidence is quite reasonably consistent with that from the Putjangan beds of Java in which broadly comparable representatives of the genus *Homo* occur.

Sir Wilfrid has argued (p. 42) that "in fact, nothing has been found in australopithecine deposits at Swartkrans, or elsewhere, to indicate with certainty that there existed contemporaneously with *Australopithecus* more advanced hominids with a cranial capacity and limb bones characteristic of the genus *Homo*." The reviewer feels strongly that these criteria are too restrictive and unrealistic. Surely it has not been essential to have such complete fossil remains present in order to recognize the presence of *Homo erectus* in the sediments of the basin at Ternifine? And only half the criteria are fulfilled in the case of the Olduvai LLK. II calvarium, and certain specimens from Java as well, and yet the presence of a species of the genus *Homo* is accepted by the author.

In taking this position, and in attributing the remains of specimens SK.

15, SK. 45, and SK. 80 (ex-"*Telanthropus*") from Swartkrans to *Australopithecus* (*africanus*), he is in fact subscribing, perhaps unknowingly, to the contemporaneity of two australopithecine taxa — *africanus* and *robustus* — as well as *Homo erectus*, accepted by him to be of equivalent age elsewhere, in Africa as well as Asia. The reviewer, who has also had the opportunity for first hand study of all the relevant specimens, is forced to disagree with Sir Wilfrid and to maintain, along with Robinson, Tobias and others, that these Swartkrans specimens *do* differ significantly in certain critical characters of structure as well as size from A. *africanus*, and in such divergence they approximate the organization characteristic of *Homo erectus*. Additional, more fragmentary remains recently recovered by C. K. Brain from Swartkrans afford further evidence in support of this view, but perhaps from an earlier range of time. Also, the Garusi (Eyasi trough) specimen — regarded by the author as australopithecine — is of an age broadly comparable with earlier *Homo erectus* from Olduvai (lower Bed II), and does not contradict this conclusion as the known structure and size of the premolars is within the range of variation of *Homo erectus*.

Thus, as Sir Wilfrid has suggested (see quote above), some forms of australopithecine, in this case A. *africanus*, did not, and perhaps could not coexist with dominant populations of *Homo erectus*.

What may be said then of the temporal duration and phylogenetic relationships of the "gracile australopithecine," *Australopithecus africanus*? Excepting the several remains from Swartkrans once attributed to "*Telanthropus*" (= *Homo erectus*), the author attributes to this taxon the hominid remains from four occurrences at three localities (Taung(s), Makapan Limeworks, Sterkfontein Type and Extension Sites). At Sterkfontein there is direct stratigraphic superimposition of hominid remains, reputedly of the same taxon, in two breccia formations. At Makapan Limeworks remains attributable to A. *africanus* have been recovered from both the lower (gray) and the overlying (pink) breccia; an uppermost breccia has also yielded a poorly preserved jaw fragment attributed to the same species. The stratigraphic relationship of the Sterkfontein breccias suggests some measure of temporal discontinuity, and the same may be said for the more substantial sequence of sedimentation in the case of Makapan Limeworks. Although there have been suggestions as to the temporal implications of the breccia accumulations in each case, it is only fair to state that the degree of continuity or discontinuity is poorly understood.

The several occurrences at these localities, and at Taung(s), can be related temporally to one another only on the basis of the composition of the associated assemblages of vertebrates. And these assemblages are adequately known only from the lower breccia member at Sterkfontein and that at Makapan Limeworks. The Taung(s) assemblage is non-comparable in composition and is ecologically distinct. There is, however, a measure of a consensus that the relationship is: Sterkfontein (Type Site) succeeded by Makapan Limeworks (lower faunal assemblage); and some probability that Taung(s) is equal to, or questionably, older than the former; the Sterkfontein (Extension Site) occurrence has been suggested to be equivalent in time to, or rather younger than Makapan Limeworks, but without adequate evidence to answer one way or the other.

However, within this "succession" there is evidence for a substantial measure of faunal turnover — either extinction, emigration, and/or appearance of new taxa — as shown by the carnivores, cercopithecoids, suids, and rodents in particular (unfortunately, the bovids are really adequately analyzed only from lower Limeworks). Although this "succession" has been treated by several authors as a single faunal "stage" it is equally as likely that two provincial faunas (at least?) are represented. Most importantly it is highly probable that a substantial measure of time is represented by this "succession."

For the moment there is no means of ascertaining absolute age(s) for all or even any part of these fossiliferous breccia formations. However, some relative measure may be afforded by comparison with the faunal assemblages yielded by radiometrically-dated sediments of Bed I in the Olduvai basin. Only a small portion of the extremely large and diverse vertebrate fauna there has been analyzed even preliminarily, but available information thus far would suggest that a single faunal stage is represented, albeit with some change in composition between the basal and uppermost sediments of Bed I (this same fauna is apparently represented in lower Bed II sediments, below the aeolian member, as well — L. S. B. Leakey, personal communication). The middle and lowermost Bed I sediments span some 2–3 hundred thousand years, on the evidence of K/Ar age determinations. As a rough estimate the total Bed I sedimentation would exceed 0.5 and approach 0.75 million. If this is in fact the case then it is not unreasonable to evaluate the aforesaid (earlier) Transvaal cave breccia succession as indicative of a time span of (minimally) 0.5 to 1.0 million years. The possibility of substantial age differences between these occurrences, and between the latter and the recognizably younger occurrences at Swartkrans and Kromdraai has not yet been sufficiently considered.

Do these successions, and the hominids yielded by them, coincide wholly or largely in time, or is there a measure, perhaps even substantial, of temporal discontinuity between southern African occurrences and the more continuous, local succession of lower Olduvai? Kenneth Oakley, in 1962, assumed a succession of Olduvai Bed I, followed by the various Transvaal breccias, followed by Olduvai Bed II. However, this relationship has not foreign origin at Sterkfontein (Extension) is still most uncertain, and been supported by the faunal or stratigraphic evidence. Other workers have recently assumed, and this seems to be the case of the author of this book, that there is broad temporal equivalence. There is in fact some faunal evidence, admittedly not wholly conclusive, to suggest that the Sterkfontein (Type Site) breccia probably antedates Olduvai Bed I sediments; whereas Makapan Limeworks and Taung(s) could either slightly antedate or overlap in time lower Olduvai. This is a matter of no little importance with regard to the interpretation of the duration of *Australopithecus africanus*, the distinctiveness and affinities to that taxon of remains attributed to *Homo habilis* from Bed I Olduvai, as well as the relationships of either (or both) to *Homo erectus*. The relationships of these taxa (or the single taxon if *Homo habilis* is to be relegated to *Australopithecus africanus*, as Sir Wilfrid, and some others, maintain) might be that shown diagrammatically if these temporal relationships are correct, as the reviewer feels is most likely.

The antecedents of neither taxon of *Australopithecus* is as yet known. Sir Wilfrid tentatively accepts, as do a number of other students of the subject, that *Ramapithecus* is a likely representative of a proto-hominid lineage, phylogenetically antecedent to *Australopithecus*. If so there is a great temporal gap — approximating at least ten million years — between these taxa. And if the latter was restricted in distribution to sub-Saharan Africa, as Sir Wilfrid (and the reviewer as well) believes, then the Pliocene history of the proto-hominids is especially interesting since *Ramapithecus* quite clearly had a pan-tropical Afro-Asiatic distribution. Unfortunately the Pliocene geologic history and vertebrate fossil record is so scantily known in Africa as to provide no evidence, as yet, to bear on this intriguing problem. However, one wonders if the lower Kaiso, Kanam, and the recently discovered Kanapoi fossiliferous occurrences (the later yielding a hominoid [? hominid] distal humerus), are in fact upper Pliocene rather than lowermost Quaternary as is now more commonly accepted.

Sir Wilfrid regards the australopithecines as carnivorous — obtaining meat both from hunting as well as scavenging — with the robust form perhaps most strongly vegetarian, as Robinson has consistently maintained. He also stresses their capability for utilizing and fashioning tools and offensive weapons — in stone as well as organic materials — for use in the food quest and also as protection against predators. In the case of the southern African occurrences, however, his evidence for stone artifact-making capabilities is slender indeed, as there is nothing of this sort known at the important Sterkfontein (Type) and Makapan Limeworks localities — and these sites have yielded the bulk of the remains of *Australopithecus africanus*. Moreover the identification of the hominid remains associated with nearly 300 undoubted artifacts and/or stone of foreign origin at Sterkfontein (Extension) is still most uncertain, and perhaps impossible to determine without recovery of additional specimens, hopefully more substantially preserved. And while undoubted artifacts are now well known at Swartkrans — though fewer in number than at

Sterkfontein (Extension) — these surely occur at a time when *Homo erectus* was already present, not only elsewhere, but at this very locality in association with *Australopithecus robustus*.

It is worth noting that the author rejects the negative stone artifactual evidence at Sterkfontein and Makapan Limeworks, although he accepts and utilizes in his argument (for differences in culturally-patterned behavior between taxa) the negative evidence at all such sites of the absence of traces of fire. Of course it is conceivable that the absence of artifacts (in stone) at the former two localities, very probably the earliest australopithecine sites as yet known, may be merely a reflection of the nature of a particular process of accumulation of sediments and vertebrate skeletal parts. However, if so there is an ill-understood contrast with the presumably similar situations — but artifact-bearing — at Sterkfontein (Extension), Swartkrans, and Kromdraai, as Robinson has repeatedly and rightly emphasized. Moreover the contrast is marked in further comparison with the splendid evidence for culturally-patterned behavior in the case of the several well-investigated occupational occurrences in Bed I at Olduvai. In the reviewer's opinion these are still problems in need of solution. Certain aspects of culturally-patterned behavior have been too readily assumed for these early australopithecines, largely on theoretical grounds, but without adequate basis in fact.

These several remarks of the reviewer are not intended to detract from the value of a book which is an important and badly needed general treatment of the earlier phases of hominid evolution, by an outstanding investigator of the evolution of man and other primates. The remarks are evoked because much of the tone of the book is set, by choice, around the resolution of a series of controversies. The attendant discussion of these matters, and the introduction of newer discoveries and related questions of interpretation, would lead the uninformed reader — for whom the book is largely intended — to accept uncritically that most problems concerning the earlier Quaternary evolution of Hominidae have been largely, even wholly, solved. Few workers familiar with the bulk of the primary data, and its limitations, would be willing to accept that such is now the case, or that it will soon come to pass. Many of the central problems are not necessarily of a morphological nature — although those too exist — , but concern matters relevant to other natural sciences and the earth sciences. In each instance there are gaps and uncertainties in data, or the lack thereof, which are essential to an adequate appreciation of many aspects of the distribution, ecological adjustments, behaviors, and phylogenetic relationships between populations and taxa of earlier Hominidae. It is appropriate, and indeed essential that these problems be stressed, and alternative hypotheses adequately set forth and evaluated, to advance further our understanding of the origin and evolution of man.

In this selection, Dr. Mann details the story of Homo erectus *using very much of the framework set out in the introduction to this section. Again we have the emphasis on function rather than form; on what our ancestors were rather than on what they should be called; and on the view that H. erectus is a transitional form not so very different from ourselves. In the constantly expanding sphere of our understanding of human evolution one important recent factor has been the narrowing of the vastness that was thought to separate us from any possible relatives. It now appears that not only can we readily reach a measure of this gulf, but, given the measure, go on to fill in the gulf with understanding gained from the data the archeologists give us concerning the way in which our ancestors lived. The major steps in the progression from ape to human are, as we have seen, already rather well delineated and H. erectus stands well along in that progression. As the Mann selection makes clear, the story of fossil man, and especially the story of H. erectus and his descendants, increasingly becomes the story of cultural man — and it is in that area that the greatest advances in the understanding of our recent past are likely to come. What we looked like in that past is a question that has often been overemphasized to the detriment of finding out what we did. The Mann article has been chosen as one illustrating a much more appropriate balance between archeology and human paleontology, which are, after all, two facets of the same existence.*

9   *Homo erectus*

The exact path taken by the ancestors of man in their long evolutionary history can never be fully known. What can be seen in the fossil record is a temporal series of remains, both cultural and biological. The biological remains, the fossils, represent all that is left of a living, functioning being. Various analyses can be applied to the bones and fairly accurate life reconstructions of the animal can be achieved. A reconstruction of the individual reveals many things, including stature, brain size, and general appearance, but this approach is essentially a static one and is only a beginning. The key to understanding the evolution of man is a knowledge of the behaviors our ancestors were capable of, since it is successful behavior that leads to a successful adaptation. Therefore, it is important to examine the fossil record with a view toward reconstructing patterns of behavior.

This perspective forms the basis of the following discussion of *Homo erectus*. *H. erectus* can be broadly dated to the Middle Pleistocene that ranges from about one million years to about 200,000 years ago (Figure 1).

The evolution of the hominids[1] during the Middle Pleistocene is the continuation of an adaptation based on a culture that probably originated with the earlier australopithecine grade. A discussion of the origins of this adaptation falls outside the scope of this paper; by the time the *H. erectus* grade of organization is reached, an adaptation based on culture is seemingly well-established. Indeed, it can be said that the hominids of the Middle Pleistocene relied on a cultural adaptation at least as much as does modern man. As will be seen from an examination of the fossil and archaeological evidence, the hominids of the Middle Pleistocene appear to have had the same kind of adaptation — hunting and gathering — that characterizes many modern groups of *Homo sapiens*. Because they are similar to modern man in their adjustment to the environment, the fossils from the Middle Pleistocene are placed in the same genus as modern man: *Homo*.

This classification, however, raises several difficulties, especially that of distinguishing those fossil forms which are placed in the taxonomic category (or taxon) *H. erectus* from those which belong in the later taxon of *H. sapiens* or the earlier taxon of *Australopithecus* (*Homo habilis*). Instances are known to paleontologists where one species evolves into another during a period of rather rapid evolutionary change. Before and after this swift evolution are periods in which very little change takes place. Obviously, in such situations specimens belonging to the different time periods are relatively easy to distinguish. At this stage in our knowledge, it does not seem likely that this type of relationship existed between *H. erectus* and the hominid populations that preceded and followed it. Rather, the evolution of the hominids is marked by gradual and continuous change from *Australopithecus* to *H. erectus*, and then to *H. sapiens*. It has been suggested that this continuous evolutionary change is responsible for the muddled state of affairs in the taxonomy of Pleistocene hominids, specifically in the matters of the taxon *H. habilis* and the origin of *H. sapiens*. These questions can be more adequately dealt with after an examination of the fossils now considered to be members of the taxon *H. erectus*.

[1] Members of the taxonomic family Hominidae, which includes man and his immediate ancestors.

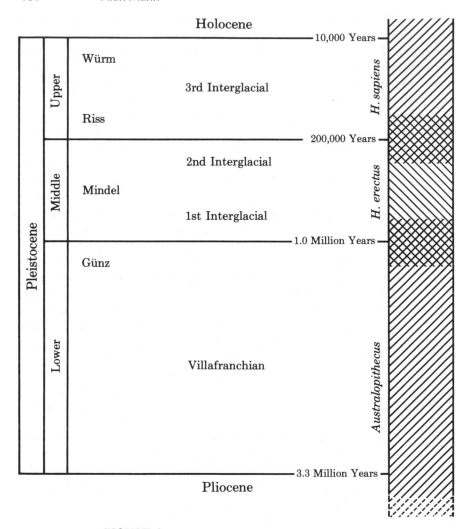

FIGURE 1

A chronology of the Pleistocene. The dates should be considered approximate.

The first evidence of fossils from the Middle Pleistocene appeared in 1891 when Eugene Dubois, a Dutch physician, reported the discovery of a skull cap, thigh bone (femur), and several small fragments, at Trinil, a locale on the Solo River, in the central part of the island of Java, Indonesia. Dubois, a truly remarkable figure in the history of human evolutionary studies, joined the Dutch Colonial Service and traveled to Java in the hopes of discovering the remains of the link between the apes and man. Several years earlier, Ernst Haeckel, a nineteenth-century German scientist, had coined a name for such a creature, if one were to be found: "Pithecanthropus," meaning ape (pithec) — and man (anthropus).

Dubois applied Haeckel's name to the bones he discovered, establishing the genus "Pithecanthropus." Since the thigh bone is indistinguishable from that of modern man, Dubois concluded that his "ape-man" walked erect in the same fashion as H. sapiens. Dubois noted this fact in devising a species name, so that the genus and species were "Pithecanthropus erectus," or erect ape-man. In the 1960s this name was dropped in favor of the term H. erectus.

To the late nineteenth century, embroiled in the controversy of organic evolution, Dubois' specimens were strikingly archaic. The skull cap, composed of thick bone, possessed large, projecting brow ridges and was low and broad in comparison to the brain cases of modern man. Unfortunately, the facial part of the skull was not found. The estimated volume of the brain case was about 800–900 cc, or about 500–600 cc, less than that usually found in modern man. At that time, the only known fossilized remains of higher primates were several Neandertals and some pieces of the fossil ape Dryopithecus. With such a small amount of comparative material, the placement of the "Pithecanthropus" fossils remained somewhat dubious. Opinions differed as to whether the skull cap and thigh bone belonged to the same individual, or whether the skull was from an extinct ape and the leg bone was that of a modern man accidentally washed into the deposit. Because of this controversy, a very ambitious expedition returned to Trinil in 1907–8 to collect additional fossil specimens. Unfortunately, no hominid remains were found. (It should be noted that recent chemical analysis has established the contemporaneity of the skull cap and the thigh bone.)

Since the time of Dubois, several important hominid fossil discoveries have been dated to the Middle and Lower Pleistocene. The material from the Lower Pleistocene, Australopithecus, was first found in 1924. This African fossil group demonstrated the existence of forms older in time and less modern human in appearance than "Pithecanthropus"; yet from a number of physical characteristics, it was undeniably hominid. Knowledge of the australopithecines contributed much toward the accurate taxonomic placement of the pithecanthropines. More direct evidence has come from the discovery, in locations scattered throughout the Old World, of additional fossils that have been placed in the same taxonomic group as Dubois' original find from Trinil.

At Sangiran and at Modjokerto, both on the island of Java, Professor G. H. R. von Koenigswald in the 1930s, P. Marks in 1953, and Professor S. Sartono in 1961 reported the finding of other fossil material. At Sangiran, Dr. von Koenigswald identified a faunal deposit containing several fossils. This deposit is very similar to the fossil-bearing layers at Trinil. These particular faunal levels have been designated the Trinil Beds. Below this deposit at Sangiran is another, known as the Djetis Beds, that has also yielded hominid fossils. The skull cap von Koenigswald found in the Trinil Bed at Sangiran was named "Pithecanthropus erectus II" and proved to be remarkably similar to Dubois's find, "Pithecanthropus erectus I." In general characteristics, both exhibit large brow ridges, thick bone, a marked waisting behind the orbits, and a low, flat brain case. Both skulls are, however, completely hominid in appearance, with little resemblance to the apes.

The hominid fossil material from the underlying and therefore older Djetis Beds has been the subject of varying interpretations. Several scientists, including Dr. von Koenigswald, view this collection, part of several upper jaws, several lower jaws, and a brain case of an infant, as being rather different from the later fossils of the Trinil Beds, and thus less like modern man. The Djetis fossils have been placed in different taxonomic categories from the Trinil material. One of them, the fossil lower jaw known as *Meganthropus palaeojavanicus*, has been assigned by Professor J. T. Robinson to the australopithecines, making it the only known occurrence of *Australopithecus* outside of Africa. Professor Robinson's suggestion has not been supported by a majority of paleoanthropologists.

Dating the Trinil and Djetis Beds has been difficult. Tectites (small black meteorites) found in the Trinil Beds are one type of a few rocks that can be dated with the Potassium/Argon process. The date arrived at is 710,000 years. Although the Djetis Beds have no date, they must be older since they underlie the Trinil horizon. The question of how much older is still being debated, with suggestions ranging from the same age as the Middle Pleistocene Trinil Beds to a Villafranchian age.

Fossils comparable to the Java specimens have been found on Mainland Asia in the Peoples' Republic of China. About twenty-five miles outside of the city of Peking lies the great cave system of Choukoutien. In the 1920s and 1930s an international team of scientists recovered the remains of approximately forty-five individuals, along with tools, evidence of fire, and thousands of animal bones. The hominid fossils were originally placed in a new taxon: "Sinanthropus pekinensis." However, their basic similarity with the "Pithecanthropus" specimens has led to the abandonment of this taxon and the placement of the Chinese material in the same category as the Java fossils.

The hominid fossils from Choukoutien include skull caps, teeth and jaws, and some postcranial bones, but as with the Java specimens, no faces were recovered. To date, we have yet to find the complete facial area of any *H. erectus* fossil.

The excavations at the Lower Cave (in the so-called Upper Cave, fully modern skulls were found) indicated an intermittent occupation of long duration by man, and revealed several important aspects concerning the way of life followed by these peoples. First, evidence shows that fire was employed (one of its earliest documented occurrences). Second, the amount of animal remains, especially deer, suggests that the people who occupied the Lower Cave were skilled hunters. Third, indications point to the practice of cannibalism.

In their physical appearance, the people of the Lower Cave, Choukoutien, are more modern looking than the Java fossils; their brain cases are larger, and their jaws and teeth smaller. This morphology is consistent with the dates suggested for the occupation of the lower cave, a time later than the 710,000 years of the Trinil Bed. A date of around 350,000–400,000 years has been given for the Choukoutien occupation, and although not arrived at through radiometric dating, the faunal and geological context makes it a reasonable figure.

Recently, additional fossil material has been uncovered in the Peoples' Republic of China. At Lan-t'ien, in East-Central Shensi Province, fossils placed in the taxon *H. erectus* have been described by Dr. Woo. The geological context suggests that these specimens, a lower jaw and a skull cap, are contemporary with the occupation of the Choukoutien caves. However, the morphological characteristics of the Lan-t'ien fossils exhibit many similarities with the earlier Javanese material; the brow ridge is large, the skull bone is thick, and the cranial capacity is about 780 cc, several hundred cubic centimeters less than that found in the Choukoutien individuals.

Although the finds from Java and China cover the known Middle Pleistocene fossil populations from the Far East, it can be assumed that the hominids of this time period were living all across Asia and that the gaps in our knowledge reflect a lack of success in locating fossils from this area and time period. Certainly the stone culture found at the Lower Cave, Choukoutien (a kit containing, among other implements, stone choppers and chopping tools) is found in many parts of Asia.

Our knowledge of the fossil remains of Middle Pleistocene hominids begins again in the Middle East and Central Europe. The evidence from the Middle East comes from the site of Ubeidiya, on the Jordan River near Lake Tiberias in Israel. The specimens consist of some small skull fragments and several teeth, recovered with animal bones and tools. The remains were at first thought to be those of an australopithecine. However, Professor P. V. Tobias, who studied the specimens, is of the opinion that they are probably members of the genus *Homo*. Because of the scanty nature of the bones, specific taxonomic placement of the Ubeidiya fossils must await the discovery of additional material.

European evidence of Middle Pleistocene hominids has significantly increased in the past few years with the excavation of the kill sites at Torralba/Ambrona in Spain, the occupation site of Terra Amata in Nice, Southern France, and the Vertesszöllös site in Hungary. However, only at the latter has a hominid fossil been uncovered. This information can be added to the lower jaw that was discovered at Mauer, a village about six miles from Heidelberg, West Germany, during quarrying activities in 1907. The Mauer, or Heidelberg jaw, is an enigma because its large, massive jawbone and no chin are combined with a set of relatively small, modern human teeth. The geological and faunal associations of the jaw are well-known and leave little doubt that it dates to the early part of the Middle Pleistocene. It has been placed in the taxon *H. erectus* by some paleoanthropologists, although many would prefer to reserve judgment until additional evidence is found.

Similarly, the back of the skull found at Vertesszöllös in 1965 has, like the Mauer jaw, been the subject of differing views. Several scientists have suggested it be placed within the category *H. erectus*. Professor A. Thoma, however, believes this bone comes from a skull larger than those usually attributed to *H. erectus*. Several additional features suggest to Professor Thoma that the Vertesszöllös occipital bone be placed in the taxon *H. sapiens* rather than in *H. erectus*.

From various parts of Africa have come a number of fossil specimens that are assigned to *H. erectus*. In North Africa, at Ternifine in Algeria, Professor C. Armbourg uncovered three more or less complete lower jaws. Professor Arambourg originally placed these fossils in a new taxon: *Atlanthropus mauritanicus*, but as the jaws clearly resemble the Choukoutien material, these North African fossils as well as the fragmentary material from Rabat, and Sidi Adbrahamin, Morocco, are usually placed in the taxon *H. erectus*. They were all found with tools of an Acheulian Industry.

Many hominid fossils have been found at sites in the Republic of South Africa, including the first australopithecine fossil at Taung, Cape Provence. In the Sterkfontein Valley, west of Johannesburg, are located a number of fossil-bearing deposits: Sterkfontein, Kromdraai, and Swartkrans. The latter has produced a great number of fossils, most of which are placed in the category *Australopithecus* (or *Paranthropus*) *robustus*. However, the deposit has also yielded a number of lower jaws, part of an upper jaw, and some isolated teeth, that were assigned to a new taxon: "Telanthropus capensis." This new taxonomic category was originally set up by Dr. Robert Broom and Professor J. T. Robinson because these fossils differed significantly from the *A. robustus* fossils surrounding them, especially in the size of their teeth. Lately, Dr. Robinson has moved these fossils into the taxon *H. erectus*. Although no normal stratigraphy or living floors are found at Swartkrans, numbers of stone pebble tools do exist. Professor Robinson suggests these tools were manufactured by the *H. erectus* peoples, and not by the australopithecines. On the other hand, Professor Le Gros Clark disagrees, maintaining that the "Telanthropus" fossils are not *H. erectus* but are *A. africanus*, the more gracile australopithecine from South Africa. A hindrance to the solution of this problem is the absence in the deposits of elements that can be subjected to an absolute dating method. The Swartkrans deposit has been placed in the lower Middle Pleistocene on the basis of the associated faunal bones.

Finally, a number of discoveries by Dr. and Mrs. Leakey at Olduvai Gorge, in Tanzania, East Africa, deserve mention. The stratigraphy of Olduvai Gorge is fairly well-known and consists of a number of beds lying on a lava base. The beds are numbered from I at the bottom through V at the top. Several sites in Bed I and lower Bed II have yielded fossils which Drs. L. S. B. Leakey, J. R. Napier, and P. V. Tobias have called *Homo habilis*. This taxon is seen as being more advanced than *Australopithecus*, but less than *H. erectus*. The size of the brain case is larger than that of *Australopithecus*, but still about 100 cc below the lower figures for *H. erectus*. The size and form of some of the teeth, as well as the conformation of the dental arch are all characters used in defining this taxon as different from both *Australopithecus* and *H. erectus*.[2] In contrast, Professor J. T. Robinson has suggested that the taxon *H. habilis* be divided into two groups: those from Bed I sharing affinities with the australopithecines, and those from Lower Bed II being viewed as *H. erectus*. The point is that *H. habilis* may represent the evolutionary transition between the australopithecine grade and the *H. erectus* grade. A layer of sand between the lower and upper parts of Bed II marks a temporal break. In the lower part of Bed II, as has been noted, are the *H. habilis* fossils. In the upper part of Bed II at the site of LLK, a skull cap has been found. This skull has large brow ridges, marked waisting behind the orbits, and is rather flat. The fossil has been called "Homo leakeyi," a term that is no longer valid, and seems to be similar to the Asian *H. erectus* fossils. It can be broadly dated to the Middle Pleistocene.

This review covers the known members of the taxon *H. erectus*. Generally, they share the following morphological characteristics: large brow ridges; marked waisting behind the orbits (post orbital constriction); low, flat skull vaults (platycephaly); a cranial capacity of between 750 and 1100 cc (comparison: *Australopithecus*: 500–600 cc; Modern man: 1350–1450 cc); greatest width of the skull being low; thick cranial bones; teeth larger than those found in modern man; some molar teeth with a characteristic crinkling of the chewing surface; no chin; and modern post cranial bones. [See Figure 2.]

In order to place in perspective these physical characteristics, data must be presented concerning the adaptive niche occupied by *H. erectus*, as well as his relative position on the hominid line. Unfortunately, many of the

---

[2] According to international rules, on setting up a new taxonomic category, the describer must, among other things, show how the new taxon differs from those most closely related to it.

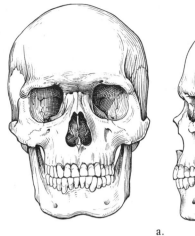
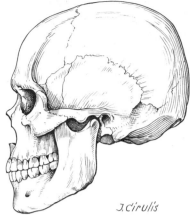
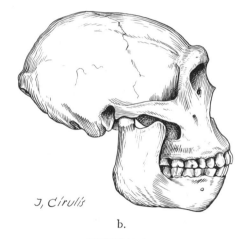
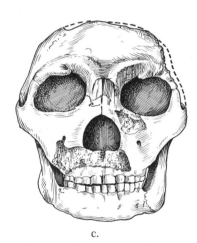

a.

b.   c.

FIGURE 2

A comparison of the skulls of modern man and *Homo erectus*.
(a) The skull of a native of Fiji, taken to represent modern man.
(b) A restoration by Professor von Koenigswald based on two Djetis Bed fossils.
(c) The reconstruction of the Lantien skull.
Note: These three drawings have been reproduced from W. W. Howells, *Mankind in the Making*, rev. ed., (New York: Doubleday, 1967), pp. 210 (a) and 160 (b and c). Reprinted by permission of Janis Cirulis.

fossils were discovered without tools or other evidence of their adaptation. Such information comes from archaeological sites such as Choukoutien, Vertesszöllös, and more importantly, those sites that have not yielded hominid fossils, but date from time periods that lead to the supposition that they were occupied by *H. erectus*, such as the kill sites of Torralba/ Ambrona, Terra Amata, etc.

The tools indicate that *H. erectus* populations throughout the Old World used a variety of implements, both unifacially and bifacially flaked. The peoples of Choukoutien employed a basic tool kit of choppers and chopping tools, whereas the industries found at Vertesszöllös and Swartkrans consist largely of pebble tools. The kits found at Ternifine and Bed II, Olduvai Gorge, are composed of bifacial tools, usually referred to the Acheulian or the Chelles-Acheul tool traditions.

The number of bones at Choukoutien and the number and size of animals found at Torralba/Ambrona indicate that the hominids of the Middle Pleistocene were accomplished hunters. Present evidence suggests that *H. erectus* differed from *Australopithecus* in the kind of hunting being carried out. *Australopithecus* probably did not hunt large animals to any great extent, whereas the presence of at least twenty elephants at Ambrona and the bones of literally thousands of cervids at Choukoutien testify to the skill of *H. erectus*. Thus may be reflected a difference between the economic bases of *Australopithecus* and *H. erectus*, an issue that will only be clarified by the excavation of living sites of *Australopithecus*. In any event, *H. erectus*, as modern human hunting and gathering societies, no doubt depended for the greater part of his subsistence not on the meat of large mammals, but on gathered plant foods, fish, shellfish, eggs, insects, etc.

The site of Terra Amata is evidence of a Middle Pleistocene open air habitation site. It reveals living structures in the form of ovoid stone circles and post holes that probably represent tent-like dwellings with coverings of skin or vegetable matter. Inside were raised platforms or pits for the building of fires.

This evidence suggests that the hunting and gathering adaptation of *H. erectus* was not very different from that of *H. sapiens* prior to the relatively recent introduction of agriculture. It is because *H. erectus* was adapted to the environment in much the same way as modern man that the genus "Pithecanthropus" was dropped and all the fossils formerly placed in that category were assigned to the genus *Homo*, but were still retained in a separate species: *H. erectus*.

Attempts at reconstructing the social aspects of *H. erectus* groups are far more speculative. Middle Pleistocene hominids certainly lived in social groups, and the house plans at Terra Amata suggest that some family unit was already in existence. It has recently been postulated that the australopithecines, like modern man, experienced a prolonged childhood dependency period that was no doubt part of the behavior of *H. erectus*. During this period, the young of the group learned those social and physical skills necessary for survival. Behavioral patterns such as belief systems and language are difficult to reconstruct at the moment. Burials, that in later time periods furnish clues to ideological systems, have not been recovered in contexts attributable to *H. erectus*.

At the beginning of this paper, it was suggested that the hominid populations of the Middle Pleistocene represent the continuation of an adaptation based on culture that probably originated much earlier in time. Around a million years ago the hominids gradually evolved into the form called *H. erectus*. Exactly when and where the evolutionary transition from *Australopithecus* took place is still a matter of investigation. The important morphological differences between *H. erectus* and *Australopithecus* involve a larger brain and smaller face and teeth. Additionally, *H. erectus* is seen to have a fully modern post cranial skeleton. The tools associated with *H. erectus* are more complex than those attributed to the australopithecines. Further along the hominid continuum, *H. erectus* is distinguishable from *H. sapiens* in precisely the same features as *H. erectus* differs from *Australopithecus*. That is, *H. sapiens* has a larger brain and a smaller face and dentition than *H. erectus*. Similarly, the culture associated with *H. sapiens* is more complex.

Clearly, the changes in brain size, faces and teeth correlate with the elaboration of culture. If culture is the basis of the hominid adaptation, then natural selection would operate for a more efficient cultural adaptation. For example, an enlarging brain is related to an increased capacity for complex cultural skills and behavior. Facial and dental reduction may be linked to more efficient tool use. These evolving characters should be seen as part of a larger complex of interrelated features, changes in one having an influence on the others. The physical appearance of *H. erectus*, therefore, is a reflection of this fossil species' place on the total hominid continuum, connecting the complex cultural adaptation of *H. sapiens* with the probable origin of this adaptation at the australopithecine grade.

The descriptions of the various specimens make it clear that all the *H. erectus* fossils are not identical to each other. The reasons for the differences are: first, population variability. Because of the nature of the mechanisms responsible for evolutionary change, all natural populations exhibit variability among their members. Other reasons for the differences seen within the taxon *H. erectus* are the spatial and temporal distributions of the fossils. Unlike the australopithecines, who seemingly were restricted to Africa, the hominids of the Middle Pleistocene are distributed throughout the Old World. It may well be that the *H. erectus* grade represents a level of cultural adaptation that allowed the hominids to expand into new environmental niches. In any event, *H. erectus* is found throughout the Old

World, and it has been suggested that the origin of modern racial groups can be dated to this Middle Pleistocene expansion of the hominids. Certainly, some of the differences between H. erectus populations in various parts of the Old World, as the racial differences between modern living groups, can be traced to the action of natural selection operating to adapt each group to its local environment.

Finally, much of the variability in H. erectus groups is related to their place in time. H. erectus is a species evolving through time, changing to better adapt to its environment. The representation on Figure 1 attempts to graphically illustrate the relationships of the hominid populations in time. H. erectus lived during the Middle Pleistocene, but the crosshatched areas between the major hominid taxa indicate that individuals living during these time periods would be difficult to distinguish, because, being transitional, they share characteristics with the hominid populations preceding and following. The taxon H. habilis seemingly fits in this area, as is probably represented by the crosshatched area between Australopithecus and H. erectus. It is for this reason that difficulties have arisen over its accurate categorization.

Similarly, the Vertesszöllös occipital bone, as well as the Cranial bones from Swanscombe, in England and the Steinheim skull from Germany are represented by the crosshatched area between H. erectus and H. sapiens. The Swanscombe remains and the Steinheim fossil have been the subjects of heated debate concerning their relationships to other hominid fossils. These specimens date from the Second Interglacial, at the end of the Middle Pleistocene, and therefore may very well be representative of the transitional populations between H. erectus and H. sapiens.

In sum, H. erectus should be viewed as the hominid population of the Middle Pleistocene that saw the continuation and elaboration of the fundamental hominid adaptation based on culture.

FURTHER READING

Day, M. H.
   1965   Guide to Fossil Man. A Handbook of Human Paleon-
          tology. New York: The World Publishing Co.
Clark, W. E. Le Gros
   1964   Fossil Evidence for Human Evolution, revised edition.
          Chicago: University of Chicago Press.
Howell, F. C .
   1967   "Recent Advances in Human Evolutionary Studies,"
          Quarterly Review of Biology 42:471–513.
Howells, W. W.
   1966   "Homo Erectus," Scientific American 215 (5):46–53.
   1967   Mankind in the Making, revised edition. New York:
          Doubleday.

III
HUMAN
VARIATION
AND
RACE

It is certainly human variation (especially in its racial aspects) that, of all areas of physical anthropology, draws the most attention from the non-specialist. We do not propose to here dwell on all the social and cultural manifestations of the recognition that men are different from one another; we do propose to probe the origins of human variation, its genetic bases, and certain aspects of race mixture. It must be recognized at the outset that on no topic of this volume is there less agreement about the answers to the questions we ask. The selections by Sarich and Stern present certain evidence and, more important, provide means of looking at their data. The reader may then make up his own mind as to whether or not the arguments presented have been convincing.

Human variation has, of course, both racial and nonracial dimensions. Although doubt exists on which of these is the more important biologically, the former definitely requires the most immediate answers. Any attempt to pose an answer must stem from a conviction that races are real entities. The selection by Sarich puts this reality on an operational basis. (It might be noted here that nowhere in that selection is race given a succinct definition. This lack is not an oversight, but stems from the author's conviction that to briefly define the term "race" often too narrowly restricts one's thinking about it. For example, one is often led to the impression that specific races can be enumerated, and to the impression that racial classifications are somehow important. The Sarich article is, if you wish, a definition of race as a whole — an attempt to place the development of human variation in a proper evolutionary context. The selection aims for understanding rather than classifying and is perhaps best characterized as trying to produce a state of mind in the reader appropriate for the attack on the many problems arising from human variation.)

The two selections from Stern's classic Principles of Human Genetics deal with specific aspects of human racial variation. In the first, he provides some data that indicate the range of genetic variation at certain well-studied loci. These and other data are then synthesized into a perspective on racial variation, in which Stern is very careful to point out several areas where appreciable care in analysis is required. (In particular are the evidential nonreality of the "pure race" concept and the necessity for recognizing that the differences between racial groups are not and cannot be constant.)

One aspect of human genetic variation has come to assume potential importance since the publication of Stern's text. This aspect comes from recent studies of protein evolution, all of which indicate that for any given protein the probability of an amino acid substitution occurring over a given length of time is the same for each lineage (see "A Molecular Approach to the Study of Human Origins"). It is difficult to explain this apparently random regularity without invoking the concept of neutral mutations — whose rate of fixation depends only on their frequency of occurrence. If then, as seems very likely, this regularity of protein evolution reflects the inexorable accretion of neutral mutations, then the large majority of all genetic changes are functionally irrelevant. Accepting that genes do evolve over time, when we look at the genetic profile of any species we should see allele frequencies at polymorphic loci varying from 0 to 1.0 depending on where in time and space our randomly evolving system is intercepted. One strongly suspects that much of the observed genetic polymorphism in man (and, no doubt, all other species) seen at a given point in time merely represents stages in this inexorable accretion. Thus, and most important, most of this allele frequency variation within and between human populations is just there without having any profound evolutionary significance.

The second Stern selection deals with the touchy topic of race mixture, as does Hardin's In Praise of Waste. Little can be added to Stern's discussion, we only emphasize that it is the individual, rather than the physical group to which he belongs, that should be the focus of our attention in social, moral, and ethical issues. These issues too often become confused with the genetic aspects of human variation. Equality is a moral, social, ethical, and legal concept and certainly not a genetic or biological one. The only realistic way to regard it is as an equal opportunity to make the best of one's hereditary material. The inevitability of equality in these cultural spheres need not, in a truly democratic society, be put off by requiring a "proof" of actual biological equality. As Dr. Alice Brues of the University of Colorado has quite cogently pointed out, the present legal status of women would hardly have been attained if we had waited for "science to prove" that the sexes were equal in all relevant behavioral and physical characters. One could argue with appreciable justification (evolutionary and otherwise) that the differences between human males and females (outside of the more obvious anatomical ones) are probably far greater and more meaningful than any possible difference between racial groups. Need more be said?

VINCENT SARICH

10   Human Variation in
an Evolutionary Perspective

At one level we are all members of a single species, *Homo sapiens*; at another, each of us is a unique individual. If one asks about the reality of human races, one is asking whether groupings at the level of populations exist between the level of the individual and that of the species, thus allowing individuals to be placed in their appropriate population by something better than chance accuracy. The process involved is readily illustrated in a thought experiment where one imagines fifty modern humans and fifty modern chimpanzees to be randomly mixed in a single group. No one would have any difficulty in reconstituting the two original fifty member sets without uncertainty or overlap. Now a precisely homologous experiment with fifty *H. sapiens* from, say, Japan, and fifty from subSaharan Africa can be carried out, and the same sorting efficiency will be achieved. Admittedly, in the latter experiment fewer sorting characteristics are available but not so few as to produce any doubt about the placement of any given individual. If we consider the whole of the human species it should be evident that other such paired comparisons can be made at or nearly at 100 percent sorting levels. These simple experiments demonstrate the reality of human physical groups (races) below the level of the species and make obvious the absurdity of the claim often made that race as a biological concept should not apply to our considerations of man.

Showing the existence of races in man is only a necessary beginning. The important questions pertain to the evolutionary meaning of this aspect of human variability. Races within a species can only develop when certain populations become sufficiently isolated from one another genetically to enable the evolution of independent changes within each population that comprise a much larger proportion of the total changes than do those introduced by gene flow from other populations. Such isolation, particularly in the case of man, has usually been geographic. It is doubtful that cultural isolation can have been maintained between any human groups for a length of time sufficient for any significant genetic differentiation between such groups to have developed. How far back in time, then, did such a geographical potential for human raciation exist? Certainly not in australopithecine and early *Homo erectus* times, for the hominid story was then a purely African one. Admittedly, the evidence supporting this conclusion is purely negative — no human fossils or, more important, no stone tools are found outside the savannas of subSaharan Africa prior to the very latest portion of the Basal Pleistocene. Human fossils are rare at best and their absence need not be persuasive evidence of man's absence, but stone tools are not. In some areas, in fact, they are so common that it is possible to not only fill a museum with them but to build it out of them as well. Thus their absence is strong, even though negative, evidence that man himself had not yet ventured out of his African homeland. Though absolute dating of this terminal part of the Basal Pleistocene is not yet possible, a reasonable estimate would place it in the area of 600,000 to 800,000 years ago. On the one hand, then, our ancestors are restricted to a geographically delimited and climatically rather homogenous area throughout which man was relatively free to travel. (Man is not evidenced as inhabiting the tropical rain forests of Africa until much more recent times — perhaps only 40–50,000 years ago.) On the other hand, however, the level of cultural achievement man had reached by this time almost insured that this state of affairs could not long continue to describe the human existence.

Only in recent years has the information gathered by the combined efforts of a number of archaeologists and paleontologists contradicted the previously prevalent notion that Africa was a cultural and biological backwater, and the real genesis of human culture must have developed elsewhere. In particular the work of the Leakey family at Olduvai Gorge that provides a magnificent and presently unique record of human achievement, spanning at least the last two million years, has shown that subSaharan Africa, far from being a cultural backwater, was indeed the cradle of all the basic physical and cultural developments that characterize the genus *Homo*. The South African evidence almost certainly takes us even further back in time and begins to fill in the precultural developments involved in the pongid–hominid transition. Before *H. erectus* expanded out of Africa, this recent evidence tells us, he possessed a relatively large brain (around 900 cc cranial capacity), was an efficient hunter of big game, had progressed far beyond the relatively simple pebble-tool kit of his ancestors, and had reached a grade of development that required only time and the inevitability of the evolutionary process to reach our modern status. No substantive evidence exists that any evolutionary change in grade comparable to that leading from pongid to hominid (involving bipedalism and reduction of the canine complex) or from *Australopithecus* to *Homo* (the introduction of a cultural system mediated by language) was involved in the *H. erectus–H. sapiens* transition. By this hypothesis, then, some pongid lineage reached a human grade of evolutionary development in Africa, and *H. sapiens* is viewed as only a somewhat advanced *H. erectus*. I would suggest that, given *H. erectus*, something akin to ourselves was evolutionarily almost inevitable.

What happened earlier in our history is a different matter. Bipedalism and loss of the canine complex were hardly an inevitable outcome of reaching a pongid grade of development (chimps, gorillas, orangs, and gibbons are still with us). Nor was a language-mediated cultural species inevitable given the early australopithecines (consider the fate of A. robustus). It is only when one gains some appreciation of the relative magnitudes of the evolutionary changes involved in hominid history that the argument to be presented concerning the development of human races becomes at least tenable. Without this scaling we can often be too readily biased by the enormous quantitative cultural changes that have occurred during the history of H. sapiens to appreciate that any underlying qualitative genetic changes are at best minor ones. Only when I look at human history in this fashion do I begin to find it possible to view within a single evolutionary picture the basic cultural unity of man in combination with his physical diversity.

Throughout the Middle and Upper Pleistocene, cultures in different areas of the world developed in essential synchrony — hence, it is often difficult to distinguish contemporaneous Acheulean tool kits from areas as far apart as South Africa, France, and India. And yet one has to allow the human groups in these areas sufficient genetic isolation over a long enough period of time to develop the levels of physical differentiation (both in phenotype and genotype) that characterize them today. I cannot see how one can possibly resolve these difficulties within a time span of 30–40,000 years, that is, as he maintains that modern lineages cannot antedate H. sapiens. As I have mentioned previously it is difficult for many to even admit the existence of human races; therefore, this highly unorthodox (but by no means original) suggestion requires appreciable justification.

The first step in the defense of this suggestion is to gain some measure of the differences between modern human races. By carrying out the rough experiments described above it can be concluded that several human groups could be sorted from one another with 100 percent accuracy. If something near this level using only visible external characteristics is required, then probably there are four major human races; two in the East (roughly Oriental and Melanesian to use terms in common usage) and two in the West (Caucasian and African Negroid). However 100 percent accuracy is considered by many biologists to be an unusually rigid criterion and often such distinct groups would be considered species. In fact 75 percent sorting accuracy is considered adequate to define a subspecific taxon. If this criterion were applied to our own species it should be obvious that a large variety of races could be so defined. This type of attempt at numerical rigidity, however, is clearly out of place here. We should by now have sufficient evolutionary sophistication to conclude that it is not very useful to place rigid constraints on what are necessarily dynamic situations. It is not possible — and, in fact, it could not be possible — to divide up the human species into races that are equally distinct from one another. As any other product of the evolutionary process, race is a dynamic entity and any attempt to create arbitrarily inflexible and unchanging groupings is bound to fail. When one looks at modern races (or any evolutionary unit) the evolutionary process is being intercepted at an instant of time and no expectation should be entertained that the characteristics of a group at that point in time should remain appropriate at a different time or place.

Now if the history of modern human races is not coincident with the history of the modern species *H. sapiens,* how far back in time does human racial differentiation go? Here the American Indians form a uniquely useful reference group. Since the discovery of the Americas by European explorers, the similarity of the native inhabitants to those of the northern Far East has been noted. The passage of time and the great increase in human knowledge concerning the population of both areas has served only to emphasize the validity of this original observation. But associated with this growing body of knowledge concerning the physical and genetic similarities between American Indian and Far Eastern populations are the facts concerning the length of time that geographic barriers have kept these two groups genetically isolated. The Americas were populated from Asia across the Bering Land Bridge that, at the time of maximum drop in sea level during the most recent glaciation, was about 1200 miles across. Exactly when the colonizing groups made it between the glaciers of eastern and western Canada along the east side of the Rockies is still a matter of some dispute. Man was definitely widespread in North America, however, by at least 12,000 years ago and had gotten to the very tip of South America by 9,500 years ago. By this time the land bridge across the Bering Strait had disappeared, making significant genetic contributions to the Americas from Asia most unlikely. One then asks: If so little physical and genetic differentiation has taken place between the related populations of the Americas and Asia in at least 12,000 years, how much time is necessary to develop situations where it is not even possible to discern relationships, either at the morphological or genetic level, among human populations except to say that they are part of the human species? The answer is rather obviously a good deal more than the 30,000–40,000 years most students of human evolution are willing to allow.

This conclusion leads to something of a quandary, however. If human racial lineages antedate the appearance of modern man, then is not a great deal being asked of parallel evolution? I have often been asked this question by students, who have pointed out the seeming incongruity of so vehemently denying the possible role of parallel evolution in developing the structural similarities among the modern Hominoidea but invoking it to explain similarities among modern human races. This apparent paradox is resolved, however, by considering the changes involved in the two evolutionary developments. In the case of man and the apes, invoking parallelism would require that a new grade of evolutionary development had been reached at least five times in essential synchrony. It has already been pointed out that this really doesn't belong in the realm of the statistically possible. On the other hand, as I have stated above, one cannot see any evidence that a comparable new grade of morphological or genetic development has been reached by H. sapiens relative to H. erectus.

What then is the exact evolutionary pattern proposed for H. sapiens? Its basis is contained in a statement to the effect that behavior tends to be one step ahead of structure and so plays a decisive role in the evolutionary process. Human behavior is crystallized as human culture and it is human culture that has been by far the most important selective agency in shaping the course of human evolution. As a famous cultural anthropologist, Walter Goldschmidt, has quite cogently pointed out:[1]

> One ironic conclusion emerging from the study of man as a biological animal is that man's cultural behavior appears to have been more influential in determining physical attributes in man than the physical attributes have been in determining the differences in culture.

Human cultural advances, insofar as they are recorded in the archaeological record, occurred in appreciable synchrony over a long period of human evolution. We have no reason to believe that at any given point in time one human group was incapable of learning some cultural novelty or advance introduced by its neighbors. Such cultural diffusion need have no genetic correlates, of course; man is quite capable of transmitting cultural information without also transmitting genetic information. In addition the nature of human geographical dispersion would mitigate against evolutionarily significant amounts of gene exchange among a number of human populations.

As H. erectus spread out of Africa into virgin territories, major increases in population must have taken place in the newly occupied areas until the carrying capacity of the land was reached. Large human populations were then present in many relatively rich areas separated from one another by what were and still are what I would term geographical filters; for example, the Sahara, the Himalayas, and the deserts of the Middle East. Man could live in these areas, but their relative population densities must have been much less than in more favored areas. Gene flow was thus first restricted by distance; its effects were further negated by the fact that the large populations on either side of these filters would tend to be little influenced genetically by the relatively small amounts of gene flow across the filters.

[1] *Exploring the Ways of Mankind* (New York: Holt, Rinehart and Winston, 1960), p. 4.

The flow of cultural information (cultural diffusion) need not be so restricted, of course — it requires only a single bearer of information and a single observer. Given this picture, one can begin to resolve what is to many the paradox of human races. One need only postulate that all populations of the genus *Homo* were capable throughout post-Villafranchian times (that is, in the past one million years) of receiving and incorporating cultural information originating in the genus. The magnitude and direction of the cultural selection pressures operating on these various human populations would tend to be much the same in all of them. Selection would be in the direction of a genetic change that would increase cultural capabilities in all populations in essential synchrony. But the specific genetic changes, because of the restricted gene flow between human populations, would necessarily be different in each major geographical area (it being highly unlikely that the same mutations would be available in all areas). This hypothesis, then, has various *H. erectus* grade human populations evolving in the same evolutionary direction under cultural selection pressures to reach a *H. sapiens* grade, but doing it with more or less genetic independence. In other words, the various human races represent nothing more, in large extent, than different paths along the journey from a *H. erectus* to *H. sapiens* grade of evolutionary development. It is not surprising that it is in precisely those parts of the skeleton (skulls, jaws, teeth) that have changed most from *H. erectus* to *H. sapiens* that the greatest differences among human races exist today.

This theory is hardly novel, but it does bring to mind the major controversies that ranged in the realm of human evolutionary studies in 1962–3 following the publication of Carleton Coon's *Origin of Races*. Coon proposed a theory disturbingly similar to the one outlined above:

> My thesis is, in essence, that at the beginning of our record, over a million years ago, man was a single species, *Homo erectus*, perhaps already divided into five geographic races or subspecies. *Homo erectus* then evolved into *Homo sapiens* not once but five times, passed a critical threshold from a more brutal to a more *sapient* state.

But Coon was surrounded by some value judgments in which he was quite validly criticized as a racist. This criticism very much overshadowed the basic truth of the theory. Throughout the book are statements that the various human lines crossed the *erectus-sapiens* "threshold" at different times; that the order of crossing was Caucasoid (naturally) then Mongoloid; then Capoid, Congoid, and Australoid follow in indeterminate order; and finally, and most mischievously, the strong implication (if not always clear statement) that the time in *sapiens* grade would tend to determine the degree of development in that grade. The conclusions one would draw are obvious.

What Coon overlooked, of course, was the continuous cybernetic interaction between human physical and cultural development and the fact that the *H. sapiens* or *H. erectus* grades are not, and cannot, be defined by the physical characteristics of the populations involved. They must be defined by their cultural capabilities as manifested in the archaeological record. The concept of a *H. sapiens* "threshold" is one that would take us back to the stereotyped typological thinking of the early years of human evolution and to the view that modern man represents a major evolutionary change from his immediate predecessors. As I have stated before, this change is true only in achievement, not in hereditary capability. And those who somehow equate achievement with capability should be reminded of the answer Franklin gave to a questioner who asked of one of his inventions, "What good is it?" Franklin replied, "And what good is a new-born babe?"

I have in lectures often termed the views put forward opposing the ideas proposed above as belonging to a "Garden of Eden" school of thought. Without exaggerating the views of scholars in this school unduly, one can summarize them as follows: *H. sapiens* represents, both culturally and physically, a major change in grade involving a complex reorganization of genetic structure relative to *H. erectus*. This change occurred in a relatively localized area and these modern and advanced humans spread out from their homeland, effectively replaced their more primitive neighbors, and thus colonized the whole world. Human races thus stem from this original colonizing population and represent differential adaptations to the selective conditions found in the various areas of the world. This picture has major problems that have forced me to take the alternate view. The cultural changes introduced with modern *H. sapiens* about 30–40,000 years ago undoubtedly represent more efficient ways of dealing with the environment even if the hows and ways of this greater efficiency are not precisely known. One problem lies in the fact that no one has been able to demonstrate any antiquity for these changes nor any early populations with which such advanced cultures can be associated. Prior to this 30–40,000 year time, only the Neandertal grade of *H. sapiens* populated all known areas. (Grade here can be used in both a cultural and morphological sense.) Thus one accepts the "Garden of Eden" school of thought for the origin of modern *H. sapiens* — a view which would necessitate the belief that the Neandertals of the world were too stupid to adopt these Upper Paleolithic cultural changes, and which is belied by the complex cultures of the Neandertals and their large brains — or one is forced to the conclusion that the Neandertal grade of human evolution led in a continuous fashion into the modern *H. sapiens* grade. The Neandertals in different areas of the world are then viewed as the immediate precursors of their modern *H. sapiens* descendants and will have to remain so until it can be conclusively demonstrated that a population culturally and morphologically more modern than the Neandertals existed at the same time they did; i.e. from 100,000 to 35,000 years ago. Francois Bordes, the eminent French prehistorian, has aptly stated the case[2] *vis-a-vis* the Neandertals:

> To conclude, it does not seem that, culturally at least, there is any great gap between the Mousterian cultures and the early Upper Paleolithic cultures that followed. One of the latter, at least, has its roots quite clearly in the Mousterian of Acheulean tradition. And even if some anthropologists deny to Neandertal man (sensu stricto) the right to be counted among our direct ancestors, one thing is sure: these ancestors of ours were at a cultural level very like that of the Mousterian peoples. So we come uncomfortably close to the old joke: It was not William Shakespeare who wrote *Hamlet*, but another man who lived at the same time and whose name was also William Shakespeare!

Now it has been argued that in certain areas of the world, notably Western Europe, the cultural and morphological changes that mark the Neandertal to modern *H. sapiens* transition are entirely too abrupt to represent a truly evolutionary change and more likely represent a replacement of one line of men with another. This possibility cannot be ruled out, but in at least one area of the world (the Middle East), this transition is well-documented over a rather short period of time. In addition, one must remember that human cultural innovation requires but a single innovator working in a proper cultural climate. Transfer of that information requires only observation and, as human culture has been the basic selective agency in human morphological evolution, major changes could occur over rather short periods of time. We are still unaware of precisely what culture-biology interactions produced the Neandertal–modern *H. sapiens* transition, as the available data are entirely too scanty, but the lack of appropriate non-Neandertal ancestors for modern man plus the Middle East evidence leaves little doubt that our understanding of the origins of truly modern man must be reached using the long-denigrated Neandertals as an evolutionary base.

Thus each of my two major contributions to this book contains a very controversial element: the idea that the hominid line is only four or five million years old is, in the current intellectual context, a radical suggestion. Nonetheless, the evidence supporting this view is about as impeccable as any molecular data can be today and we have already seen the enormously simplified and rigorous reconstruction of the course of human evolution that it makes possible. Although our necks may be out a long way on the question of hominid origins, we have little fear for them. The picture drawn here concerning human racial variation I would place at an entirely different level of confidence. In my weaker moments, in fact, I sometimes seriously

[2] *Science*, 134 (1960), pp. 803–810.

question it. But the questioning process usually ceases when I again look at the alternatives that have been suggested. Admittedly the data and logic involved in concluding that human racial lineages antedate *H. sapiens* do not compare either in amount or quality with those bearing on the question of hominid origins. They are, as I have pointed out, consistent only with the conclusions drawn. The major objections raised are raised not so much on the quantitative data but on one's intuitive feelings concerning the meaning of human differences. The differences are small (even minor) compared to the similarities of all human populations. Evolutionarily, however, this is expectable. Purely in terms of time, for example, we are talking about roughly four million years of common evolutionary history involving two major changes in grade that all modern humans happen to share, compared with the possibly one-half million years involving no major new evolutionary grade changes that separate some human groups. Put in such temporal perspective the actual degrees of difference and similarity begin to make some sense.

Another objection that has been raised states that it borders on the statistically impossible for several (the number five is often used) *H. erectus* populations to have independently and in parallel evolved into a more or less corresponding number of *H. sapiens* populations. Now if: (1) it is required that such a process occur purely by chance, (2) the possibility of functionally equivalent but genetically different solutions to the same evolutionary problem (in this case, human cultural selection pressure) is denied; and (3) the genetic gap between *H. erectus* and *H. sapiens* is viewed as large, then the hypothesis supported in this chapter can be disproved. Each of the three points has been dealt with previously and even if the available data are insufficient to allow an unexceptionable conclusion to be drawn, it does appear to me that the most viable hypothesis remains the one proposed here. This hypothesis, if substantiated by further research, can also have enormous practical value to the field of physical anthropology. A great deal of effort has been, and may well continue to be, extended in the attempt to demonstrate the selective meaning of specific human differences. It has been suggested here that such attempts may well be for the most part exercises in futility. One wonders how many research projects have been undertaken and how much valuable time (not to mention money) has been wasted because the basic framework within which to study human evolution was not erected before attempts to answer much more complex questions of detail were made.

It has already been pointed out that many of the differences in body structure that characterize modern human groups are probably individually selectively meaningless, representing only a few of the possible paths from a *H. erectus* to a *H. sapiens* morphology. Thus the important matter is the amount of change over time that developed in cybernetic association with human cultural evolution. This, as far as we can see, does not vary from human group to human group. The physical differences are there, however, and serve as a reminder that man has a long history — a history which the species collectively spent in much of the Old World and which produced modern men of equal genetic potential to operate within the human cultural context, but which also necessitated that different parts of the species developed that potential along different evolutionary paths.

11 Genetic Aspects of Race

There is no full agreement among students of the systematics of animals and plants as to what constitutes a "species." In general, however, separate groups of organisms are regarded as belonging to different species if they are more or less *reproductively isolated,* a term which signifies limitation or lack of interbreeding under natural conditions.

The criterion of reproductive isolation is independent of the more obvious structural differences among organisms. While many groups of structurally different organisms do not cross with each other, there are also numerous examples of reproductive isolation in spite of very small or nonobservable morphological differences, as well as of strikingly different populations without reproductive isolation. Such populations are able to retain their differences because of geographical or other isolating factors.

Often, two strikingly different groups of organisms inhabiting different regions are connected by a more or less continuous series of intermediate types. Despite the range of variability, all these organisms form one single unit, differentiated into subgroups which, in different regions, replace each other. Even members of the subgroups which are most distinct morphologically can, in many cases, interbreed freely if brought into contact. Many systematists call the large group a *species,* and the groups out of which the species is composed its *subspecies.* There are species which are not subdivided into subspecies; others in which only two or a few subspecies can be distinguished; and still others, sometimes called *polytypic species,* in which a great many subspecific types exist, each of which inhabits a different region.

A taxonomic observer of mankind, using the criteria which have just been described, would classify man as a single species subdivided into numerous subspecies. There is no doubt about the existence of morphologically different groups of mankind; these form the various races studied by the physical anthropologist. Undoubtedly, too, there are many intermediate populations among the different groups, forming either a more or less continuous chain of connections or consisting of "hybrid swarms" — the

From *Principles of Human Genetics,* Second Edition, by Curt Stern. W. H. Freeman and Company. Copyright © 1960.

products of interbreeding and consequent segregation of genetic traits derived from different races which were once separated and later came into contact.

As in other polytypic species, the subdivisions of mankind are not all of equivalent rank. There are major races, as the Mongoloids and the Caucasoids, for example, and minor variants, as the Mediterraneans and the Alpines, and many groups of intermediate taxonomic rank. Because all degrees of differences occur between human populations, there is no generally accepted system of classification. The term human race will be defined later in this chapter, and it will be seen that there are no sharp genetic criteria by which to distinguish different degrees of racial differences. As far as is known, members of every human race can successfully hybridize with members of every other. These phenomena — morphological and reproductive — have led the taxonomist since Linnaeus' time, two centuries ago, to assign a single species name, *Homo sapiens*, to all mankind.

GENETICS OF RACIAL DIVERSITY

It is one thing to recognize the existence of racial diversity and another to define it in terms of the underlying genetic facts. We shall attempt the latter after familiarizing the reader with specific examples of types of genetic diversity among human groups. Our discussion assumes that racial diversity has a genetic basis and is not exclusively conditioned by environment. This premise is undoubtedly true for many of the differences among groups which are studied by the physical anthropologist. Color of skin and hair; shape of hair, nose, and lips; amount of body hair; prominence of cheekbones, and large differences in stature and in many other traits are highly independent of the climatic, nutritional, or cultural environments in which human beings are reared. Whether or not there are mental differences of genetic nature among races will be discussed in the next chapter.

Genetic analyses of the main differences between human races are few and incomplete. Such differences are probably based on differences at several if not many loci. Some examples are the dark pigmentation of the Negroids and the lighter of most of the Caucasoids; the kinky hair of the former and the straight or wavy hair of the latter; the different configurations of lips, noses, eyelids, and other facial features among Mongoloids, Negroids, and Caucasoids; and the differences in body build of African Pygmies, Hottentots, and Polynesians.

Results of crosses between members of the different races consist mostly of data on first-generation hybrids. The phenotypes of such hybrids are mixtures of dominant and intermediate expression of individual traits.

Thus, the hair type of first-generation mulattoes is similar to that of the negro parent, while the pigmentation is intermediate between negro and white.

It is not correct to use the words dominance, recessiveness, or intermediateness in a genetic sense for these first-generation hybrid phenotypes. The genetic terms were coined for the types of expression of heterozygous allelic pairs in comparison to the homozygotes (A^1A^2 as compared to A^1A^1 and A^2A^2). Whether the distinguishing racial traits are based on allelic differences at single loci will remain unknown until later generations have been studied. Most of the limited number of such studies are fragmentary, but it is safe to say that, in general, the genetic differences underlying opposite traits are polygenic. Thus, while the kinky hair of the negro appears in first-generation negro-white hybrids, in later generations a whole array of different hair types is found. First-generation children from marriages between American Indians and negroes frequently show the straight hair of the former, but, again, various grades and types of hair occur in later generations. The polygenic determination of pigmentation differences between whites and negroes has been discussed earlier[1].... The discussion of the inheritance of quantitative characters given there is relevant to the majority of the main racial character.

Another difficulty in the genetic interpretation of phenotypic differences among races is the possibility that different genotypes have resulted in similar phenotypes. Thus, the absence of crosses between such groups as African negroes and the small groups of negritos in Southern India, Malaya, Java, and the Philippines leaves an open question of whether their similar characteristics of skin color and hair type have the same genetic basis or are the phenotypically similar products of different genotypes.

Antigenic Differences

In order to avoid such uncertainties, anthropologists in recent decades have studied racial differences in genetically well-defined characters, particularly blood groups and types of hemoglobin. Two discoveries of general importance have resulted from these studies: (1) there are striking differences in the frequencies of various alleles in different races and racial variants; and (2) these differences are usually merely relative. Most human groups have the same array of alleles at the different loci, even if in different proportions. Table 1 shows that the blood-group alleles I^{A1}, L^{Ms}, R^0, R^1, R^2, and probably P and Fy^a are found in all six human groups listed. Several other alleles, such as r', r'', R^z, and Lu^a, which are rare wherever they occur, may well be present even in those races for which they have not yet been recorded.

---

[1] [Ed. note: See Curt Stern, *Principles of Human Genetics* (1960), chapter 18.]

TABLE 1. FREQUENCIES IN PER CENT, OF
VARIOUS BLOOD GROUP ALLELES IN SIX RACIAL GROUPS
BELONGING TO FOUR MAJOR RACES

Genetic Loci	Caucasoid		Negroid	Mongoloid		Australoid
	Basque	Other		Asian	Amer. Indian	
I^{A1}	20	20–30	10–20	15–25	0–55	20–45
I^{A2}	3	4–8	5	0	0	0
I^B	0–3	5–20+	10–20	15–30	0	0
L^{MS} }	55	20–30	7–20	4	15–30	0
L^{Ms} }		30	30–50	56	50–70	26
L^{NS} }	45	5–10	2–12	1	2–6	0
$L^{N}{}_{s}$ }		30–40	30–50	38	5–20	74
r	48–53	30–40	10–20	0–7	0	0
r'	1–3	0–2	0–6	0	0–17	13
r''	1	0–2	0–1	0–3	0–3	0
R^0	1	1–5	40–70	0–5	0–30	9
R^1	38–42	30–50	5–15	60–76	30–45	56
R^2	5–7	10–15	6–20	20–30	30–60	20
R^z	0	0–1	0	0–0.5	1–6	2
P	?	40–60	50–80	1–12	20–60	?
Lu^a	?	2–5	0–4	15–20	0–10	0
Fy^a	?	40	<10	?	0–90	?
Di^a	?	0+	0	90	0–25	0

Note: The frequencies given are sometimes based on a single or a few
samples. The ranges are based on from two to many samples. Altogether,
the data are somewhat selected and intended to show general trends only.
For details, consult the original sources: Boyd, Mourant, and Wiener and
Wexler.

There are, however, some alleles which are common in some races and
apparently absent in other: I^{A2} is restricted to Basques, other Caucasoids,
and Negroids; I^B appears in these groups as well as in Asian Mongoloids but
not in American Indians and Australian aborigines (Australoids); and r has
a high frequency in Basques, other Caucasoids, and Negroids and a low
frequency in Asian Mongoloids but is lacking in American Indians and
Australoids.

The major races have long been differentiated from one another on the
basis of their external physical characters. It is significant that the study of
blood groups leads to a similar classification. Wiener, Boyd, and Mourant
have pointed out that most people can be classified into six "serologic

races," which coincide fairly well with the differentiation according to external physical characters. Caucasoids are characterized by possession of I^{A2} as well as I^{A1}, high frequency of r, and total or near absence of Di^a; Negroids, by possession of I^{A2} as well as I^{A1} and high frequency of R^0; Asian Mongoloids, by absence of I^{A2}, low frequency of L^{MS} and L^{NS}, and high frequency of R^1 and Fy^a American Indians, by absence of I^{A2}, I^B, and r and low frequency of L^{NS}; and Australoids, by absence of I^{A2}, I^B, L^{MS}, L^{NS}, and r and high frequency of L^{Ns}. The Basques of Spain and southern France belong physically to the Caucasoid race, though they are to some degree culturally and linguistically separate. (It is believed that they are the remnant of an early European population which has been largely replaced by later arrivals.) Serologically the Basques are distinguished by very low frequency of I^B and high frequency of r.

Table 1 shows also that within each racial group there is often great variability of allele frequencies. We shall later discuss some aspects of these very interesting and equally complex variations.

Differences in Hemoglobin Types

There are some striking associations between racial groups and incidences of alleles for certain types of hemoglobin. One of the most significant is the high frequency of the allele for hemoglobin C in Equatorial West Africa and its virtual absence elsewhere. The allele for sickle-cell hemoglobin is found in wider groups of African negroes as well as in various Mediterranean people and a few Asian groups, and the gene for thalassemia is restricted to Mediterraneans and dispersed populations of Asia. The very rare presence of these alleles in northern and western Europeans and their descendants in the United States is perhaps the result of past intermarriages with Mediterraneans. . . .

Other Differences in Allele Frequencies

The genetic "polymorphism" of blood-antigen types is certainly representative of a great number of other traits. The genetic basis of some of these polymorphic characters is more or less well known, but information on racial differences is limited. Among these traits are type of singing voice, "secretor" property, pattern of finger ridges, and ability to taste phenylthiocarbamide (PTC).

The proportions of people with basso or soprano voice decrease from northern to southern Europe. Assuming the correctness of Bernstein's theory of the inheritance of singing voices in Europeans by means of a pair of alleles . . . the gene frequency for the basso-soprano allele in the geographical range studied has been calculated. It was concluded to have a maximum of 61 per cent along the northwest coast of Germany and a minimum of about 12 per cent in Sicily. Although this specific interpretation of the polymorphism of singing voice has to be abandoned, there is undoubtedly a genetic basis for it, and differences in allele frequencies must account for the different frequencies of types of voice in different populations.

The frequency of the gene Se (for secretion of the ABH substances into body fluids) is approximately 50 per cent in Caucasoids, only 38 per cent in American negroes and probably less in African Negroids, and rises to nearly 100 per cent in American Indians.

TABLE 2. RACIAL VARIATIONS IN ABILITY TO TASTE PHENYLTHIOCARBAMIDE[a]

Racial group	No. tested	Tasters (%)
Australoids	152	51
American whites	>6,000	65–75
Egyptians	208	76
American negroes	>3,000	91
African negroes	>1,000	91–97
Chinese	>200	89–94
American Indians	>1,000	90–98

[a] Valls, 1958.

A final example concerns the ability to taste PTC. The frequency of tasters ranges from only 63 per cent among Arabs to 98 per cent among American Indians; expressed in terms of nontasters, these numbers are 37 and 2 per cent (Table 2). In view of the recessive nature of the allele for nontasting, we obtain a range of allelic frequencies from over 0.6 to 0.14. While there is little doubt about the hereditary nature of the taste-polymorphism, it is too early to assume that the differences in frequencies of tasters are the result of differences in the frequency of the t allele only. The somewhat variable frequency of the trait among whites and its sex modification in many racial groups suggest that when the frequency of modifying genes is studied, the interracial variability may be found to depend, at least in part, on genes at other loci.

There are some data on differences among races in frequencies of red-green color blindness and ability to smell hydrocyanic acid, but the evidence is insufficient for making valid comparisons.

The finding of so many relative differences in the frequencies of alleles suggests that even apparently absolute differences in traits between two races may be dependent on alleles which occur in both of them. If the differences in skin color between Negroids and Caucasoids are based on a polygenic system involving five or more loci, then it would be possible to account for the dark pigmentation of the African Negro by the presence of alleles for darkness with frequencies of, say, 99 per cent and presence of alleles for lightness of 1 per cent. Inversely, the Caucasoids may possess the alleles for darkness in frequencies of 1 per cent and those for lightness of 99 per cent. With such large, but not "all-or-nothing," differences in allele frequencies, practically all members of one group would be dark and practically all of the other group light.

A GENETIC DEFINITION OF RACE

We are now ready to approach the problem of a genetic definition of race. Let us begin with a discussion of a dictionary definition:

RACE. A division of mankind possessing constant traits, transmissible by descent, sufficient to characterize it as a distinct human type; a permanent variety of the genus *Homo*. . . ."

It will be seen immediately that this definition does not fit the anthropological concept of race. All people belonging to blood group O constitute a division of mankind fulfilling the specifications outlined; yet, this group of O people is composed of individuals from all anthropological subdivisions of man. Or, if a more superficially obvious character, e.g., albinism, were chosen, it would be true that albinos constitute a division of mankind according to the definition given, but individual albinos differ from each other in the most diverse respects.

It may be wondered whether the difference between anthropological races and "artificial" groups, such as those cited above, is essentially dependent upon the number of genic differences involved. This is not likely to be the case, although it is unknown how many loci are involved in racial differentiations. Whatever the number of the loci differentiating two specific races, the number will be different for another pair of races. Phenotypically, nearly or fully Caucasoid segregants are rarer among the offspring of first-generation hybrids between Caucasoids and Negroids than among the corresponding offspring of Causasoid-Mongoloid crossings. This suggests that a smaller number of genic loci is involved in the phenotypic differences between the latter two races. Whatever the number of loci concerned in the determination of these interracial differences, it would probably be possible to select groups of individuals within any one of the anthropological races which are distinguished by as many, or even more, intraracial genic differences. Yet, while the term race is applicable to Caucasoids and Mongoloids, it would not be applicable to two groups within the Caucasoids or Mongoloids which were defined artificially by the sum of alternative genotypes (and phenotypes) in regard to blood groups, hair color, eye color, taster ability, hair type, form of nose, mouth, etc., etc.

The dictionary definition would be improved if the following italicized words were added:

RACE. A division of mankind, *inhabiting a limited geographic area or areas, and . . ."*

The addition would then make the definition applicable to the majority of cases. However, there would be important exceptions. For example, gypsies are characterized by a number of physical features which separate them racially from typical Caucasoids; yet, they inhabit the same geographic areas as the latter. The same is true for the "racial minorities" all over the globe. Nor are the exceptions restricted to minorities. In some areas of the southern United States, Caucasoids and Negroids are present in equal proportions.

These exceptions all have in common an element closely related to geographic distribution. In the past, gypsies and other fractions of geographically coexistent populations were limited to geographic areas different from those of the rest of the population with whom they now live together. Should we, then, improve the definition further by adding a reference to the historical background which originally involved geographic separateness? Again, this would not satisfy the facts completely. There is good evidence that many of the now existing minor racial types are the results of past mingling of originally geographically separated races. Thus, the Japanese are believed to be the offspring of Malayan, Mongolian, and, perhaps, Polynesian immigrants into Japan who have intermarried among one another and also with the aboriginal Ainus. Knowledge of this hybrid origin does not run counter to the recognition of the Japanese as a single, somewhat distinct racial group.

What, then, is the difference between a country where gypsies and other racial types occupy the same territory, and Japan, where descendants of different races, too, live in the same geographical region? The difference results from the two different systems of mating. In respect to gypsies, barriers exist which lead to preferential marriages of gypsies with gypsies, and of nongypsies with nongypsies. Among the Japanese, on the other hand, mating barriers between the originally separate races have largely disappeared. The anthropological term "race" thus becomes allied to the genetic term "isolate."

A genetic definition of race must take into account the fact that all populations consist of individuals who are heterozygous for many loci and many alleles. There is no "pure" race — a designation which, in genetic terms, would signify homozygosity and isogeneity of all individuals.

The study of blood-group genes has shown that races often differ only in the relative frequencies of alleles, and this phenomenon may be true for most loci. A race, then, is a group of individuals whose corporate genic content, sometimes called the *gene pool*, differs from that of other groups. The members of a race retain the differences, more or less, over the course of generations because geographic or cultural isolation results in only a small amount of genic exchange between them and members of other races. We may now summarize our discussion by the following definition:

"RACE. A geographically or culturally more or less isolated division of mankind whose corporate genic content (gene pool) differs from that of all other similar isolates."

Does this definition coincide with the everyday concept of race? The definition includes this concept but goes beyond it. It fits the anthropological characterization of the major groups of mankind as well as of the minor racial types, since they are all endowed with different genic contents and are more or less isolated from one another by geographic or social barriers. In addition, the genetic definition considers as "races" different groups of individuals who are fully or partly isolated but whose genic contents are so slightly different from one another that our language has no word to characterize these groups as separate entities. For example, during World War II, it was found in northern Wales that the ABO frequencies of blood donors with Welsh family names differed from those of donors with non-Welsh names (Table 3). There were more O and B individuals and fewer A and AB among the Joneses, Williamses, Robertses, and other people with Welsh surnames than among the people with English names. The differences in allele frequencies for both sexes are significant. Obviously, then the genic content of the group of Joneses, Williamses, etc., is distinct from that of the rest of the population among whom they live, a difference which can only be due to some genetic isolation between the two groups. Yet, we would hardly call the Joneses, Williamses, etc., a different race.

TABLE 3. PERCENTAGE FREQUENCIES OF ABO BLOOD GROUPS AMONG DONORS WITH WELSH AND NON-WELSH FAMILY NAMES[a]

Men and single women donors with	No. of individuals	O	A	B	AB
Welsh family names	909	52.7	35.0	9.7	2.6
Non-Welsh family names	1,091	46.6	42.0	8.3	3.2

[a] Roberts, Ann. Eugen., II, 1942.

The dictionary definition cited earlier tries to circumvent the difficulty by inserting the specification that the traits which are possessed by a race should be "sufficient to characterize it as a distinct human type." Unfortunately, however, the definition does not clarify what is to be regarded as "sufficient" for this purpose.

The difficulty is inherent in the facts of nature. There exists a continuous series of degrees of difference in the genic content of isolates, from the slight differences between the Welsh isolate and the population of which it is a part to the obvious differences among the major races of the anthropologists. The biological phenomenon is the same, irrespective of the size of the difference. The basic genetic similarity of all differences among isolates results in arbitrary decisions as to when to apply the term race and when to regard its use as inappropriate. A problem of this kind is frequently met. Natural bodies of flowing water of different width and depth are called brooks, creeks, streams, and rivers. No sharp definition can be drawn up to separate these different terms from one another, although there is no doubt about which term to apply to the Mississippi or, conversely, to a very narrow and shallow current.

There is not only a wide range of genic diversity between different groups but also many degrees of isolation. Absolute isolation of different human groups hardly exists, since contacts between such groups have always resulted in some interbreeding. The degree of isolation, itself, is variable not only from group to group but also with time. In historical periods of mass migration, barriers to interchange of genes have always been decreased. Technical developments in modern transportation, which facilitate and increase contact between formerly geographically isolated groups, have led to equivalent results. Global wars, too, with their shifting of large military forces into foreign areas, have contributed to the breakup of genetic isolation, either through legally sanctioned marriages or from illegitimate unions.

Frequencies of Specific Genotypes in Different Races

Let us assume that two races possess n loci, $A^1A^2, B^1B^2, C^1C^2 \cdots N^1N^2$, each of which occurs in two allelic forms, with the frequencies $p_{A^1}, q_{A^2};$ $p_{B^1}, q_{B^2}; p_{C^1}, q_{C^2} \cdots p_{N^1}, q_{N^2}$ in race I and the frequencies $p'_{A^1}, q'_{A^2}; p'_{B^1}, q'_{B^2};$ $p'_{C^1}, q'_{C^2} \cdots p'_{N^1}, q'_{N^2}$ in race II. In both races, there will be individuals who are homozygous or heterozygous for either one of the alleles of any one locus. Consequently, an N^1N^1 individual taken from race I cannot be assigned to his race on the basis of his constitution at the one N locus. However, a priori, the probabilities of his belonging to race I or II may be different, the proportion of the expected frequencies of N^1N^1 individuals in the two races being $(p_{N^1})^2$ and $(p'_{N^1})^2$, respectively.

If we assume that the allele frequencies p and q for every locus are 1/10 and 9/10 in race I, and that the allele frequencies p′ and q′ for every locus are 9/10 and 1/10 in race II, the probability that an N^1N^1 individual will occur in race I becomes $(p_{N^1})^2 = 1/100$, and that he will appear in race II $(p'_{N^1})^2 = 81/100$. Thus, the probabilities that an N^1N^1 individual will be a member of race I or II differ from each other in the proportion 1:81, so that the probability that an N^1N^1 individual belongs to race I is 1/82 and to race II is 81/82. If an individual's genotype were known to be $A^1A^1N^1N^1$, his chance of occurring in race I would be only $(1/100)^2 = 1/10,000$ as opposed to the chance $(81/100)^2 = 6,561/10,000$ of his occurring in race II. Therefore, the probability of an $A^1A^1N^1N^1$ belonging to race I and not to race II is 1 out of 6,562. Clearly, the more loci known, the more reliable may be the assignment of an individual to his race. However, not only is there a small uncertainty, even in favorable cases, but there are genotypes which have rather similar probabilities or even an equal probability of belonging to either race. Among these genotypes are the complete heterozygotes. The probability of a person being heterozygous for n loci is $(2pq)^n$ in race I, and $(2p'q')^n$ in race II. In our example where pq $(1/10 \cdot 9/10)$ is equal to $p'q'(9/10 \cdot 1/10)$, there would be an even chance that an A^1A^2, $B^1B^2 \cdots N^1N^2$ individual would belong to either race.

In general, gene frequencies in two races will not be as "symmetrical" (1/10:9/10 vs. 9/10:1/10) as in our two assumed populations. Consequently, it will usually be possible to discriminate with a high probability between the two possibilities. It must be emphasized, however, that these calculations apply only to races that are absolutely isolated genetically and not to races between which there is some degree of miscegenation. Particularly between the minor anthropological subdivisions, intermarriages are frequent, or have been so in the past. For example, in the course of many centuries, the Nordic, Alpine, and Mediterranean racial variants of Europe have interchanged genes freely. Consequently, allele frequencies for different loci are probably rather similar in these racial subtypes. The result is that it is often difficult to place a given individual in one or another of these groups. Indeed, such an attempt may become meaningless, since segregants from the same parental pair may show phenotypes characteristic of different minor racial divisions.

In view of the imperfections of any definition of the term race and particularly in view of the fateful misuses of the term, some geneticists are inclined to strike the word race from modern vocabulary, substituting words like "population" or "ethnic group." Since, however, the word race will probably remain in our language, it has been retained in this book and is used, without value judgment, in its scientific sense.

REFERENCES

Boyd, W. C.
  1950 *Genetics and the Races of Man.* Boston: Little, Brown.
  1950 Cold Spring Harbor Symposia on Quantitative Biology "Origin and Evolution of Man," *Cold Spring Harbor Syp. Quant. Biol.*, 15:1–425.
Mourant, A. E.
  1954 *The Distribution of the Human Blood Groups.* Springfield, Ill.: C. C. Thomas

Rosin, S.
    1956   "Die Verteilung der ABO-Blutgruppen in der Schweiz."
            Arch. Julius Klaus-Stift., 31:17–127.
Vallas, A. Medina
    1958   "Estudio antropogenetico de la capacidad gustativa para
            la fenitiocarbamida," *Fac. Cienc. Univ. Madrid.*
Wiener, A. S. and I. B. Wexler
    1958   *Heredity of the Blood Groups.* New York: Grune &
            Stratton.

12   Genetic Aspects of Race Mixture

Whenever history brought together two or more races in the same territory, unions of persons of different races occurred. This interbreeding, called *miscegenation* (from the Latin *miscere* = to mix, *genus* = race), proceeded sometimes at a slow pace and at other times rapidly. Often, complete "amalgamation" or "assimilation" of the different groups was the end result. Before the particulate nature of the hereditary material was understood, it was thought that such joining of the germ plasms of the races would result in a new, homogeneous population. The recognition of the existence of separate genes has, of course, changed this expectation. Recombination of the different alleles brought into the gene pool of a mixed population results in the production of numerous diverse genotypes in proportions that are predictable if the allele frequencies are known.

Segregation of allelic differences brought into a mixed population should increase its variability, as compared with the variability within each parent race. However, a comparison of the variability of the mixed population with that *between* the parent races shows a decrease in variability, since statistical measurements of variability are less dependent upon the rare extreme variants of group than upon the distribution of the majority around the mean. Expressed differently, the *intra*racial variability within the mixed group is less than the *inter*racial variability before mixture.

The specific application of these considerations to human miscegenation on a population scale depends on the number of loci, on the phenotypic expression of polygenic genotypes, and on the relative sizes of the two parent races involved in any specific crossing.

In a population derived from negro-white mixtures, a trait like skin color shows a greater variability than is found in the parental races. Other traits may be less variable. In fact, it has often been found that many traits do not vary appreciably more in the mixed population than within the parental groups. There are several ways in which this low variability may be interpreted. Perhaps the most probable explanation, advanced by H. J.

From *Principles of Human Genetics,* Second Edition by Curt Stern. W. H. Freeman and Company. Copyright © 1960.

Muller, is that if the intraracial variability of a character in each of the two parent races is due to numerous recessives of individually rather low allele frequencies, and if these genes are at different loci in the two races, then the variability of the mixed race would be lower than that of either of the parent races. This is a consequence of the relative lowering of each allele frequency due to "dilution" (by intermarriage) of the concentration of alleles present in one, but not in the other, race. This dilution results in a lower frequency of homozygous recessives in the new isolate and, thus, in a lower number of phenotypes which vary from the mean. Opposite in effect to this lowering of the variability is the segregation of interracial differences. It is not to be expected that the two factors affecting variability, dilution and segregation, will always compensate for each other completely. Hence, a mixed race may show increase of variability in some traits, decrease in others, and no, or little, change in still others. That the changes in variability observed in mixed populations of negro-white, Tahitian-white, or Hottentot-white intermarriages have been small may be taken as an indication that the differences between individuals within the parental groups are of magnitude comparable with the differences between the groups.

NEGRO-WHITE MISCEGENATION IN THE UNITED STATES

One of the most important examples of miscegenation, both because of the number of individuals involved and because of its contemporary historical significance, is that between the white and negro populations of the United States. Neither group was racially uniform, in the sense that neither consisted of a single random-mating isolate, but the whites stemmed mostly from western and central Europe and thus, probably, were less differentiated into genetically different groups than the negroes, who came from widely separated parts of Africa. The slight initial genic isolation between the white subgroups has had a strong tendency to disappear, although geographic and religious factors, as well as new immigration, have retarded their complete amalgamation. The different negro subraces, likewise, underwent a process, by intermarriages, of gradual transformation into a single Negro race.

Superimposed on these two separate processes of amalgamation within each of the two major races, miscegenation has occurred and continues to occur. Negroes, whites, and American Indians have been involved in this miscegenation, but the discussion will be restricted to negroes and whites, since the over-all contribution of the American Indians to the gene pool of the other groups has been very small. This is proven by comparisons of the frequencies of blood-group alleles among the three groups.

The Colonial period and the succeeding decades before the emancipation of the negro slaves were the most significant periods of miscegenation. Miscegenation, primarily between white men and negro women for more than a hundred years, had led to the existence of a very large number of first-generation hybrid mulattoes. Although half their genes were derived from whites and half from negroes, socially the mulattoes were classified together with negroes, as "colored" people. Accordingly, they married either with each other or with negroes who had no white ancestors. The result of this system of mating at first was an infiltration of "white" genes into the colored population without an appreciable reciprocal gene flow from negroes to whites. Lately, as a result of the segregation of alleles concerned with the more obvious characters which differentiate whites from negroes, colored parents have produced children whose skin pigmentation, hair type, and facial features are similar enough to those of whites for them to "pass" for whites. The segregants undoubtedly carry various combinations of less obviously recognizable genes of negro derivation than those responsible for the traits mentioned above. They also contain heterozygously recessive alleles concerned with some of the more obvious differences between whites and negroes, as well as alleles which, in specific combinations with alleles at other loci, determine genotypes characteristic of negroes. Consequently, individuals who have "crossed the color line" and have "white" children represent a channel through which various genes derived from negroes flow into the white population. Thus, the initially one-sided gene flow, from the white to the negro population, has developed into a mutual exchange of genes.

The frequency of white or near-white segregants is probably higher than would be expected from random mating within the negro population. There is a tendency for positive assortative mating among negro individuals; for example, lightly pigmented persons preferentially marry light ones. This mating preference favors the reconstitution of homozygosity for pigmentation alleles derived from the Caucasoid race; that is, it favors the production of individuals who function in the transfer of genes from the negro to the white population.

The process of extraction of alleles for light pigmentation from the negro population and the return, by means of "crossing the color line," of these light alleles to the white population from which they were derived is bound to continue — with the result that the negro population will be drained of those alleles or combinations of alleles which make for the more striking anthropological white phenotypes, particularly light pigmentation. It may be expected, therefore, that the American negro population, whose mean coloration is lighter than that of the original Africans, will gradually darken again due to selective "back-migration" of white genes.

This process will be counteracted by continued miscegenation, legitimate or illegitimate, between whites and negroes. The time span of a human generation is not negligible if it is measured against historical periods of one or two centuries. For whites and negroes in the United States, this time span certainly has been much too short to result in a complete breakup of genic isolation. Possibly, in the future, miscegenation will increase, or continue long enough, so that a single random population will finally be produced. It is more likely that selective mating of whites with whites and negroes with negroes will uphold the relative genic isolation between the two groups for a long time, but that an inconspicuous gene flow in both directions, as described, will continue.

What will the final consequences of these processes be, in terms of the over-all genic differences which existed between the original whites and negroes? There will be a tendency toward equalizing the frequencies of any one allele in the white and negro groups, except for those genes which are concerned with the most obvious racial characters. This equalization of numerous allele frequencies will proceed fastest for loci which are not chromosomally linked to those genes for which racially assortative mating exists, as for genes concerned with pigmentation. Even for loci linked to them, crossing over will tend to establish an equilibrium in which the original racial linkage combinations will occur no more frequently than exchange combinations. The result will be that the white and negro populations will become similar for most allele frequencies for which they were different before miscegenation and will remain different only in those probably fewer loci which contribute in an appreciable degree to superficial diversity of Caucasoid and Negroid individuals.

The gradual breakup of isolation for most genes has an important bearing on the genetic evaluation of segregants in future generations. Apart from genes causing obvious phenotypic differences, the least African-like members of the white group will belong to the same array of genotypes and with equal probability distribution as the most African-like members of the negro group. Even at the present time, the skin pigmentation of white-negro segregants is but a poor indicator of their total genotypes.

THE CONSEQUENCES OF MISCEGENATION

Many persons regard miscegenation as undesirable. So far as it focuses attention on sociological problems arising from unsolved difficulties in the attitudes of races toward one another, the question of the undesirability of miscegenation does not fall within the province of the biologist. Nor is it the geneticist's task to evaluate the historical consequences of a gradual disappearance of the diversity of cultures as a possible result of extensive racial intermingling. Nor are the psychological conflicts which may confront an individual whose parents belong to two racial groups with widely different cultures of primary genetic concern. The opinion is often expressed, however, that there are biological reasons for the undesirability of racial hybridization. The most important arguments for this opinion center around views concerning (1) the breakup of well-adapted racial genotypes; (2) the origin, in the first or later generations, of disharmonious gene combinations; and (3) the superiority of certain races over others. We shall take up these arguments in the order given and further divide our discussion by considering physical characters first and mental ones later.

Physical Traits

Racial Adaptations. It is indeed possible that some of the major racial physical characters are the result of selective forces which acted against certain genotypes in one isolate and favored their appearance in others. Such adaptations may be in response to environmental (ecological) factors. With pigmentation, which has often been cited in this connection, two different and opposing selective forces are known: an advantage, in that dark pigmentation provides a shield against strong sunlight, which may cause burns; and a disadvantage, in that, as a shield, it may decrease the amount of vitamin D which is formed in the body from ergosterol by natural irradiation. The darker pigmentation of the inhabitants of tropical regions thus may be regarded as an adaptive protection against intense sunlight, and the lighter pigmentation of northern people as an adaptation which permits enough of the less intense light rays to penetrate the skin and help manufacture vitamin D. Other traits also have been interpreted as ecologically adaptive. The long, narrow nose of Caucasoids is thought by some anthropologists to allow for warming up cold outside air before it enters the lungs, while the shorter and broader nose of Africans seems more suited to their evenly warmer surroundings. The lean physique, with its long arms and legs, of inhabitants of deserts, whether in North or South Africa or in Australia, seems to be an adaptation to the heat of these regions, since the relatively large amount of body surface provides for more cooling evaporation than compact bodies.

It is difficult to prove the correctness of such interpretations, but it seems likely that some, even if not all, racial characters represent adaptations to the specific environments in which the major races evolved. It is questionable, however, whether the value of these adaptations is still as great as it may have been in the past. Technological developments, particularly those of the last century, have so greatly changed man's environment and his ability to cope with it (and greater changes are bound to come) that adaptations to former environments are becoming largely obsolete; i.e., they lose their positive selective value. If this is so, then the breakup of formerly adaptive racial genotypes is of little concern.

Regardless of whether many racial characteristics are of ecological adaptive significance, the proper working of any human body depends on the harmonious adjustment of its different parts and functions. We may speak of this adjustment as *internal adaptiveness.* The blood-pumping function of the heart must be fitted to body size; the size and activity of the different glands of internal secretion must be delicately related to one another; the proportions of limbs to trunk and of various bones to one another must be fitted within the limits of normality. It may be wondered whether different human races contain different gene combinations which provide, within each race, the necessary internal harmony. If this were so, the breakup of former racial isolates would justifiably be a matter of concern. It appears, however, that internal adaptiveness should not be conceived as the ability of an organism to fit together, in a harmonious way, separately determined parts. Rather, the sizes and the degrees of function of organs are genetically provided with a wide range of possible expressions, and the specific expressivity that will result is dependent on developmental interrelations. The marvelous ability of an organism to regulate — that is, to respond in an adaptive way to a great variety of conditions — is responsible to a large degree for internal adaptiveness. If one kidney is removed, the other kidney compensates for the loss by increasing its activity; or, if a bone is broken and heals in an abnormal fashion, it rebuilds internal structure in a new manner best fitted to cope with the different mechanical stresses imposed on it. It may be assumed, similarly, that, in general, a developing human being will form during his embryogeny and later an internally adaptively balanced system, regardless of the gene combinations he inherits from his ancestral race or races.

Disharmonious Gene Combinations. The regulatory abilities, or developmental homeostasis, of organisms makes the occurrence of disharmonious phenotypes rare. It is, however, conceivable that different parts of the body may sometimes be genetically determined in a sufficiently independent manner so that actual incongruities may arise. Such disharmonies occur occasionally when different species of animals or plants are crossed with each other. Disharmonies have also been described within a single species, namely, in crosses of widely different breeds of dogs. Thus, some hybrids between a short-legged, slender-bodied dachshund and a long-legged, heavy St. Bernard have the short legs of the first and the large body of the second breed, so that the body drags on the ground.

As instructive as this example is in showing the limits of regulatory development, it is hardly comparable to human race crosses. The dachshund is a disproportionately dwarfed animal, corresponding to chondrodystrophic human dwarfs and not to naturally occurring human races. Differences between human races seem to be dependent, not on a few genes which independently determine striking properties of parts, but rather on polygenic combinations of which each single gene affects to a small degree one or more characters, so that the various allelic combinations of the system are able to direct development toward a reasonably harmonious system. This seems to be the explanation for the fact that no well-substantiated examples of disharmonious constitution resulting from miscegenation have been reported.

In this connection, a very special case may be recalled: the Rh incompatibility between pregnant Rh-negative mothers and their Rh-positive embryos. If two isolated human races existed, one isogenic for the allele R, the other for r, the pathological phenomenon of Rh-determined erythroblastosis fetalis would not be known in either race. If the two races intermarried, many disharmonious mother-child combinations would appear, resulting in a disease which might then be called typical for miscegenation. There are races — the Mongoloids, for example — which have a frequency for the allele r of nearly 0.0. No known race has an r allele frequency of 1.0, but intermediate frequencies occur. These differing allele frequencies account for the apparent absence of Rh erythroblastosis in Mongoloids and presence in Caucasoids.

Let us imagine the immigration of whites into China and of Chinese into a country inhabited by whites, and the miscegenation of the immigrants with the native race. In China, no erythroblastosis fetalis will occur in the first generation of intermarriages between Chinese women and white men, since all Chinese women are Rh positive and not subject to Rh iso-immunization. However, in the marriages between white immigrant women and Chinese men, the disease will affect some of the children, since about 16 per cent of white women are Rh negative and can be iso-immunized by fetuses, all of whom have inherited the R allele from their fathers. In later generations, the relative frequency of erythroblastosis in the population of China, now of mixed Chinese-white origin, will be less than in the first generation, since the frequency of the r allele and, therefore, of rr women will be lower than among the original whites due to the decreased frequency of r after dilution with the R allele of the original Chinese. Still, the frequency of the r allele will be higher than it was before the white immigrants came. Hence, rr women will result as expected from random mating, and some of them will have erythroblastotic pregnancies. Thus, from the point of view of the Chinese, and judged purely from Rh incompatibility, miscegenation will have had permanently bad effects.

The results will be very different in the "white country" with its Chinese immigrants. None of the Chinese women married to white men will add to the fetal disease, but Chinese men married to white women will cause the appearance of a higher frequency of erythroblastotic children than among marriages of white men and white women. In later generations, the frequency of the r allele in the white population, now of mixed white-Chinese origin, will be *lower* than before the RR immigrants came; the frequency of rr women will be correspondingly less, and the incidence of the disease will be lower. Thus, again, judged purely from Rh incompatibility, miscegenation will be found to be permanently beneficial.

Racial "Superiority." The argument that certain races are superior to others and that miscegenation involving the superior type is bound to destroy its excellence has rarely been used in connection with purely physical characteristics. While it is likely — though not established — that some races have a better genetic endowment than other races in regard to normal eyesight, hearing acuity, endurance of extreme temperature, longevity, and so on, it is improbable that some races contain many or all of these desirable traits and that others lack most or all of them. It would be difficult to give an objective rating to races, because they form different combinations of genic endowments — some resulting in many excellent phenotypes of one kind, and others in less frequent excellent phenotypes of another kind.

The same difficulty in evaluating relative superiority exists in regard to what has sometimes been called *race pathology,* the study of diseases in relation to race. It has been found that certain diseases are nearly unknown in some races and that the frequency of other diseases varies from race to race. Environmental differences may account for many such variations. Moreover, where a genetic basis is well established, differences in the frequencies of the disease-conditioning alleles often account for the observed racial differences. Examples of such differences ... are thalassemia, which is mostly restricted to people of Mediterranean racial background, and sickle-cell anemia to negroes. The frequency of erythroblastosis fetalis depends on the highly variable frequency of the different R alleles in different races. Other more or less well-substantiated examples are the rare occurrence of scarlet fever among Mongoloids and Negroids as compared to Caucasoids, and the less severe course of the disease when it does appear in the former races; the less frequent occurrence of tuberculosis among Jews as compared to members of many other racial variants; and the more frequent occurrence of infantile amaurotic idiocy among Jews as compared to Caucasoid non-Jews.

Public health statistics contain further data on different frequencies of various diseases in different racial groups, and the causes of some of these diseases are known to have a genetic component. Frequently, however, the penetrance of this component is dependent, to an unknown degree, on complex external circumstances, such as social status and its interrelation with housing, nutrition, type of occupation, etc. It would, therefore, be premature to draw general conclusions regarding differences in racial frequency of pathogenic alleles.

The examples given for racial differences in hereditary diseases should not overshadow the large number of diseases for which no striking difference exists. One of the most extensive compilations on the subject is Komia's two-volume *Pedigrees of Hereditary Diseases and Abnormalities Found in the Japanese Race,* which comprised probably all such pedigrees ever published in Japan up to 1943. The list is similar to a recounting of a great number of the frequent and the rarer abnormalities well known among Western peoples: albinism, ichthyosis, harelip, arachnodactyly, hemophilia, diabetes mellitus, cataract, blue sclerotics, partial and total color blindness, Huntington's chorea, amaurotic idiocy, deaf-mutism, and many others. In contrast to genes which differentiate the normal characters of Japanese from those of Caucasoids, most of the alleles for pathological traits are found in both groups. Specific allele frequencies are not known, however, and it is likely that quantitative differences exist in the incidence of alleles involved in the different diseases. It is also possible that some hereditary, apparently identical diseases or abnormalities in the two racial groups may be caused by genes at different loci.

If two different races possess different frequencies of certain pathogenic alleles, miscegenation will result in a decrease of the allele frequency in the mixed population, as compared to the frequency in the original race which has the higher incidence. As we have seen earlier, for recessive traits, this will result in a lower *total* frequency of the affected homozygotes. Miscegenation, then, like the breakup of isolates within racial groups, will result in a reduction of pathological conditions. This may be illustrated by an example for sickle-cell anemia. If, in a racial isolate of 1,000,000 people, the frequency of $Hb_1{}^S$ is 6 per cent, then $0.06^2 \cdot 10^6 = 3,600$ individuals are affected by the homozygous disease. Should miscegenation occur with another isolate consisting of 9,000,000 people in whom $Hb_1{}^S$ is virtually absent, then after panmixis only 360 affected individuals would be produced.

Heterosis. Hybridization between different species or breeds of animals or plants often results in increased size, productiveness, and resistance to diseases or other unfavorable conditions of the environment. This phenomenon has been referred to as *the stimulating effects of hybridity, hybrid vigor,* or *heterosis.* The causes of heterosis may be diverse in different crosses, or different causes may be jointly effective in a single cross. Indeed, full clarification of the phenomenon of heterosis has not been obtained, but two main theories seem to contain important elements of truth, as demonstrated by experimental tests.

One theory, in simplified form, is that vigor results from the collaboration of many loci; that different species or breeds are not likely to carry all the favorable alleles at the various loci concerned; and that, therefore, hybrids may combine in their genotype favorable alleles from both parents. If these favorable alleles are dominant, then their effect in the first-generation hybrids will be apparent as increased vigor. Theoretical examples of genotypes fitting this explanation have been given . . . on polygenic inheritance, the simplest case being a pair of *AAbb* and *aaBB* parents and their *AaBb* hybrid. The other important theory concerning causes of heterosis assumes that heterozygosity of single loci may result in increased vigor as compared to the vigor of the constituent homozygotes; in other words, the heterozygous constitution AA' may confer on an organism a more vigorous phenotype than either AA or A'A'.

The first of the two theories depends on the existence of dominant genes for vigor. Such dominance has been well established in specific cases — for example, by Mendel, in peas, for an allele for tall, over dwarf, size. Similarly, in mice, normal size is dominant over pituitary dwarfism. Although no conclusive evidence is available, it is possible that normal breeds may differ in both dominant and recessive genes for vigor. If two isogenic breeds are, respectively, *AABB* and *aabb* where *A* is a dominant and *b* a recessive allele for increased vigor, then the hybrids, *AaBb*, would show no change in vigor if the A allele for increased and the B allele for decreased vigor balance each other (Figure 1, I). If dominant genes for vigor are in excess over recessives, heterosis will result (Figure 1, II); and if the recessive genes for vigor are in excess (or to say it differently, if dominant genes for decreased vigor are in excess of those for increased vigor), then the offspring of hybridization will be less vigorous than either parent (Figure 1, III). The breakdown of human isolates within a given race, as well as miscegenation between major racial groups, may well result in no change of some traits, improvement of others, and deterioration of still others.

The same may be true if the second theory of heterosis holds. In addition to increased vigor of heterozygotes for a single locus, mutual interference in the action of two alleles may result in decreased phenotypic effectiveness. Very often, heterozygosity for single loci has no perceptible effect.

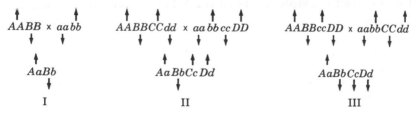

FIGURE 1

Three crosses between strains which differ in several loci concerned with increased or decreased vigor. Because of compensating effects of dominant and recessive genotypes at these loci, it is assumed that all strains are equally vigorous. Upward arrow = increased vigor; downward arrow = decreased vigor. I. If A increases and B decreases vigor, then the vigor of the hybrid is like that of the parents. II. If A, C, and D increase, and B decreases vigor, then the vigor of the hybrid is increased. III. If A increases, and B, C, and D decrease vigor, then the vigor of the hybrid is decreased.

Heterosis and Human Stature. It is well known that the average body size has increased during the past century in various European countries, the United States, and Japan. Part of this increase undoubtedly is the result of improved external conditions. In addition, it has been suggested that the breakdown of isolates has furnished a genetic basis for heterosis. The most impressive study is that by Hulse on various physical measurements of the descendants of villagers from the Swiss district of Ticino. Because the villages in this mountain district are rather isolated from one another, a very high percentage of marriages has been between individuals within the same village. As a result of this inbreeding, many inhabitants of a given village have specific traits, such as big noses, which distinguish them from inhabitants of other villages. Hulse has compared the offspring of parents from the same village (endogamous marriages) with those of parents from two villages (exogamous marriages). Each of the two groups of offspring could be further subdivided into (1) those who remained in their native area, (2) those who had emigrated to California, and (3) those who were born in California of immigrant parents. It is noteworthy that these data show a decided influence of the environment, in that the men born in Switzerland were about 4 cm shorter than those born in California (Table 1). More important than this, however, is the fact that, in all three subdivisions, the mean stature of the exogamous group was approximately 2 cm greater than that of the endogamous one, the over-all difference being statistically significant. As with stature, several other physical measurements gave larger mean dimensions for the exogamous than for the endogamous group. It is likely that a common cause underlies these differences: a prolonged period of bodily growth in the children and young adults of exogamous parentage. This is interesting in view of the findings by Morton that the birth weight of Japanese infants from nonconsanguineous, exogamous marriages was not greater than that from consanguineous, endogamous ones. It is possible that these offspring might differ in size in adulthood, after completion of growth.

An interpretation of the Swiss data in terms of heterosis is based on the assumption that the individuals who enter into exogamous marriages are not genetically different from those who marry endogamously. As far as is known, this is true.

The inhabitants of the different Swiss villages are, of course, all members of the same racial group. It is not known whether heterosis also occurs in interracial mating, but it would seem likely.

Mental Traits

There is no doubt that racial differences in psychological traits exist. Attitudes vary among different races, and their study is the object of

TABLE 1. MEAN STATURE, IN CENTIMETERS,
OF ADULT MALE OFFSPRING OF EXOGAMOUS
AND ENDOGAMOUS MARRIAGES OF SWISS
NATIVES OR THEIR DESCENDANTS[a]

Subgroup	Exogamous	Endogamous
(a) Swiss	168.51	166.21
(b) Emigrants	168.71	166.90
(c) Californians	172.33	170.50

[a] Hulse, 1958.

special sciences, such as social anthropology. It is clearly true that psychological attributes of races are greatly influenced by the particular historical, cultural, and sociological environment. It is difficult enough to define an over-all social psychology, but even when some valid approximation can be made, it seems to apply only to specific historical periods, or, if the race occupies different parts of the globe, only to specific regions. Differences in group psychology are also well known in different social layers of populations presumably rather genetically homogeneous.

. . . The study of the hereditary components of mental differences among individuals is still in its infancy. Progress is slow, mainly because of the lack of tools for accurately measuring mental traits independent of the environmental factors which are known to influence them. No determination of allele frequencies concerning normal mental attributes in different races has been made, nor will such a determination be possible until specific genes can be singled out for study. At present, all inferences regarding differences in the mental endowment of different races remain conjectures. Nevertheless, such conjectures are justifiable, provided that their hypothetical nature is kept in mind.

Biological arguments against miscegenation as it concerns mental traits assume that there are basic mental differences among races and that these are at least partly determined by different genetic endowment. Such discussions emphasize the first two arguments which were discussed in connection with physical traits, namely, the breakup of well-adapted racial genotypes and the origin of disharmonious gene combinations, as well as the third, the supposed existence of superior races. "The psyche," writes von Verschuer, "is a more sensitive reagent [than the body]. Disharmony of genes, therefore, will probably become apparent more easily in psychological than in physical disturbances." He adds, significantly — and scientifically — "There exists, however, a lack of really convincing data." An opposite point of view is held by other writers, who doubt the existence of well-adapted and of disharmonious gene combinations which affect mental traits. This opinion is guardedly expressed by Dobzhansky and Ashley

Montagu: "...genotype differences in personality traits, as between individuals and particularly as between races [are probably] relatively unimportant compared to their phenotypic plasticity. Instead of having his responses genetically fixed, as in other animal species, man is a species that invents its own responses, and it is out of this unique ability to invent, to improvise his responses, that his cultures are born." These authors, as well as others, stress evolutionary factors which "in all climes and at all times have favored genotypes which permit greater and greater educability and plasticity of mental traits...." In other words the range of expressivity of genotypes concerned with mental traits is considered to be unusually wide.

The consequences of this point of view for miscegenation are, obviously, that there is no specific racial adaptiveness in mental traits, but that mental harmony is potentially present in all human beings. This also means that mental disharmonies resulting from hybridization should not be ascribed to genetic causes.

The two points of view are, of course, not mutually exclusive. Stressing possible genetic factors in racial mental differences does not deny plasticity, and stressing plasticity leaves room for genotypic differences. Even though we lack exact knowledge, we may still be rather confident of the existence not only of great plasticity, which is an obvious phenomenon, but also of genotypic differences in racial endowment. Mental traits are correlated with material physical factors, among which the organization of the nervous system and the hormonal constitution are the most important. Delicate and far-reaching interrelations may mold the psychology of each individual in conformity with all aspects of his physical make-up. Since genic differences influence all parts of the body and since differences in allele frequencies have been established for various genes in different races, one may expect some genetic influence on mental traits. The important problem is how great this influence is in differentiating races mentally. How does it compare with the inherent plasticity of mental traits, which may diminish or obliterate phenotypic expression of genotypic divergence; and how does it compare with external factors, which cause different expressions of like genotypes in different individuals and different groups?

In an attempt to answer this question, the facts of history are often cited. The cultural achievements of different races are very diverse, and such differences in achievement are taken as proof of different genetic endowments of mental traits. In such discussions, particularly, the concept of a scale of racial superiority is employed, the measure being achievements in such fields as mechanical inventions, abstract thought, social and political organization, religious creativity, and accomplishments in architecture, sculpture, music, and other arts. The scientist and the historian alike regard established differences in achievement as very inadequate evidence of genetic causation. Not only each individual but, even more, societies seem to be similar to electronic amplifier systems, in which the relation between intake and output is most complex. The development of any society is intricately conditioned by history. The fortuitous appearance or lack of appearance of some external circumstances which provide stimuli of just the "right" intensity to specific cultural endeavors may, with all probability, determine the most divergent future developments. Similarly, the appearance or lack of appearance of a specific influential individual at a specific moment may possibly decide the course of a culture, although here, as in the case of external circumstances, opinion cannot point to controlled experiments in history.

In this connection an opinion voiced by Lord Raglan is relevant: "It has been said against the African Negroes that they never produced a scientist; but what kind of a scientist would he be who had no weights and measures, no clock or calendar, and no means of recording his observations and experiments? And if it be asked why the Negroes did not invent these things, the answer is that neither did any European, and for the same reason — namely, that the rare and perhaps unique conditions which made their invention possible were absent!"

Remote indeed seems the time when a reliable statement can be made regarding a possible genetic component in the cultural achievements of different races.

Apart from the statement itself, it is pertinent to ask whether an objective scale of superiority is possible if we take into account cultural achievements which defy a simple hierarchy of values, such as European Gothic art as compared to Chinese T'ang art; if we consider simultaneously excellence in different fields, such as Roman law and Buddhist thought; and if we include negative values, which stem from ruthless acquisitiveness, coercion, and intolerance.

If, for the sake of argument, it is assumed that the different achievements of different races have some genetic foundation, it is, without doubt, true that variation in individual endowment shows a very wide range in every race. Although methods of testing the hypothesis are lacking, it may be assumed that the ranges of mental endowment of individuals of different races overlap greatly. Therefore, it would probably be possible to find individuals in each race who are mentally superior to the majority of individuals in their own and in every other race.

A genetic explanation of the proposed wide overlap would suggest the existence not of absolute differences in the presence or absence of specific alleles among races but of differences in allele frequencies. In addition, it would involve the assumption that many loci are involved in mental endowment. Such a genetic basis may lead to various kinds of racial differences, namely, variations in mean endowment, in relative frequencies of specific endowments, and in range. How such variations would be mirrored in racial achievement will be estimated differently by different men. What importance should be ascribed to differences in the average endowment of two groups, as compared to differences in the frequency of a few exceptional individuals? How important are variations in the frequency of a large, better-than-average group? How great is the drain on a group's achievement if the distribution of grades of endowment is biased too heavily on the poorer side? To ponder questions like these not only shows our inability to answer them rationally, but, even more, brings to light the inadequacy of an approach which attempts to analyze the history of cultures in terms of allele frequencies.

Confronted with the lack of decisive evidence on the genetic consequences of miscegenation for physical and mental traits, the conservative will still counsel abstention, since the possible ill effects of the breakup of races formed in the course of evolution will not be reversible; whereas the less conservative will regard the chance of such ill effects as small and will not raise his voice against the mingling of races which, from a very long-range point of view, is probably bound to occur anyway. It should not be forgotten, however, that the problem of race is only partly genetic; men will have to consider the biological, sociological, and ethical problems when they attempt to plan for the future.

REFERENCES

Alvarez, J. J.
   1951   "Studies on the A-B-O, M-N, and Rh-Hr Blood Factors in the Dominican Republic, with Special Reference to the Problem of Admixture," *Am. J. Phys. Anthrop.*, 9:127–148.
Benedict, Ruth
   1934   *Patterns of Culture.* Boston: Houghton-Mifflin. (Reprinted 1946. New York: Penguin Books.)
Coon, C. S.
   1954   "Climate and Race," *Ann. Rep. Smithsonian Inst.*, 1953:277–289.
Coon, C. S., S. M. Garn, and J. B. Birdsell
   1950   *A Study of the Problems of Race Formation in Man.* Springfield, Ill.: C. C. Thomas.
Dobzhansky, Th. and M. F. Ashley Montagu
   1947   "Natural Selection and the Mental Capacities of Mankind," *Science*, 106:587–590.
Glass, B.
   1955   "On the Unlikelihood of Significant Admixture of Genes from the North American Indians in the Present Composition of the Negroes of the United States," *Am. J. Human Genet.*, 7:368–385.

Howells, W. W.
   1955   "Universality and Variation in Human Nature," *Yearb. Anthrop.*, 1955:227–236.
Hulse, F. S.
   1958   "Exogamie et hétérosis," *Arch. Suisses d'Anthrop. Gen.*, 22:103–125.
Penrose, L. S.
   1955   "Evidence of Heterosis in Man," *Proc. Roy. Soc., B.*, 144:203–213.
United Nations Educational, Scientific and Cultural Organization
   1952   *The Race Concept.* Paris: UNESCO.

GARRETT HARDIN

*Little can be said to improve upon this offering by Hardin,
chosen as perhaps the best (and certainly the most original)
essay in his superb volume* Nature and Man's Fate. *The
perceptive student of the evolutionary process can readily draw
from his own studies certain basic requirements necessary to the
development of new and better ways of existence. At least some
of these requirements can be generalized to processes other than
those of strictly organic evolution. In particular is the recognition
that any success is necessarily built upon the ruins of many
failures. One had thus best be rather careful about deciding what
sort of "waste" is in fact wasteful. One might also take
cognizance of the fact that it is easy and shallow to harp upon
failure — an emphasis that so often leads to the depressing habit
of holding one mistake against someone, no matter what his
record of accomplishment. One often forgets that the best way
to never be wrong is to never commit oneself. Mentioned here is
a single example of what might be drawn from Hardin's article,
and it is left to the reader to evolve his own insights — such
insights being necessarily a personal matter.*

13   In Praise of Waste

On they go — an invincible army yet not a victorious one. The
aristocrats, the elect, the chosen, the Best People — all the words
that describe them are false, and all attempts to organize them
fail. Again and again Authority, seeing their value, has tried to
net them and to utilize them as the Egyptian Priesthood or the
Christian Church or the Chinese Civil Service or the Group Movement, or some other worthy stunt. But they slip through the net
and are gone; when the door is shut, they are no longer in the
room; their temple, as one of them remarked, is the Holiness of
the Heart's Affection, and their kingdom, though they never
possess it, is the wide-open world.

E. M. Forster

Modern science is the product of two great revolutions in thought, one that we call the Newtonian revolution, the other the Darwinian. It is often implied that the principal distinction between these two is that one took place in physics, the other in biology. In reality, neither was so confined and the difference between them is more profound. Without intending to belittle the Newtonian revolution we may, with some justice, say it was mainly a semantic revolution. Before Newton, the motions of the world were rigidly determined: some thought the planets were kept in their courses by personal angels who controlled them, as it were, at the end of a leash. After Newton, the motions were still rigidly determined — but now by impersonal forces. God had given way to Gravity — but still the world moved the same.

The Darwinian revolution involved a far more profound reassessment of the sense of the world, resulting in a view that no merely verbal substitution could make consonant with the old. It was for this reason that the reaction to the change was many times more emotional than had been the reaction to the earlier revolution stemming from physics. Taste, if you please, this sample from an anonymous analysis in the *Athenaeum for* 1868:

> In the theory with which we have to deal, Absolute Ignorance is the artificer; so that we may enunciate as the fundamental principle of the whole system, that, IN ORDER TO MAKE A PERFECT AND BEAUTIFUL MACHINE, IT IS NOT REQUISITE TO KNOW HOW TO MAKE IT. This proposition will be found, on careful examination, to express, in a condensed form, the essential purport of the Theory, and to express in a few words all Mr. Darwin's meaning: who, by a strange inversion of reasoning, seems to think Absolute Ignorance fully qualified to take the place of Absolute Wisdom in all the achievements of creative skill.

The typographic emphasis brings to mind the Russian writer, Chekhov, who, setting out to ridicule the simplicity of a loving woman, ended in creating a paean of praise in his short story "The Darling." So also must this English critic have intended to damn Darwinism beyond hope, though he ended by epitomizing its essence admirably. *In order to make a perfect and beautiful machine, it is not requisite to know how to make it.* Quite so.

It is surely improbable that a perfect and beautiful machine could be made without foreknowledge of what was wanted: but only improbable, not impossible. It does not matter that it is *highly* improbable, for the Darwinian system of natural selection is equal to the task. Natural selection, as R. A. Fisher has pointed out, is a mechanism for generating improbabilities. Such a mechanism was utterly undreamt of by the Newtonians.

To Darwinians, Design emerges from blind Waste. "To be an Error and to be cast out is a part of God's Design," said William Blake. How old is this thought? Who can trace the earliest embryological stages of so tenuous an entity as an idea? Perhaps it is centuries old, but certainly its form was not unambiguously clear until Robert Malthus wrote his *Essay on Population* in 1798. This much misunderstood work, yearly buried by liberal critics and yearly resurrected by its own vigor has (entangled in its many errors) a correct view of stability achieved through waste — the Malthusian cybernetic scheme of population. From the superabundant vitality of nature comes the ever-present threat of geometric increase, but this is opposed by the limitations set by the environment. The result is a cybernetic equilibrium achieved through waste, an equilibrium that may, it is true, be subject to temporal shifts, but an equilibrium nonetheless. Forethought, planning and charity are either of secondary importance, or are self-defeating in such a system. It is a "tough-minded" view of life, a view that has been singularly identified with English thinkers; particularly, it is interesting to note, with sons of Cambridge: Malthus, Darwin, Galton, Fisher, Keynes, Charles Galton Darwin and J. B. S. Haldane (who was not always a Communist). All of these men were either trained at Cambridge, or taught there at one time. Ideas have a sort of heredity of their own.

In one context or another, with more or less qualification, these men have asserted that the world is capable of governing itself — wastefully perhaps, but adequately. This is a tough view. It has been opposed from 1798 down to the present day by another stream of thought and feeling, the tenderer view that it is our humane duty to maintain a minute control over the system of nature, trying always to eliminate waste and suffering completely. The two streams of thought have, in fact, waxed in strength together. During most of man's history, the greater part of mankind — at least in the Western world — has had a pretty tough attitude toward life. The *idea of cruelty* — i.e., cruelty as something to be abhorred rather than enjoyed — scarcely existed. The gentle Jesus was a real exception among men. Beginning apparently in the late eighteenth century, a significant quantitative change in the heart of mankind began to take place: Christians started to become *christian*. Perhaps I am my brother's keeper, men said, as they became concerned about the cotter's Saturday night; the wee . . . sleekit . . . tim'rous beastie; the girl on the Bridge of Sighs; Black Beauty; the neighbor's dog; the lace-maker; the woman in the mine — naked, on all fours — drawing the coal cart; the chimney sweep's cancerous little devil; Oliver Twist; Uncle Tom and Little Eva; and — significant name! — Captain Bligh's *Mr. Christian*.

Why the new concern with cruelty? Perhaps in part because, with the Industrial Revolution, things changed for the worse, rapidly, in Blake's dark, satanic mills. Physiological psychology tells us that it is not the absolute state of a sense organ that we perceive, but the rate of change. (The scalding hot bath of the Japanese is bearable so long as you hold *very* still.) The principle applies to cultural evils as well. Cruelty, if traditional and constant, may not be perceived as such; but let it suddenly double, however low the base from which it begins, and it will be abhorred.

The increasing concern with cruelty and suffering may also have been due in part to a change in perspective. In the middle ages it was common for the population of a city to be lowered as much as 10 percent in a single year as a result of disease or famine; even a lowering of 25 percent was not unknown. In a world so filled with suffering not caused by humans it would, to some, seem rather out of perspective to complain of a little human fun (like the Spanish Inquisition, say). As the suffering and death from seemingly divinely caused diseases decreased — as it did even before Pasteur and bacteriology — man's view of his own cruelties changed, perhaps because they loomed larger proportionately. Cruel fate was becoming reformed; cruel man now looked crueler. Tender-minded poets and novelists were determined that he, too, should reform, and quickly.

Into this world of tender intentions burst Malthus, asserting that suffering was inevitable, simply because population had the capability of increasing more rapidly than the means of subsistence. A reasonable balance between population and subsistence — a decent scale of living for some — could be maintained only if others suffered from insufficient means of subsistence. Nor would it be a true solution for the *haves* to divide their means with the *have-nots* — this would merely encourage the production of more have-nots, and hence greater misery for all. In a famous passage Malthus said:

> A man who is born into a world already possessed, if he cannot get subsistence from his parents on whom he has a just demand, and if the society do not want his labour, has no claim of *right* to the smallest portion of food, and, in fact, has no business to be where he is. At nature's mighty feast there is no vacant cover for him. She tells him to be gone, and will quickly execute her own orders, if he do not work upon the compassion of some of her guests. If these guests get up and make room for him, other intruders immediately appear demanding the same favour. The report of a provision for all that come, fills the hall with numerous claimants. The order and harmony of the feast is disturbed, the plenty that before reigned is changed into scarcity; and the happiness of the guests is destroyed by the spectacle of misery and dependence in every part of the hall, and by the clamorous importunity of those, who are justly enraged at not finding the provision which they had been taught to expect. The

> guests learn too late their error, in counter-acting those strict
> orders to all intruders, issued by the great mistress of the feast,
> who, wishing that all guests should have plenty, and knowing
> she could not provide for unlimited numbers, humanely refused
> to admit fresh comers when her table was already full.

This sentiment provoked a storm of protest from the *literati*, who were now making the cause of the poor and the unfortunate *their* cause. The wealthy Percy Shelley saw a great social threat in "sophisms like those of Mr. Malthus, calculated to lull the oppressors of mankind into a security of everlasting triumph." His friend Henry Hazlitt asserted that "Mr. Malthus's gospel is preached only to the poor."

This is not the place to examine Malthus's thesis — or rather, his theses, for there were several. We need only point out that the early decades of the nineteenth century saw an establishment of sharp lines of battle between — shall we say? — *humanitarians* and *analysts*. (It is difficult to name the factions without arousing prejudice.) It must not be supposed that men like Malthus were inhumane; in his personal relations with family and friends, Malthus was the kindest and most considerate of men. But in his public statements he insisted on the primacy of analysis in the attack on social problems, whereas his opponents insisted on the humanitarian treatment of all existing people — particularly the poor and unfortunate — in the hope, or belief, that future generations would present no problem. The here and now is much more real than the there and tomorrow. The humanitarians won the minds of common men (who are, in the nature of things, the majority). The analysts continued their activities, but rather quietly. They knew that at the slightest public utterance an avalanche of criticism was awaiting them.

This recognition must certainly have been one of the factors contributing to Darwin's twenty-year-long hesitation to publish. He undoubtedly saw that his "struggle for existence" — remember the phrase was coined by Malthus — would be viewed as a rationalization for the oppression of the poor. (Spencer's phrase, "the survival of the fittest," suggested this possibility even more clearly.) The *Origin of Species*, when it finally appeared, significantly contained absolutely no mention of the possible implications of the theory for the political and social behavior of human beings. Darwin kept his kind eyes averted from the human problem and deprecated the inferences of others from his theory. In one of his letters to Lyell he wryly remarked, "I have received, in a Manchester newspaper, rather a good quib, showing that I have proved 'might is right,' and therefore that Napoleon is right and every cheating tradesman is also right." He was personally as little in sympathy with what came later to be known as "Social Darwinism" as were his bitterest enemies.

IMPOTENCE PRINCIPLES

In the minds of most laymen, and indeed of many scientists, science is primarily an activity in which one discovers how to do today what was yesterday thought impossible; for many, science is a faith that nothing is impossible. But to the more profound students of the philosophy of science such a faith is impiety. The history of science may quite properly be variously interpreted; for one thing it may be correctly interpreted as the search for the definition of the impossibilities of this world. Edmund Whittaker, a mathematical physicist, has called these the *impotence principles*. It is difficult to word such principles in an unexceptionable way, and the number of them known is, so far, small; but their number is increasing, and the wording of them is growing in precision.

A few examples may help our understanding. In mathematics, there is an impotence principle that may be stated: "It is impossible to trisect an angle with straightedge and compass." This is true. Or rather, there is something true which this statement is aimed at. Actually it *is* possible to trisect an angle with these instruments if one will be satisfied with an approximate answer — which is all we ever need in daily affairs. In the light of this fact, we may revise the impotence principle thus: "It is impossible to trisect an angle *exactly* with straightedge and compass. . . ." Is it true now? Well, not quite. By resorting to an infinity of operations with these tools, exact trisection is possible. Of course, an infinity of operations is, in a practical sense, impossible. But this theoretical possibility may make us propose another revision: "It is impossible exactly to trisect an angle with straightedge and compass, *in a finite number of steps*."

Is the impotence principle now correctly stated? Are there other loopholes in the wording? Perhaps; perhaps not. But whether we discover them or not, we believe that we are dealing with a genuine principle of impotence. We may not soon — perhaps not ever — state it perfectly, but we believe it is *there*. Only if some things are impossible can other things be. The task of science is to discover, and put into words, the impotence principles. In mathematics these include the non-trisectability of angles, and the rule that a circle cannot be squared. In physics, the first and second laws of thermodynamics are impotence principles. These laws not only rule out the possibility of perpetual-motion machines; they also rule *in* all the other wonderful machines we have invented. Impotence principles are not merely restrictive; in the larger framework of science, they are also permissive.

The recognition and acceptance of impotence principles do not come easily. On a thoroughly rational level, we can always doubt whether a particular impotence principle is truly such, or accurately stated. We have been wrong in the past in believing things are impossible. Lord Rutherford, to the day of his death in 1937, thought it would never be possible to harness nuclear power; Simon Newcomb, on the eve of Kitty Hawk, thought human flight impossible. We have been wrong before. We can be wrong again.

Less defensible is opposition to impotence principles because of a psychological need of an unbounded world. This is the only remaining source of opposition to the well-established impotence principles. Those who have had any contact with angle-trisectors, circle-squarers, or the inventors of perpetual-motion machines will attest to their being a very queer bunch of people, indeed. It is not their proposals that merit study, but their personalities. What defect in their character is it that makes them unwilling to accept the idea that perhaps they cannot have everything they want? Whatever it is, it is akin to the immaturity of the spoiled child and the compulsive gambler.

IMPOTENCE PRINCIPLES OF EVOLUTION

It is an evidence of the maturing of biology that it, too, is accumulating impotence principles — not as precisely stated or as certain as those of the physical sciences, perhaps, but just as important in their implications. Let us review the impotence principles that have to do with evolution.

I. *Weismann's Principle* of the separation of soma and germ plasm is certainly a principle of impotence. It might be called the anti-Lamarckian principle. One suspects that a convincing theoretical justification of the necessary character of this principle could be given, though this has not yet been done. In the meantime, Weismann's principle rests on a large mass of negative evidence. There is no repeatable positive evidence for Lamarckism, in experiments properly carried out. Conceivably, such evidence might turn up tomorrow. To the professional biologist this seems most improbable, and his attitude toward the Lamarckian is much like that of professional mathematicians toward the circle-squarers, before the time of Lindemann. To paraphrase Poincaré — Which is the more probable: that this new publicity seeker has proved that Lamarck was right after all, or that the world is the richer by one more fool?

II. *The Competitive Exclusion Principle.* No two organisms that compete in every activity can coexist indefinitely in the same environment. To coexist in time, organisms that are potentially completely competitive must be geographically isolated from each other. Otherwise, the one that is the less efficient yields to the more efficient, no matter how slight the difference. When two competing organisms coexist in the same geographical region, close examination always shows that they are not *complete* competitors, that one of them draws on a resource of the environment that is not available to the other. The corollary of the principle is that where there is no geographical isolation of genetically and reproductively isolated populations, there must be as many ecological niches as there are populations. The necessary condition for geographical coexistence is ecological specialization.

III. *Waste.* Waste, in the Darwinian cybernetic scheme, produces not only progress, but also the conservation of what is. There is no heredity without its tax of mutation; most mutations are bad; their production and elimination are a kind of waste. The sentimentalist who seeks to eliminate the waste in a species by preserving all of the mutants and breeding equally of all genetic types ultimately brings about the extinction of the entire species. It is a throwing of good money after bad. It is the saving of pawns and losing the game.

IV. *In a state of nature, each lethal mutation causes one "genetic death,"* *on the average.* This fact is called the Haldane-Muller principle. Different systems of mating, with different degrees of inbreeding, cause different degrees of loss among immediate offspring. If there are many recessive lethals in common between two closely related partners, the loss among their offspring will be greater than the average in the population. By out-breeding they could avoid this personal loss, but only by saddling it onto later generations. Mathematical analysis shows that the loss is precisely the same, whatever the mating procedure. Sexual reproduction is a kind of stirring of the genes. Ultimately, the lethal mutation must be paid for by death. It is just a question of what "ultimately" means. The removal of a gene from the population is spoken of as "genetic death."

V. *In a state of nature, all bad mutations are, in their cumulative,* *ultimate effects, equally bad.* Science, which begins as common sense, in its fullest development produces concepts that seem most surprising to "common sense." The impotence principle just given is a fine example of this truth about science. To say that a gene that is only mildly harmful to the individual is just as harmful to the race as is one that is completely lethal seems to be flying in the face of reason. But such is the case. This is another aspect of the Haldane-Muller principle; it is demonstrable by a simple mathematical analysis, which may be found in Crow (1957). The sense of the demonstration can be given in words.

When we say, "Gene A is not as bad as gene B," what do we mean? How do we measure "badness" in nature? The only acceptable way, in an evolutionary sense, is by its effect on success in leaving progeny. The "worse" the gene is, the greater the diminution in progeny it causes in early generations, and consequently the sooner the gene is completely eliminated. A gene that causes only slight damage in each generation does so for many generations. These two factors — damage in one generation, and number of generations sustaining damage — bear a reciprocal relation to each other. As a result, the total damage of a gene, summed over all generations, is a fixed quantity, the same for all deleterious genes. In saying this, we assume a population of static size. For a population that is constantly growing in size, the situation is slightly altered: in this case, the less harmful genes exact a greater numerical toll than the more harmful, because a larger proportion of the loss is postponed to the later generations when the population is larger. So, if we have our eye cocked on the human situation of the past three centuries, during which the population of *Homo sapiens* has been increasing, we should be not less, but more concerned about the ultimate cost of the mildly defective genes. In a static population, all defective genes cost the same; in an expanding population, lethal genes are the cheapest tax of all to pay.

CAN GENETIC WASTE BE ELIMINATED?

Some of the preceding impotence principles included the unexplained phrase "in a state of nature." The meaning and the reason for the qualification should be fairly clear: the principles apply to all organisms except man, organisms that do not consciously control their breeding. Man, *if* he consciously controls his breeding, may be said, in some sense, to be living not in a state of nature, in which case the problem of the losses exacted by mutation need to be examined all over again. Can man alter these losses?

Certainly he can increase them. In fact, he is increasing them now deliberately (though not intentionally) by increasing the general radiation level through medical X rays, atomic bombs and atomic-energy installations. How much he is increasing the mutational losses in man through his present actions we do not yet know: nor do we know how much he will increase the general radiation level in the future. We play with atoms because we believe there are benefits to be gained from our play. We know there are losses. Ethics is not so well-developed a science that it can tell us how to balance possible profits and certain losses. At the present time, unavoidable mutations cause the production of about 2,000,000 defective babies per year throughout the world. Suppose we increase radiation to such a level that it brings about an ultimate increase in the number of defective babies produced each year by 200,000. Is this a trivial addition or not? Is it small in comparison to the gains brought by atomic energy? How can we say?

Can man decrease natural losses? Yes, eugenists say. Let us see what it signifies to say *Yes* — what means may be used, and what their cost is.

First means: "loading the scales." Suppose we take albinism as an example. Undoubtedly, there are natural disadvantages to being an albino. Eyesight, for example, is adversely affected. In a state of nature, each new mutation would ultimately be eliminated, with a constant loss. Each genetic death would, in a particular social order, entail a certain emotional cost, in human suffering. A eugenicist might propose to minimize the emotional cost by invoking immediate genetic death among albinos — not necessarily personal death, be it noted, but non-reproduction, the evolutionary equivalent of death. If failure to reproduce involves no emotional cost, then non-reproduction of a disadvantageous type (like albinos) will certainly decrease the magnitude of the loss to society. If non-reproduction is itself emotionally painful, then no answer can be given until we learn how to reckon up accounts in emotionality — how, for instance, to weigh the grief of childlessness against the guilt feelings caused by the recognition that one has deliberately brought handicapped children into the world. It is not for the biologist to give an answer. However, he insists on reminding moralists of these facts: (1) There is no such thing as a "reproductive instinct" — only an urge for certain sorts of sensual stimulation. (2) The act of fertilization is only a small part of the experience of parenthood; adoptive parents often feel that they are truly parents. (3) Different societies, with different values, will equate the opposing interests differently.

There is one important limitation to eugenic action that needs to be stated. In a diploid organism, elimination of a disadvantageous recessive gene takes place more slowly the rarer the gene is. This fact follows from the Hardy-Weinberg law. . . . If selection is exerted only against those that show it, it follows that selection (whether natural or artificial) has very little influence on a gene that is already rare. This is no argument against the elimination of rare, deleterious genes — Huntington's chorea and hemophilia are still undesirable conditions — but it is a caution against optimism. We can't expect to do *much* good by preventing rare homozygotes from breeding. (We can only do harm by allowing them to breed, however).

Second means. By "making book" on breeding. One may not be able to identify the heterozygotes of an unwanted gene, but one may be able to state the probability of their existence. For instance, the sister of a hemophilic man has a fifty-fifty chance of being a carrier of the gene. If she has the gene, a child of hers has one chance in four of being hemophilic. Therefore, without knowing her genotype, she knows that if she is to have a child the chance that it will be hemophilic is 1 in 8. For so serious a condition as hemophilia this would be regarded by most civilized and sensitive women as too great a risk. If those who have a significantly high probability of being the carriers of bad recessives refrain from having children, the gene frequency will fall.

Third means. By the positive identification of heterozygotes. There is some indication that the blood-clotting ability of women heterozygous for hemophilia is poorer than it is in homozygous normals. If this is so, then heterozygotes can be identified positively, instead of merely probably. From an emotional point of view, this would be a definite advance. It may be irrational for women to become mothers when they have a probability of 0.5 of being carriers, but many do. We all are guilty of wishful thinking; and there is something healthy about having a bit of the gambler's spirit. ("The ship that *I* am on won't go down," said D. H. Lawrence contemptuously, during a terrible voyage to Australia.) *It is not I who have bad genes, says Everyman the Gambler*. Positive identification of heterozygosity would cut down on the gambling.

Fourth means. By positive eugenics. Gene frequencies can be changed in a favorable direction as well by encouraging the breeding of favorable types. Since negative eugenics involves what some regard as infringement of personal liberties, one might suppose that positive eugenic measures would be viewed with greater favor, but such a supposition does not reckon with human nature. *No one is my superior; but I will accept you as an inferior* — this is the basic presupposition of the competitive social animal. Men accept to a greater or lesser extent, segregation and sterilization of mental defectives, but not the designation of a select group as "State Breeders." The measure that honors a few degrades the egos of many. From Plato's *Republic* to Muller's *Out of the Night*, the dream of positive eugenics has been utopian, in a derogatory sense.

And yet, we may someday come to it. Though probably by a roundabout route. In fact, there is already in existence a social practice that is, in fact, a form of positive eugenics, though the motivation for it is quite different. This is the practice of artificial insemination by a donor other than the husband. It is used to remedy the defect of a childless marriage. That it has the effect of a positive eugenic measure seems highly probable from the following facts. Semen donors are chosen very carefully on the basis of their superior physical and mental health, and freedom from known genetic defects. In the nature of things, donors probably are genetically superior to most husbands, for it is seldom that a nubile girl will choose her husband as carefully as a mature physician will choose a semen donor. On the average, donor insemination upgrades the human stock. (Since most donors are, for convenience's sake, medical internes, this is a new reason for maintaining high standards of admission to medical school.) How many babies are produced every year by this method is not a matter of record, but competent specialists estimate the number at 1,000 to 10,000 per year in the United States. As the practice becomes more widely known, and as the shock of novelty wears off, we suspect that resort to it will become more common. With 10 percent of all marriages being involuntarily unfertile, half of them presumably because of male sterility, and with the supply of adoptable orphans becoming increasingly outstripped by the demand, there is a large field for donor insemination.

COMPETITION IN THE EVOLUTION OF MAN

Many biologists — I confess I am one — find few things so dreary as a discussion of the "missing links" in man's evolution. Whether this or that jawbone found in a distant gravel bed of uncertain age is part of an evolutionary series that leads directly to modern man, or is instead a relic of a dead end, is so exasperatingly undecidable a question that I cannot maintain an interest in it.

Yet there is a way of looking at man's evolution that is not without interest. Try as we will to be objective and modest, we cannot but conclude that man is a very remarkable animal, perhaps the most remarkable of them all. In what way is he remarkable, and how did he get this way?

There is no objective way of picking out man's most remarkable or characteristic features, but probably most of us would agree that any such list should include his eyes, his hands and his speech. He owes the development of at least the first two of a life in the trees, which his more monkey-like ancestors led. Such an animal, swinging from limb to limb, needs not only delicately grasping organs, like the hands, but also good eyesight. Its vision need not be as keen as that of a hawk, for the problems of arboreal life are more local, but the three-dimensionality gained by having both eyes directed toward the same scene is of vital importance. This orientation of the eyes and the eventual diminution in the importance of the sense of smell ultimately led to the relatively flat, snoutless face of the anthropoids. Had our ancestors never taken to the trees, our idea of facial beauty would undoubtedly have been much different: something more like a collie's head, perhaps.

And *speech.* Here, as we know, is the most remarkably human trait of all, but how can we descry its evolution, since it leaves no fossils? We can only guess at it. The word "speech" actually stands for a complex of ideas. We can only gloss over some of them. Undoubtedly vocalization was in the beginning only for the conveyance of emotion, as it is for most animals now. *Look out! Food! Sex!* (What an inadequate word) *I'm mad* . . . Then somewhere along the line, sounds must have become identified with objects — perhaps food objects first. Thus, perhaps, were nouns developed. And then somehow, two modes of statement were developed: a reportive and an expective (to follow hints of Whorf's). The distinction was between what is (or was) and what will be (*I hope.*). These led eventually to what we recognize as tenses, the reportive mode to the present and past tenses, the expective to future and conditional. Elaboration followed elaboration until we find, in some languages, more than a dozen tenses. Man's ability to conceive of the non-existent (in the future tense, for example) found a different outlet among the nouns in the development of verbal substantives for the non-substantial: *existence, good, justice, energy, power, entropy, spin, curl.*

The ability to create "concepts" is truly wonderful — but has it done more harm or more good? In its pathological aspects, it has resulted in such dreadful productions as Plato's dialogue *Euthydemus.* (Perhaps Popper was right, in *The Open Society and Its Enemies,* in identifying Plato as one of the arch-enemies of society.) On the other hand, the fruitfulness of the major concepts of physics and chemistry makes one rather proud of man. And concepts themselves occur in various grades of generality, forming a hierarchal complex that has not yet been explicitly described. Language is a wondrously subtle and complicated tool; by far the greater part of it is to be found only in mathematics. That which most men call "language" is only a small part of man's concept-handling machinery, scarcely the ABC's of it.

Speech has developed far beyond any *merely* emotive needs, yet it undoubtedly had its origin in emotion, and very likely in emotions evolved by social situations. The stock from which man sprang was undoubtedly a social one — more so than that of most animals. It has often been remarked that the excessive sociality of the monkeys and apes (as it might seem to other animals) is probably a consequence of their excessive sexuality (again, "excessive" from a biased point of view). Most of the vertebrates are only intermittently sexual; the restriction is connected with the hazards of having offspring out of season. The primates, probably because they underwent a considerable part of their evolution in the relatively seasonless tropics, became all-year breeders. The selective advantages of seasonal frigidity and seasonal impotence disappeared. With the continuous interest in the opposite sex, there developed a need for more elaborate and satisfactory forms of social discourse than are required by the merely momentarily amorous. With sociality came conflict, and as sociality became the norm, conflict became an ever-present force in life. A species can survive such an erosive force only if it evolves modes of conflict that permit competition to be worked out by means that stop far short of the lethal point. Threat replaces attack, a snarl replaces a slash. Ultimately (in part at least) words replace weapons. The ability to communicate well, to subdue an enemy with words that evoke the support of the bystanders, becomes of paramount importance. In the social arena, tact becomes of greater value than overt aggressiveness.

Sociality is no one thing: it is many things, many units, with which the individual identifies to varying degrees. Within the greater unit of tribe, clan or nation, the much smaller unit of the family has been of paramount importance in lessening the degree of competition. Because the members of a family are unequal in fact they can live together amicably; specialization permits coexistence. The parents, different sexes, *are* different. They can accept a child because it is inferior. The antagonism that develops when an offspring grows up and competes as an equal with a parent is obvious in other animals, and is often only thinly disguised among humans. The importance to a fetus of being an only fetus has already been pointed out by Bolk: non-competition permits delayed maturity. In the months and years after birth, the same principle applies. An only child, lacking competition with litter-mates, can take its time in maturing. Slower maturation permits greater indulgence in wasteful play, lesser responsibility, greater juvenility, more interest in such non-practical affairs as the sciences and the arts. Good and bad are two faces of the same coin. Were humans to be born regularly in litters, one would predict they would be more competitive, more aggressive, more practical and faster maturing; also less interested in the daydreaming that is the necessary soil of the arts and sciences. (Technology, however — the application of the science already known — is possible in a completely competitive society.)

David Riesman's distinction of inner-directed and other-directed men is of interest in this connection. The child who is brought up by himself is ideally situated to develop whatever inner-directness is inherent in his genes, for he has no equals, no direct competitors. Isolation favors the development of a strong self-image. But if he has a twin, or brothers nearly his age, or if families band together to raise their young in nurseries, then the child is subjected to the pressure of "others" and will become as other-directed as his genes permit. This is the biology that explains the tendency that Riesman points out — that increasing population promotes other-directedness. First the environment influences personality. Secondly (but more important in the long run), the environment selects for those genetic types that are capable of developing the kind of directness it promotes. So the species changes: but it is still called man.

The other-directedness (ultimately the tradition-directedness) that comes with dense population is but a manifestation of unavoidably increased intraspecific competition. Among the impotence principles of socio-biology is surely this: *competition is inescapable*. That species which has succeeded in eliminating all other species as competitors, ends by becoming its own competitor. The world, in spite of comic-strip science, is a limited one. Man, freed of the population-controlling factors of predators and disease organisms, must — willy nilly, like it or not — control his own numbers by competition with his own kind. By taking thought he can elect the kind of competition he employs; but he cannot escape all kinds. This is not to imply that the election is a trival matter. Surely there are few who would not prefer the endemic celibacy of the Irish to the ritual blood sacrifices of the Aztecs, who, at the dedication of the temple of Huitzilopotchli in 1486 slaughtered at least twenty thousand victims (by the most conservative accounts), tearing the hearts out of the living bodies. There surely can be no serious question as to which behavior is preferable, but we should note that, though both practices have a religious "reason," both are, in the eyes of a biologist, competitive techniques associated with the threat of overpopulation, however unconscious of that threat the practitioners may be. The question is not whether competitive techniques shall be employed, but what techniques, and by whom.

The game must go on: that is Nature's command. But it is up to man to determine the ground rules and the teams. The determination of the rules is principally the responsibility of the specialist in ethics. The delineation of the teams — well, that is a task for which many disciplines are needed. It may be that no synthesis of all the relevant considerations is yet possible. But such a synthesis is one that we must work toward. The biologist, with the wisdom gained from a century's preoccupation with evolution, has some things to say about the choosing of the teams.

ONE WORLD — OR MANY?

Few dreams are as pervasive in our time as the dream of "One World," a brotherhood of man, a world in which we are all members of the same team, a world in which competition is at an end. It is an ancient dream, rooted in the fantasy of "The Kingdom of Heaven" of pre-Christian days. It is a noble dream, one that has agglomerated to itself much that is gentlest and finest of man's aspirations. It is a growing dream: in the last century it has increasingly shaped men's political actions in the world at large. The "best" elements of our society believe in it — those who are most liberal, most tolerant, most loving in their attitudes toward other men. Those who strongly repudiate the dream include many with whom one hesitates to associate — men who may be ignorant, narrow-minded, sadistic, or intolerant. Yet a biologist, however much he may dislike the complexion of this group, can hardly throw in his lot with the opposing camp, those who think that One World is both possible and the best of all possible worlds.

In the first place, in a profound sense, One World is a mirage. To eliminate all international competition by abolishing nations would be but to intensify the competition between other groups within the single society — the competition for wealth and honor between labor unions and white-collar workers, for example, or between skilled and unskilled workers, or between farmers and city dwellers. International competition is replaced by class competition. Can one get rid of classes? Possibly. Karl Marx thought so. This man, militant atheist though he was, gave a new lease to the religious idea of the Kingdom of Heaven in his dream of the Classless Society. One nation in our time has tried to achieve this Kingdom of

Heaven on earth, with what results we have seen: in proportion as class competition has decreased, so has the competition between individuals increased in intensity and vindictiveness. The complete elimination of classes would mean the installation of a dog-eat-dog society. In recent years, there has been a reverse tendency in the Soviet heaven, a formation of new classes (bureaucrat versus subject, party member versus citizen, intellectual versus clod), and consequently an increase in social stability. Competition there must be, even in One World. The choice is in the number of teams — which may vary from a minimum of two to a number equal to the population of the entire world — and in the rules of the game. (Is the penalty of defeat to be death, sterilization, celibacy, or what?)

One World in the sense of a competition-free world is impossible. Is it possible in any other sense? Certainly it is possible in a political sense; in fact, the superlative military weapons we have devised seem to indicate that One World is inevitable, in some sense. But is it desirable? Here the biologist, flying in the face of recent tradition and apparent logic, must answer *No*. Such a minority position certainly needs to be justified.

Any position rests on assumptions, which are themselves "taken for granted," i.e., not proven. An important premise of what follows is the assumption that the continued survival of mankind is desirable. This can certainly not be proven from any point of view that is demonstrably "objective," but most men will be willing to accept it. Accepting it, we see immediately, in terms of the picture of evolution developed in the last chapter, that the wisdom of man's dream of One World is highly questionable, to put the matter mildly. Any species that becomes one big melting pot of genes puts (to change the metaphor) all its eggs in one basket. There are countless adaptive peaks available; the one-population species can occupy only one. If circumstances change rapidly, it may be unable to adapt, and so will perish. Conspicuous success in evolution, as in human affairs, is all too likely to be the prelude to extinction. That the dinosaurs should have become extinct at the end of the Mesozoic Era is no cause for wonder; what needs explaining is how such highly successful forms lasted as they did.

It is not that the relatively unsuccessful have a better chance of survival *because* of their deficiencies. Rather, their advantage comes when their lack of success results in the species being broken up into many separate breeding populations, among which there is very little interchange of genes. Under these conditions, there is a great increase in variety within the species, each isolated population necessarily differentiating into a different race. (*How* different will depend on many factors, including the extent of environmental differences.) With a greater variety of harmonious genotypes in existence the species is better adapted to face a varying and unpredictable future. Not all of its breeding populations may survive a change; but the chance that at least some will is greater than it would be for a single, large population. And those races that survive a change can then repopulate regions left vacant by those that have succumbed.

Such is the picture presented to us by a spelling out of the consequences of biological inheritance. But man is subject also to a kind of inheritance that we may call cultural. Will this not alter the picture? We don't know. The Mendel of cultural inheritance has not yet appeared. But there are strong intuitive reasons for believing that the mechanism of cultural inheritance will, if anything, merely increase the contrast in the picture. The loss of adaptability of a species is the result of the inevitable tendency of a breeding population to become genetically uniform. Surely we, in our time, have seen enough of social power to realize that the pressure toward uniformity is even greater in the cultural realm than it is in the biological. As Phyllis McGinley, in *In Praise of Diversity*, complained:

> One shrill, monotonous, level note
>   The human orchestra's reduced to.
> Man casts his ballot, turns his coat,
>   Gets born, gets buried as he used to,
> Makes war, makes love — but with a kind
> Of masked and universal mind.[1]

Genuine tolerance of human variety has been strongest in frontier situations, where men competed with Nature rather than with other men. With the closing of frontiers and the increase in pressure of population, tolerance of real diversity becomes more difficult and the movement toward uniformity much accelerated. The conclusions of the Wrightian picture of evolution are undoubtedly strengthened and exaggerated when we include cultural inheritance in a social animal. Diversity within the species demands isolation of populations — many worlds, not one.

HOW REGULATE COMPETITION?

To the biologist it is clear that the best chances for man's long-time survival depend on the fragmentation of the species into well-separated populations. But it would be foolhardy to say what form the separation should take. It might be a matter of nations, as we know them; or some sort of caste system, that would permit genetic isolation with geographic unity; or — far more likely — some new kind of communities that are neither nation nor caste nor anything that has yet been conceived of. We can hardly talk in term of units that have not yet been invented, so

[1] From *Times Three* by Phyllis McGinley. Copyright 1953 by Phyllis McGinley. Reprinted by permission of The Viking Press, Inc. and Martin Secker and Warburg Ltd.

we must talk in terms of units that now exist, to develop the consequences of inter-group competition further. Some error in prediction will certainly result; we can hardly estimate its magnitude; we can only try to remember it exists.

If one were to conceive of the present world reorganized as if by magic into a system of worlds that would give man the best chance of survival, it might be into many nation-like communities. The biological differences between communities would be not differences of single genes, but of whole constellations of genes. The cultural differences would be also in terms of constellations of culture traits. Just as the fitness of a gene does not inhere in the gene itself but rather in a whole complex of genes, so is the fitness ("wisdom" or "morality") of culture traits a property of the complex, rather than of the individual elements.

If there are separate communities, there will surely be competition between them. But of what sort? Plainly, there must be ground rules to prevent the use of any competitive device that could permit one community to eliminate all others, thus instituting One World. This means, of course, the successful outlawing of atomic bombs and, indeed, of all international warfare as we now know it. But it means something else as well: the elimination of one of the most potent means of warfare known, though one not often recognized as such.

Suppose that in this universe of many communities, one of them, say a remote tribe of very primitive aborigines — let's call them the Polyovacians — announce that they have it as a matter of divine revelation from their god (whose name is Ova) that it is a sacred duty of all men to indulge in sexual intercourse whenever the divine spirit moves them and that intercourse must never be in the slightest way altered by foresight, device, or restraint; and that their god Ova has revealed to them that all life is sacred and must not be extinguished, no matter what the circumstances. What will happen if the Polyovacians develop such a set of religious beliefs, and the rest of the world does not? If the rest of the world believes in sexual restraint, plainly the Polyovacians will outbreed all others and will ultimately replace all other peoples just as surely as if they had used atom bombs. The elimination of warfare by military means is tolerable only in a world that has outlawed reproductive warfare. The competitive use of human gonads in a pacifistic world is every bit as vicious and productive of suffering as is the militaristic use of atomic bombs.

Plainly there must be some sense in which our world must become One World. There must be a few moral principles that are accepted by all, if all are to survive. But these moral principles should be only such as will assure the continuing existence of the smaller units. Beyond that, it is very questionable whether man has the wisdom to go. It seems very doubtful that any body of united nations can draw up a universal bill of human rights that will not do more harm than good if put into effect. There are millions of different constellations of genes that *work*, that produce organisms that are fit for some sort of life. May there not also be very many constellations of moral principles that will work, too, in one sort of life or another? The good constellations in either case are only a tiny fraction of all that are possible, but this fraction is surely a large number. It may be hard to resist trying to punish a society whose moral practices are repugnant to us, but only a policy of live-and-let-live will permit the development of the variety of communities that is needed to insure man's continued existence.

Our kind of community has as a foundation stone the doctrine of freedom of speech. We have learned by bitter experience that this must not be interpreted to mean that "men have freedom to speak only the truth," for who is to determine the truth? Freedom of speech, to mean what it says, must mean freedom to lie; otherwise the phrase is a mockery. Is it not dangerous to permit the broadcasting of falsehoods? Indeed it is. But we must have Milton's firm faith that

> . . . though all the winds of doctrine were let loose to play upon the earth, so Truth be in the field, we do injuriously by licencing and prohibiting to misdoubt her strength. Let her and Falsehood grapple; who ever knew Truth put to the worse in a free and open encounter?

In the realm of inter-community affairs an analogous moral principle must be espoused — freedom to err. Within a single community there cannot be freedom of action for individual members. It will not do, for example, for a community that disapproves of murder, to wink at murder by individuals who want to be free. But, as between communities, there must be freedom for each community to determine its own moral principles. Other communities must be free not only to live morally (by our standards) but also to live immorally (again by our standards). Put bluntly, every community must be free to go to hell in its own way, so long as its action does not endanger the continued existence of other communities. A community must, for instance, enjoy the freedom to breed itself into a state of starvation, if it so wishes, without a finger being lifted elsewhere to interfere with its stupidity. To interfere, to save it from the consequences of its own immorality is but to postpone and aggravate the problem, and to spread the moral infection. By not interfering, however, we make it more probable that a community will see its error in time, will see that a moral principle of unlimited reproduction is incompatible with the principle of unlimited use of medicine in the prevention of crowd diseases. If we have any responsibility at all with respect to other communities, it is only because we ourselves failed in the past to see the cultural incompatibility of the above-mentioned principles and freely gave of our medicine without at the same time seeing to it that the gift was coupled with the principle of birth limitation.

IS THIS UTOPIA?

Library shelves groan with utopias, blueprints of ideal communities, of varying degrees of realism and phantasy, motivated by varying degrees of pathological psychology. Is this just another utopia that has been sketched in the preceding section? At first glance it might appear so; yet will I argue No. At worst, what has been sketched here is a utopia-generating system.

Utopias, however much they vary, agree in two characteristics. The societies they sketch have a high degree of rigidity and finality; and they seek to eliminate all waste, which is variously conceived in terms of economic waste, human suffering, or moral turpitude. The student of biological evolution cannot accept a utopia that embodies either of these features. Evolution is an unending process, in which waste plays an indispensable role. Until proof to the contrary is forthcoming, the evolutionist must assume that man is a part of nature. The biologist sees no end-state for man and his society, which must continue evolving until the day of extinction. No one has conceived any substitute for the mechanism of evolution (whether biological or social) that does not necessarily involve variation and selection — that is to say, waste. Man, the slender reed that thinks, can alter the force and direction of natural forces somewhat, but only within limits. The wisdom of so doing is at least questionable. Who is so wise as to descry the lineaments of man a thousand millennia from now, using these now as guides for consciously warping the course of human evolution toward these goals? And as for waste, the more we try to eliminate it, the more we are impressed with its protean changeability and elusiveness. The time-study man who saves a thousand man-hours by altering work procedures may be astonished to find himself faced with a sitdown strike that costs a million man-hours; reducing the waste of walking to work by inventing horseless carriages may ultimately double the time wasted in transportation by making possible the modern city and its congestion. And so it goes. We have no scientific theory of waste yet, but all men of experience and realism recognize its ubiquity and its inevitability. We can often exchange one kind of waste for another; and we can sometimes — though not as often as we like — decrease it somewhat in amount. But always we must live with it. If we are wise, we even make waste work for us a bit.

IN PRAISE OF WASTE

When did man first perceive that waste may be fruitful? We do not know: the history of waste is yet to be written. But it may plausibly be argued that conscious charity owes its origin at least in part to a subconscious realization of the value of waste. Most interesting of early prescriptions for charity is the Jewish "Law of the Corner," which is given thus in Leviticus *(19:9–10)*: "And when ye reap the harvest of your land, thou shalt not wholly reap the corners of thy field, neither shalt thou gather the gleanings of thy harvest. And thou shalt not glean thy vineyard, neither shalt thou gather every grape of thy vineyard; thou shalt leave them for the poor and stranger." Such a directive sprang, no doubt, in part from a tender heart; but it may also have indicated an embryonic recognition of the danger of an unmodified competitive exclusion principle in human affairs — a recognition that if competition were pure and unbridled, the more efficient man (the landowner) would starve out the man who was less so (the poor and the stranger), coupled with a surmise that perhaps this eventuality might not always be best or right. In Deuteronomy *24:19* there is a further injunction: "When thou cuttest down thine harvest in thy field, and hast forgot a sheaf in the field, thou shalt not go again to fetch it: it shall be for the stranger, for the fatherless, and for the widow ..." Thus there came into being that curious entity of Jewish practice known as "that-which-is-left-through-forgetfulness," which belongs to the poor. The devout were urged always to see to it that something was left through forgetfulness. It is certainly difficult to remember to forget. It is no wonder that the principle of the deliberate tithe — one tenth of one's income given to charity — later replaced so operationally difficult a procedure as deliberate forgetfulness.

The first glimmerings of the importance of waste are quite old, but waste did not really come into its own until the last of the eighteenth century, with the work of economists, particularly of Adam Smith (and later Ricardo). Before them, many economists dreamed of a world made perfect and waste-free through law — through regulations governing the prices of commodities, for example. It was Smith's insight that showed that the world works very well with waste. In effect, Smith said that the world is best and most equitably governed when waste governs it. It does not matter if some men place too high and others too low a price on a commodity. The former goes bankrupt from too little business, the latter from too much; their wiser competitor survives. Through waste, we learn what is the "right" price. Such a cybernetic system is infinitely flexible. Every day, even perhaps every hour it can adjust to the slightest change in circumstances. Adaptation is made possible by waste. That which man's poor intellect may be incapable of creating directly can be produced indirectly through the waste-actuated Smith-Ricardian cybernetic system.

It was Darwin's genius to show that the same system would explain the fact of biological adaptation. Design in nature required no supernatural intelligence to explain it; a cybernetic system based on waste rather than intelligence does so just as well. There is a perpetual production of mutations that are random with respect to need, which means that most of them are bad. They are an unavoidable form of waste. But no matter. Should external circumstances alter the meaning of "fitness," the species is instantly prepared to alter to meet the new demands, through mutations that a moment before were bad, but are now good. A supernatural Designer might, one suspects, occasionally doze and neglect to redesign some of his million different children to meet changing circumstances. But not the impersonal Darwinian system of mutation and natural selection. The needs of the emergency are met through the adaptability conferred on the organism by ever-present waste. No organism is infinitely adaptable of course: the new environment cannot suddenly be too different from the old, else the species simply becomes extinct. (Here we see a difference between gods and Nature. Gods, addicted to miracles, probably do better in the great emergencies, great demands being more worth the while of a divine intelligence. Nature, more humble, works only by littles.)

Evolution has involved not merely the evolution of species but the evolution of systems of evolution. An example of one such evolution at this higher level of meaning is found in the displacement of haploidy by diploidy. The waste in both systems is precisely the same, but in diploidy it is paid for on the installment plan. The diploid species accumulates debts to nature, debts that are paid for, for the most part, by a posterity remote from the generation in which they were incurred. "Am I rich?" a Texas oil magnate asked, repeating the query of a reporter. "I guess you might say I am; I have a million dollars in debts." So it is with organisms. Diploid species are immensely richer in debts than haploid. Out of this genetic richness, multitudinous new combinations of genes are evolved, and (by a magic known only in nature?) an occasional combination of genetic "debts" turns into a new asset, an asset which a more honest, more efficient haploid would, in all probability, never uncover. Diploidy gains its first advantage because of its relative irresponsibility; ultimately it is superior because it is more creative. The association of creativity with a modicum of irresponsibility is not confined to nature.

That the magnificent progress of historical evolution is impossible to the cybernetic process conceived in the most narrowly Darwinian terms has been an intuition of countless minds. Efforts to conceive of other processes have not been wholly happy. Lamarckism, entelechy, *élan vital*, orthogenesis and the hopeful monster are only a few of the terms associated with the less fortunate efforts. More successful have been Wright's, and Fisher and Ford's proposals that Nature may suspend, as it were, the ordinary laws of accounting — now and then and for a while — during which moratorium improbable new combinations may be thrown together to be tested later. Wright works the miracle by the errors of small numbers; Fisher and Ford by the extravagance of unaccustomed prosperity. Both involve an increased measure of irresponsibility; both increase waste; both are creative. This description might be regarded as a paean to inefficiency, but we must not forget that inefficiency is creative only when it is limited. Natural selection is the firm's auditor. If one threw him out forever, the result would surely be ugly chaos. But by postponing his visits now and then while the treasurer places a few three-horse parlays on long shots, an occasional fortune may be made: a new adaptive constellation of genes. Most of the time, of course, the result is closer to bankruptcy — but, no matter, for Nature is infinitely wealthy. Thus Nature shows she knows the meaning of Keynes's famous advice: "The poor man should never gamble; the rich man should do nothing else."

THE COST OF THERAPY

Again we ask our question: *Is man a part of nature?* At times we have answered *Yes*, at times *No*. Perhaps in our time the latter answer is the one more often given. We are terribly clever people, we moderns: we bend Nature to our will in countless ways. We move mountains, and make caves, fly at speeds no other organism can achieve and tap the power of the atom. We are terribly clever. The essentially religious feeling of subserviency to a power greater than ourselves comes hard to us clever people. But by our intelligence we are now beginning to make out the limits to our cleverness, the impotence principles that say what can and cannot be. In an operational sense, we are experiencing a return to a religious orientation toward the world.

That this orientation was lost for a while was perhaps — at least from a certain point of view — good for man. Man refused to accept the world as it is, and out of this *impiety* came technological science. No world of thoroughly pious men could have achieved what we have achieved. In spite of all that may be said — and much truly said — about the perils of eating of the tree of knowledge, we do not honestly regret that we did so, whatever the final outcome. It has been a wonderful adventure, this science of ours, and we would not have even suspected its magnificence had we not impiously refused to accept the world as it appeared to be. By so doing we have plunged beneath the appearance, ultimately (we believe) to discover the real. Impiety, coupled with honesty, will lead us finally to a new and defensible piety.

The scientific temper has been one of rejection of the appearances of the world, and among the appearances most vehemently rejected has been the wastefulness of life, wastefulness of many sorts — of fuel, of natural beauty, of human spirit, of time. The rejection has been productive of much good. We now make two blades of grass grow where but one grew before; we make one lump of coal do the work of four; we save the countryside from devastation by industrial fumes by collecting and making a profit out of the contaminants; we save the lives of jaundiced babies; we restore madmen (some of them) to useful life; we prevent the erosion of the spirit of the poor by taking care of the young. By these and countless other means we have immensely reduced some of the wastes to the world — though, be it noted, not entirely without introducing new wastes of our own invention. But as we have really come to grips with the question of waste, we have discovered its power, the extent to which it is unconquerable. The Second Law of Thermodynamics tells us not only that a perpetual-motion machine is impossible, but it also defines the limits of efficiency, *i.e.*, the extent of irreducible waste, for our machines. Engineers long ago gave up even thinking of circumventing this impotence principle. To try seriously to do so is a sign not of commendable ambition, but of emotional immaturity.

In biology, the wastefulness of mutation is a great impotence principle. Laymen sometimes ask: May we not someday learn how to control the mutation process, so that we can produce only those mutations that we want? Good ones. Thus permitting idiots to give birth to Einsteins. After all, when science has done so many other wonderful things, may it not learn to tailor-make mutations?

It is a plausible surmise. But no geneticist known to me holds out the slightest hope for such a discovery. The reasons are hard to put into words, but they are felt to be very strong reasons. Perhaps the simplest way to put the difficulty is in terms of scale, as has been done for the Second Law of Thermodynamics by Leo Szilard. James Clerk Maxwell, as a fantasy, created a demon who could sit at the door between two equal temperatured rooms and, by allowing only fast-moving molecules to go through in one direction, and only slow-moving ones in the opposite way, could, without the expenditure of energy, eventually bring into being rooms of different temperature. This is, as we know, contrary to experience. Szilard has shown that the impossibility (or rather, the exceedingly high improbability) is connected with the scale of the molecules relative to the demon; involved is a matter of information and its cost. Now genetic theory is by no means so far advanced as to permit a similar analysis, but intuitively it appears that scale is again involved, that the cost of directively controlling mutations will far exceed the value received. Mutations, we are sure, are just naturally wasteful; refusing to accept the waste is a sign of emotional immaturity.

This is not to say, of course, that the waste cannot be reduced. It can. But to see in what sense we mean "can" we must look at "it" again, *i.e.*, at waste, trying to define it more closely.

The Haldane-Muller principle says that every bad mutation causes one genetic death. Genetic death is a subdivisible quantity: it may occur by degrees and over many generations. A lethal gene kills at one fell stroke — this is death as we ordinarily conceive it. But a gene that has a selective worth of 0.9 diminishes the reproductivity of every individual in which it shows by 10 percent. If we multiply the fraction of the population that suffers this loss by the amount of loss each individual suffers, we come out with the number 1, no matter what the selective worth. This then is an impotence principle: each bad gene, no matter how bad, causes exactly one genetic death. But it does not follow from this that there is nothing that can be done to diminish the loss to human beings. To say nothing can be done is to assert that death is the only form of human waste, a thesis that surely few would hold. The sub-lethal gene does not merely diminish the reproductivity of its possessor, it usually also diminishes his vigor, his health, his *joie de vivre*. We would be little concerned if genetic death were the only consequence of Huntington's chorea, Mongolism, phenylketonuria, pyloric stenosis, or fibrocystic disease of the pancreas. But these conditions cause other losses that we state in terms of human suffering. These losses can be reduced.

Until very recent times, the only method of attacking the problem of suffering was by medicine. Medicine is surely one of the glories of mankind, but we are now perceiving its limitations. For a disease in which it is accurate to say that the hereditary component is negligible — say, for smallpox — medicine has been an unalloyed blessing. But where the hereditary component is great — for instance in phenylketonuria — we have our doubts. Let's see what these are by examining phenylketonuria more closely.

Phenylketonuria is a chemical disease. One of the twenty or so amino acids present in proteinaceous food is called phenylalanine. Most people can change this into tyrosine which is used in synthesizing various constituents of the body. But a person who has a double dose of the phenylketonuria gene cannot do this: the phenylalanine is changed instead to the ketone, phenylpyruvic acid which appears in his urine, hence the name. If this were all, there would be no need to worry. But for some reason that is not yet understood, the deranged metabolism affects the brain, causing the phenylketonuria child to develop into an idiot or, at best, into a moron. The hair is unusually light in color also, perhaps because there isn't as much tyrosine available for melanin formation.

Since the results seem to stem from the abnormally high concentrations of phenylalanine in his system, some workers have recently devised a tailor-made diet of specially selected substances that do not include the offending amino acid. The diet is expensive. But, it is maintained, if the phenylketonuric child is early identified and kept on such a diet, it will develop with an I.Q. several points higher than it would otherwise. Is this not progress? *No*, says Dr. J. E. Cawte of Australia, who writes:

> The new clan of treated phenylketonurics cannot be assumed to be a happy one, or one with a high proportion of well adjusted

individuals. Conceding for the moment that the phenylketonuric, if he sticks to his diet, will retain much of his intelligence, it is safe to predict that he will be miserable. One of his life's basic processes for satisfaction, his food, has been seriously tampered with and replaced by a conflict. Eggs, milk, cheese, meat, fish, poultry, most fruit, even ordinary bread, are taboo for his table. He will consume a diet which will be cunningly prepared and flavored, but we can hardly say that he "eats food". . . .

More than this, the legitimate diet permitted him conceals risk. He must plot a careful course between the Scylla of too little phenylalanine and the Charybdis of too much. Too little will lead to tissue breakdown, generalized amino-aciduria, and return of the old biochemical abnormalities. Too much will intoxicate his neurones and start his progression down the slippery slope of mental dullness. The margin for error in a given case may not be great.

So the act of eating, instead of being pleasurable, is beset with difficulty and anxiety of a degree which the diabetic, or even the obsessional neurotic, never encounters. Furthermore the phenylketonuric child will learn guilt as the response to natural appetite, while he is too young to appreciate that it is not his craving that is dangerous, so much as the medical progress which has landed him in his predicament.

How will the poor phenylketonuric handle these problems? Because he is not likely to be of exceptional intelligence or adaptability, it is not going to be easy for him to find satisfaction compensating for all this. The less stable ones will not need to turn to alcohol for oblivion to the burden imposed by medical science. All they have to do is substitute milk or some such beverage for the wine with which disappointed Omar Khayyam, in that profane poem, proposed to fill another and another cup to drown the memory of this impertinence. They can cloud their consciousness on bacon and eggs.

KOMM' SUSSER TOD

"All of us," said George Eliot, "get our thoughts entangled in metaphors, and act fatally on the strength of them." Colorfulness is one of the hazards of communication. The apt metaphor cuts two ways and in the end may do more harm than good. Muller's phrase "genetic death" is a dangerous one. Our traditional reaction to the word "death" is so automatic, so unthinking, that we suppose quite unconsciously that "genetic death" is wholly undesirable. This is far from the truth. Genetic death is not always to be shunned; it is often to be welcomed.

We do not say that the cause of the genetic death is to be desired; the cause is a "bad" mutation, and we mean *bad*. The cause is not desired, but we must accept it. Having received the mutation, the question is: How are we to pay for it? What does it cost?

It has two costs. The primary one we have already seen: genetic death. Every bad mutation has the same cost, in this sense: precisely one genetic death, one extinction. ("*After the first death there is no other. . . .*") Genetic death may be variously subdivided. With a dominant lethal mutation it occurs in one stroke. With a recessive sublethal mutation it is spread over a number of generations, depending on its seriousness and on the mating system. All its partial deaths add up to 1. In a state of nature, the total cost, in terms of reproduction, is constant.

But there is another cost that is not constant: this we may call the suffering-cost, for want of a better name. This is not constant. A lethal gene acting before birth costs the least. About 10 percent of all human pregnancies end in spontaneous abortion. Of these an appreciable fraction, apparently more than half, is attributable to lethal genes. The suffering involved is certainly not great, perhaps none for the embryo and seldom much for the mother or disappointed relatives. Even gentler in their action are the still more lethal genes that cause the death of the embryo in the first week or two of its existence. Such an embryo is conceived, started on its way, and then killed by its genes without a twinge of pain or regret in the mother, who idly wonders how it happened that menstruation came a few days late. With really lethal genes, death comes softly.

It is the sublethals that exact the highest price in suffering. Consider hemophilia. Who can add up its total cost in terms of fear and the foreboding of a death brought on by some minor and unforeseeable accident? The cost to the hemophiliac himself is not all: he has parents, perhaps later a wife. All these share in the suffering-cost.

In a state of nature each bad gene causes one genetic death. Man can delay or avert this if he wishes — but only at the expense of increasing the suffering-cost. Hemophiliacs are now kept alive by frequent, sometimes daily, blood transfusions. We can, if we wish, encourage them to have children. Suppose we saw to it that hemophiliacs had, on the average, precisely as many children as normal people, what would be the result? Genetic death would thus be completely eliminated, but the cost in suffering would be established as a perpetual and continuing cost, a sort of overhead if you wish. However small the cost might be per generation, it would increase without limit as time went on. Every bad mutation is a sort of fine levied against mankind. We can either pay the fine promptly or we can delay or avoid payment altogether — by paying in another way.

We are in the position of the traffic violator who can either pay a fifty-dollar fine *once* in court, or can pay one dollar hush money every week to a dishonest officer to keep from having the violation reported. In the long run, even the cheapest blackmail charge mounts up to more than the most expensive fine. In the long run, unobstructed genetic death is the cheapest way to pay for the unavoidable misfortune of mutation.

THE PREDICAMENT OF MAN

Is man a part of nature? Insistently this question returns to us as we lay bare layer after layer of truth. The progress of our knowledge of man has in large part been achieved by successively deeper insights into the senses in which man is seen to be part of nature. Yet at the same time, we see with increasing clarity senses in which man may properly be said to be *not* part of nature, to be something standing outside of nature, something unique in nature, a being wonderfully unique in his capabilities, and wonderfully, painfully unique in his predicament.

What man's predicament is entirely escaped the early eugenicists. The utopia of classical eugenics is nowhere clearly and completely outlined, but it was something like this. It was a world in which breeding is controlled by the state. (Not marriages, necessarily, for this can be separated from breeding, especially by using artificial insemination.) The markedly "unfit" are prevented from breeding. What does one mean by "unfit"? Principally those defective in intelligence (since the plans are drawn up by a very intelligent person). But such "negative eugenics" is not enough. As was said in 1952 by Charles Darwin's grandson, Charles Galton Darwin:

> This restraint of the breeding of the feeble-minded is important, and it must never be neglected, but it cannot be regarded as a really effective way of improving the human race. If by analogy one wished to improve the breed of racehorses, one might accomplish a little by always slaughtering the horse that finished last in every race, but it would be a much slower process than the actual one of sending the winner to the stud farm.

So utopia must include positive eugenics as well. We must, by artificial insemination or other means, make it possible for the "fittest" to have more than the average number of children. But how do we decide who the fittest are? Here's the rub. Fittest is a relational term: an organism's fitness refers to its fitness for a particular environment. The environments of men are many and various. Bernard Barber (1953) points out that one describes some 17,000 different jobs in modern society. This is admittedly an incomplete list, though on the other hand not all these jobs are different in terms of their demands on genetic endowment. But there must be thousands of genetically different environments into which humans can fit. If we conceive of a utopia in the simplest form possible, as consisting of a director and his people, we can easily postulate that the director could selectively breed his subjects so as to increase the fitness of each occupational group for its particular occupation. He could, in fact, breed improved successors for all the occupations save one: *his own*. As C. G. Darwin puts it:

> If the director had foreseen his death, he would have tried to produce a successor to himself. Since his profound belief in heredity had been so fully confirmed by the remarkable changes he had made in his subjects, he would naturally expect that it would be one of his own sons that would be best fitted to succeed him, but his difficulty would be just the same if he were trying to find a successor elsewhere. The matter is on quite a different footing from all his other decisions. For the others he could say: "I have improved all our breeds, by seeing which son improved on the qualities of his father. That is why I select you." For his own successor the utmost he could say would be "I am selecting you in the hope that you may be a better director than I have been. But I have no idea how you will set about it, since *if I had known what I was failing in, I should have set it right myself.*"

In the last phrase, to which italics have been added, the author has pointed out a weakness of the eugenic utopias that seems to have escaped the attention of most of the eugenicists from Francis Galton's day to the present. It is of more than a little interest to note that the author is not only the grandson of Charles Darwin, but also is a distant cousin of Galton's. Thus, in our own time, significant contributions to evolutionary thinking continue to be made by a member of a family that, with Erasmus Darwin, began thinking about the matter more than a century and a half ago. The Darwins have become one of their own best arguments for hereditary and evolutionary principles in man, even to the extent of pointing out how exceptional man is.

How is man to control his own evolution? How can he possibly have the wisdom to do so? How can the animal-that-makes-himself conceive the best possible image to mold himself into? We see no answer to this problem. The worst of it is, we have forced ourselves into a position in which we *have* to give an answer. In the days before Pasteur man's population was maintained approximately constant from generation to generation by a cybernetic system in which the principle feedback element at the upper limit was disease. The crowd-diseases — smallpox, cholera, typhoid, plague, etc. — are, by the ecologist, labeled "density-dependent factors," whose effectiveness in reducing population is a power function of the density of the population. No growth of population could get out of hand as long as the crowd-diseases were unconquered, which means that man did not have to sit in judgment on man, to decide who should have a cover at Nature's feast and who should not. With the development of bacteriological medicine, all this has been changed. Now, the feedback control is man himself.

The reality of this truth is temporarily obscured by the increasing of the size of the feast, through technological advances, but the increase is only a passing phase which must soon come to an end. (Even now, for the majority of the people of the world, there has been no increase per person.) Having eliminated all other enemies, man is his own worst enemy. Having disposed of all his predators, man preys on himself.

"Man preys on himself . . ." — the language is too colorful. Many eugenicists, from Plato onward, have postulated severe controls: infanticide, involuntary sterilization, and putting males out to stud. No such direct and controversial measures need be used to achieve genetic effects. Controls, to be effective, need operate with no more than statistical precision. No judgment need be passed on individuals; it is enough if a law affects the reproductivity of one definable class more than another. If it does, it will have genetic effects, and may be called a eugenic law, whether it is consciously such or not, whether its eugenic effects are good or bad. Taxation is a measure that is notoriously impossible to free from eugenic side effects. Consider the income tax in the United States. By creating a deduction for each child that is a constant figure regardless of parental income, the poor are encouraged to have children, while the rich are discouraged from doing so, since the cost of bringing up a child is unavoidably proportionate to one's income rather than a fixed cost. If the poorer taxpayer is genetically superior to one who is richer, the eugenic effect of this law is good. If the deduction for dependents were a proportionate one (rather than a constant), its eugenic effect would be different. What is desirable is not here in question. The point is, it is difficult, if not impossible, to draft a law, any law, that is without eugenic effects.

"*Man is condemned at every moment to invent man.*" So said Jean Paul Sartre, in another context. By his every law and action, in this finite, crowded world, the man of today invents the man of tomorrow by affecting the reproduction of competing genes differently. Does man do well in this inventing? If so, it is only by chance, for he pays little attention to the eugenic consequences of his laws. As the world becomes more crowded, he may pay more attention, and here enters another danger — the danger arising from his limited wisdom. In principle, no definitive answer can be given to C. G. Darwin's objection; the only hope is to "spread the bets" enough to hit on the right answer somewhere, sometime.

In *Heads and Tales*, the sculptor Malvina Hoffman tells a charming story of a Mohammedan who made for her an exquisite tiled fountain, perfectly paved — except for one tile which was conspicuously missing. When Miss Hoffman asked why he had deliberately introduced this imperfection he replied, "Only Allah can create the perfect."

However curious this sentiment may seem to us, we recognize it as a piety. Something of this piety must enter into our making of man. If we deliberately make man in the best image we can conceive, insisting that every tile be in place, the result will surely be unhappy, because our wisdom is not perfect. As we increasingly take tighter hold on our own destiny we must see to it that a considerable measure of disorder is retained — out of humility. Waste and disorder, properly controlled, are fruitful of good, as we have seen at many levels. The Law of the Corner, tithing, diploidy and fragmentation of a species into many separate breeding populations — all these, in their various ways, mitigate the full severity of the logical working out of the Competitive Exclusion Principle. They increase the variety of life by saving part of the relatively "unfit" — as defined by today's world — for possible use in the different world of tomorrow. Those who, in the name of whatever principle, seek to put an end to all waste threaten a very foundation stone of evolution and progress. However different they may be in ideology, Capitalist and Socialist all too often, in the name of efficiency, join hands in throttling life.

SCIENCE AS WASTE

Just as biological evolution has been made immensely more luxuriant and productive through mechanisms that prevent complete efficiency in the working out of the competitive processes, so also has social evolution progressed most rapidly under circumstances that insured a considerable measure of waste. Countries that have been fully populated for long periods of time — e.g., classical China — have produced a negligible amount of science. The reason is not difficult to find. Science — pure science — is, in its inception, pure waste. An item of information in pure science "pays off" in a practical way only after it has long been in existence and has been combined with other items of pure science. We are reminded of the new mutation, which is almost always bad, but which — if protected by diploidy — may eventually be able to combine with other and similarly "wasteful" genes to produce a new and superior constellation of genes. Diploidy is the great protector of novel genes; prosperity is the great protector of novel thought. A people whose nose is constantly to the grindstone of poverty cannot look up to see the world as it is; all that exists is the nose and the grindstone. A people living under completely Malthusian conditions cannot discover even so much as the Malthusian principle. Science is not produced by eternally busy, miserable people. The flowering of science in the Western world in the last four centuries paralleled the increase in prosperity. Cause? Effect? Both. However the new science got started (prosperity was only a necessary condition, not a sufficient); once started, it produced more prosperity as an effect which fed back into the system as a cause. Science and technology make a system with positive feedback. No such system can go on forever in a finite world. How it will stop, and when, we cannot but wonder.

And who is it that makes science? Who, indeed, makes poetry or music or art, or any of the creations that stretch the minds and spirits of men? The normal psychiatry of occupations is just beginning to be explored. We know little for sure about this problem. But already there is enough biographical detail to suggest the form of the answer.

Darwin's life is symbolic. His *Autobiography* clearly and unconsciously reveals two elements that are needed to produce any creative genius: irresponsibility and alienation. Is this surprising? We do not ordinarily count these as desirable things; surely they are not so when present in the extreme. But in small measure they are essential to the development of the creative spirit. When Darwin, in about his seventeenth year, learned that his father would leave him enough property so that he need never work, he gave up all pretense of preparing himself for a professional job. The roster of scientists of the eighteenth and nineteenth centuries is replete with the names of men of wealth: Darwin, Galton, Lyell, Cavendish and Boyle, to name only a few. Wealth relieves one of the responsibility of making a living; one then *may* become a scientist. (Why wealthy men of our time do not do so we will see later.)

He who is to see what other men have not seen must, in a real sense, become alienated from the crowd. The manner in which this alienation occurs is subject to an infinity of permutations.

> Most wretched men
> Are cradled into poetry by wrong:
> They learn in suffering what they teach in song,

said Shelley. How great the wrong must be is problematical. For many a scientist of the nineteenth century the process of alienation began when he embarked on an extended journey: so it was for Darwin, Hooker, Huxley, Galton and von Humboldt. A man of the twentieth century might suppose that these voyagers had many companions, but not so. In a world in which class distinctions were so much a part of a man's unconscious, no man's world was very populous. Darwin on the *Beagle*, surrounded by lowly sailors, was virtually alone. His only real equal, his cabin-mate, Captain Fitz-Roy, was himself so weird a psychiatric specimen that young Charles had to withdraw into himself to preserve his sanity. Thus began his alienation.

Alienation breeds alienation. Through the lens of his loneliness Darwin saw the world as it was, not as people thought it. In the Galápagos he apprehended the fact of evolution. Then began his real ordeal. The feeling that he was about to commit murder (as he expressed it to Hooker later) now became part of his daily burden. Illnesses of the voyage that may have been initially "organic" continued at the psychic level. Fearing the disapproval of his fellows, he withdrew from their fellowship, which he so dearly loved, and holed up in Down for the rest of his life, thus creating the conditions for thinking even more alienating thoughts. There is positive feedback in this system, too.

But there is a limit to the alienation a man can endure and still retain his sanity. In some way every great creator must find a companion. For some, it is the felt presence of a past master, who may, from long study, seem like an actual contemporary, like a household spirit. For other thinkers, support comes with the vision of an understanding posterity. ("My time will come," said Mendel, who had spoken in vain to the scientists of his own age.) Still others, most fortunate of all, find a living confidant. For Darwin, it was Hooker — Hooker, the sad young botanist; Hooker, who was near enough to Darwin's age to be an equal, but just young enough to be forever the admiring disciple. To Hooker, Darwin poured out his heart in hundreds upon hundreds of letters. In the strict sense, this was the great love affair of Darwin's life. It made his alienation from the mass of society bearable and productive.

NURTURING THE SPIRIT OF SCIENCE

The problem of fostering science is one of the great unsolved problems of our day. T. H. Huxley once remarked that the new truths of science begin as heresy, advance to orthodoxy, and end up as superstition. It is not science in its last two phases that we are interested in promoting: such kinds of science can take care of themselves all too well. It is young science, new science, science that is heretical that is our problem. How do we encourage this?

It is not enough merely to vocalize in favor of heresy. Surely we in our day know all too well the harvest that comes from this kind of cultivation.

> Heretics choose for heresy
> Whatever's the prevailing fashion.

So Phyllis McGinley has lampooned the efforts of those who have as their *goal*, heresy. And she's right. It is not possible to found an effective Society for the Cultivation of Heresy. Heretics are lonely seers. They cannot be institutionalized.

We cannot deliberately produce heretics. But we can make the conditions favorable for their spontaneous generation. We can see to it that a substantial minority have available to them that indispensable ingredient of heretical and creative thought, irresponsibility. In the past, men of wealth have had this gift. Now they seem not to have. *Fortune* magazine, after making a survey of the sociological origins of science, came to the conclusion that "the broadest generalization that may be made is that scientists tend to come from the lower-income levels." Many students of law and medicine have their schooling entirely paid for by the family; among graduate students in science, such support is rare — their families seldom have money.

The wealthy of our age are probably the most responsible Croesuses the world has ever known. Inherited wealth is almost universally acknowledged by its recipients to carry with it a heavy load of obligation — obligation to one's forebears to preserve and increase the wealth, to one's successors to pass it on, and to society as a whole *to do good.* The wealthy eccentric is a nearly extinct dodo. The man of wealth is now an other-directed man. He may become a lawyer or a doctor. But not a scientist. He is too much a part of the world to achieve the alienation required to be creative. (What millionaire today would have the nerve to do what Darwin did — retire to a "non-productive" life in the country *to think?*)

The discipline of science has little to recommend it as a way of life to those well supplied with this world's goods and breathing an atmosphere of fellowship and togetherness. Its appeal, like that of professional sports and the performing arts, is to the relatively impoverished. For the ambitious youngster of the lower classes these three routes offer the best avenues to social promotion. These occupations, perhaps more than any other, offer rich rewards to inner-directed men, rewards based almost entirely on individual merit; family and connections count for little. In terms of basic biological endowment the rich, one would suspect, are at least as well fitted to become independent thinkers as the poor; but their environment is unfavorable to independence.

If we lived in a non-competitive One World the non-creativity of what is undoubtedly a genetically superior class would not matter; but this is not One World, and does not promise to be. The world is highly competitive and shows signs of becoming more so. The creative spirit that characterizes, but is not confined to, science is of great competitive value. How can we establish the conditions needed for this creativity?

There was a time when hereditary wealth, coupled with a tolerance of eccentricity, created the necessary conditions. In the more recent past, freedom from workaday cares and responsibilities has been more often furnished by an academic position. Scientists occupying university posts produced so much pioneering research precisely because they weren't paid to do it. For, as the Nobel laureate, J. J. Thomson, remarked:

> . . . if you pay a man a salary for doing research, he and you will want to have something to point to at the end of the year to show that the money has not been wasted. In promising work of the highest class, however, results do not come in this

regular fashion, in fact years may pass without any tangible results being obtained, and the position of the paid worker would be very embarrassing and he would naturally take to work on a lower, or at any rate a different plane where he could be sure of getting year by year tangible results which would justify his salary. The position in this: You want this kind of research, but, if you pay a man to do it, it will drive him to research of a different kind. The only thing to do is to pay him for doing something else and give him enough leisure to do research for the love of it.

As it became generally realized that an important fraction of the world's research in pure science was done by academic men, administrators defined research as part of the job, and made productivity in research a criterion for advancement. The consequences of this meddling have been about what one would expect. There is now a tendency to choose projects that are pretty sure to give quick results, and to avoid questions on tabooed subjects. This is why so little work is done in human heredity, so little inquiry made into human differences. As research has become more expensive, the academic man has had to develop a talent for begging. He gets subsidy from foundations by telling committees what he hopes to accomplish with their money if he gets it. The successful beggar often gives more attention to the committee than he does to the scientific problem. The result: other-directedness is introduced into a realm where it has no business being, the realm of inner-directed science. Orthodoxy is encouraged. This may not be too bad for what we *call* "science," for its fields are almost all freed now of conflict with tradition, and its methods systematized to the point where innumerable and immensely important discoveries can be made by men who are not in the first rank of the heretics. But there is need for the spirit of science to move into the fields not now called science, into fields where tradition still holds court. We can hardly expect a committee to acquiesce in the dethronement of tradition. Only an individual can do that, an individual who is not responsible to the mob. Now that the truly independent man of wealth has disappeared, now that the independence of the academic man is fast disappearing, where are we to find the conditions of partial alienation and irresponsibility needed for the highest creativity?

If we solve this problem, we can expect progress to be made in fields more important to man's welfare than is science as presently conceived. Social inheritance will be based on new foundations, and ways will be found to secure the blessings of non-material inheritance without nullifying the implications of genetic recombination. Light will be thrown on the problem of the value of life.

Authors of the greatest persuasiveness seem to be convinced that tomorrow is the world of the other-directed man. Perhaps they are right. No one sees how this eventually may be easily avoided in a Pasteurian world. However, no fate may ever be said to be an inevitable one for man, for merely saying so may alter the truth. (Here is a mode of truth, undreamed of and unallowed for in what we now call science. Here is a problem that requires its own Bolyai and Lobachevsky.) Even other-directed men may be rational, and if rational, may be convinced of the necessity of cherishing those not of their own kind. The inner-directed man, he who is answerable only to his own conscience, is always a thorny tablemate, doubly so when Nature's board is crowded. To ask that all men be inner-directed would be quixotic in the extreme; but it is not unreasonable to ask that other-directed men add the care and nurture of a small corps of inner-directed men to their tithing duties. It is not planning that is needed here, certainly not organization. It is, rather, a systematic allowance for waste, for heterodoxy, for the unforeseeable. It is perhaps not even understanding that is demanded — that would be asking too much of other-directed man — but something in the nature of faith. Faith in the future, and faith in the fruitfulness of waste, properly allowed for.

Those who have painted pictures of an organized heaven have, implicitly or otherwise, appealed to the esthetic sense in man to try to gain assent to their plans. We know now that a completely planned heaven is either impossible or unbearable. We know that it is not true that design can come only out of planning. Out of luxuriant waste, winnowed by selection, come designs more beautiful and in greater variety than ever man could plan. This is the lesson of Nature that Darwin has spelled out for us. Man, now that he makes himself, cannot do better than to emulate Nature's example in allowing for waste and encouraging novelty. There is grandeur in this view of life as a complex of cybernetic systems that produce adaptedness without foresight, design without planning, and progress without dictation. From the simplest means, man, now master of his own fate, may evolve societies of a variety and novelty — yes, and even of a beauty — that no man living can now foresee.

REFERENCES

Anonymous
    1868   *Athenaeum*, No. 2102, 8:217.
Barber, Bernard
    1953   *Science and the Social Order*. London: Allen and Unwin.
Cawte, J. E.
    1956   "A Note on the Future of Phenylketonuria," *Jour. Mental Sci.* 102:805–811.
Crow, James F.
    1957   "Possible Consequences of an Increased Mutation Rate," *Eugenics Quarterly* 4:67–80.

Darwin, Charles
  1868   *The Variation of Animals and Plants under Domestication.* London: Murray.
  1909   *The Foundations of the Origin of Species.* (Francis Darwin, ed.) Cambridge: University Press.
  1927   *The Origin of Species,* 6th ed. New York: Macmillan.
  1951   *On the Origin of Species by Means of Natural Selection,* or *The Preservation of Favoured Races in the Struggle for Life,* 1st ed. New York: Philosophical Library.
Darwin, Charles Galton
  1952   *The Next Million Years.* London: Hart-Davis.
Darwin, Francis, ed.
  1887   *The Life and Letters of Charles Darwin.* New York: D. Appleton.
Darwin, Francis and A. C. Seward
  1903   *More Letters of Charles Darwin.* London: John Murray.
Eliot, George
  1872   *Middlemarch.* (Many editions.)
Fisher, R. A.
  1930   *The Genetical Theory of Natural Selection.* Oxford: Oxford University Press.
Fisher, R. A. and E. B. Ford
  1950   "The 'Sewall Wright Effect,' " *Heredity* 4:117–119.
Hoffman, Malvina
  1937   *Heads and Tales.* New York: Scribner's.
Huxley, Leonard
  1900   *Life and Letters of Thomas Henry Huxley.* London: Macmillan.
Keynes, John Maynard
  1926   *The End of Laissez-Faire.* London: Leonard and Virginia Woolf.
McGinley, Phyllis
  1954   *The Love Letters of Phyllis McGinley.* New York: Viking.
Malthus, T. R.
  1803   *An Essay on the Principle of Population.* London: J. Johnson.
Muller, H. J.
  1935   *Out of the Night.* New York: Vanguard.
Plato
  1937   *The Dialogues of Plato.* (B. Jowett, trans.) New York: Random House.
Popper, K. R.
  1945   *The Open Society and Its Enemies.* London: Routledge and Kegan Paul.

Ricardo, David
1911 *The Principles of Political Economy and Taxation.*
London: J. M. Dent.
Riesman, David
1950 *The Lonely Crowd.* New Haven: Yale University Press.
Shelley, Percy B.
1818 *Revolt in Islam.* (Many editions.)
Smith, Adam
1776 *The Wealth of Nations.* (Many editions.)

IV
BEHAVIORAL
STUDIES:
PRIMATES

PHYLLIS DOLHINOW

A brief survey of the diversity in kind and behavior of the living nonhuman primates is presented in this article. The topics discussed, although far from an exhaustive coverage, are representative of major areas of current investigation on monkeys and apes. The selection is intended to indicate those areas of emphasis in which attempts are being made to correlate information from many aspects of biology, behavior, and environment in order to understand primate adaptations.

For example, major types of organization of primate social groups are considered in relation to the habitats in which they occur. Factors such as population density, food abundance, seasonality and dispersion, water supply, sleeping trees, and predator pressure are all reflected in group organization patterns, in individual patterns of behavior, and often in the morphological specializations of both males and females of a species. Four predominant types of social groupings are described and representatives of each type are mentioned. However, here, as with other topics, emphasis is placed on the tentativeness of each generalization. The experience of the past few years of research indicates that future studies of additional kinds of primates and a clarification of the ranges of organization and behavior within species will undoubtedly make it necessary to modify and reformulate generalizations. On the basis of present knowledge, common features of life among all types of social groupings are considered briefly. The structure of each group as related to patterns of individual interaction and spacing, to communication patterns, and to ontogeny of behavior patterns is discussed.

Finally, attention is turned to the usefulness of living primate behavior as comparative data in the reconstruction of the evolution of hominid social behavior patterns. Emphasis is placed on the appropriateness of certain kinds of comparisons, depending upon closeness of evolutionary relationships and similarities in complexes of behavioral and morphological adaptations. Caution must be exercised in comparative studies since many species of nonhuman primates are used in reconstructing man's evolutionary history when the resemblances of specific adaptations are often only superficial.

14 The Living Nonhuman Primates

MAJOR KINDS OF PRIMATES

The living primates constitute an amazing variety of forms and live in many habitats from tropical forest to the temperate zones of the Old and New Worlds. Within each region they have adjusted to many different habitats — by morphological and locomotor features as well as by patterns of individual and group social behavior. Of the more than fifty living genera with at least two hundred species, only a few have been studied in their natural habitats, and the ones that have been studied in this way are far from representative of even the major types of primates.

Primate taxonomy has been a subject of great controversy and of argument over the details of classification (Simpson 1945, 1949, 1962, and 1963, Piveteau 1957; Fiedler 1956, Clark 1959; and Napier and Napier 1967). However, some major divisions of the primates are recognized by almost all taxonomists. Since it is traditional to begin with the most primitive primate form, the tree shrews, this discussion will start with them, even though doubt exists on whether they are really primates or, instead, the most primatelike of the insectivores. Tree shrews are very primitive in most structures and lack the basic adaptations of the hands and feet that enable primates to climb by grasping. In addition, many features of the tree shrew's skull, teeth, and brain are characteristic of insectivores rather than primates. Van Valen (1965) and others have suggested that, because of certain aspects of their morphology, the tree shrews should not be included among the primates. This conclusion is confirmed when behavior patterns are considered, since those of tree shrews are very different from those of the vast majority of primates.[1] However one may regard the tree shrews, the separation of the tree shrews and the prosimians occurred more than sixty-five million years ago.

The suborder Prosimii contains lemurs and tarsiers (in addition to the tree shrews if they are included among the primates). Prosimians dominated in numbers and variety the early period of primate evolution and at the time were found in North and South America, Europe, Asia, and Africa. At least sixty genera of prosimians did not survive to the present; these, plus the surviving genera, represent a great diversity of forms. At present, prosimian distribution is a small part of its former extensive coverage of the world. No New World forms survive, and those in the northern and temperate regions of the Old World have also become extinct. The lemurs

[1] Preliminary work along the lines described in Chapter 5 suggest that the tree shrews do not appear to be as distinct from the prosimians as this discussion indicates (Sarich, personal communication.)

have been divided into two major groups, the Lemuriformes and the Lorisiformes; the former are limited to Madagascar and the latter include all the other lemurs on the mainland of Africa — the galagos, and the pottos. The Asian forms include the lorises.

Most of the living prosimians are small and nocturnal. The exceptions are on the island of Madagascar, where prosimians have radiated independently of those of the African mainland for the more than thirty million years that the island has been separated geographically. Only these forms are diurnal, possibly in part because the island has no monkeys to compete for food or living space.

Some scholars regard the tarsier, of all the prosimians, as closest to the line leading to the monkeys and eventually to man (Clark 1959). The tarsier is a very small jumping nocturnal primate approximately the size of a two-week-old kitten. Today only one form survives, in Borneo, the Philippines, and the Celebes, a marked contrast to its former widespread distribution.

All the lemurs and the tarsier have hands and feet that can grasp, but they also retain claws on some digits in addition to nails on others. Lemurs have a claw on the second toe, and the tarsier has claws on both the second and third toes that have been described as "toilet" claws. A very specialized and rather improbable-looking Madagascar prosimian, the Aye-Aye, has nails that are histologically very similar to claws. All the other nonhuman primates, the monkeys and apes, have only nails.

In contrast to monkeys and apes, the prosimians are characterized in general by their dependency upon the sense of smell and on tactile sensations from vibrissae to obtain information about their environment. Reliance on olfaction more than on vision is far more characteristic of primitive mammals than it is of most living primates. Many prosimians have special scent glands that are used in social interactions within and among groups to mark territories. In contrast, few monkeys use scent-marking and instead depend on visual, gestural, and vocal communication signals to mediate social relationships. The relative importance of different sensory modalities may be seen in the structures of the skull and the brain of different primates.

The Ceboidea, New World Monkeys, are composed of a great variety of different forms that represent very ancient lines of evolution. New World monkeys evolved from New World prosimians rather than from a monkey ancestor in common with the Old World monkeys. The many similarities in morphology and behavior between Old and New World forms are all the more remarkable, since their histories have been separate since the Oligocene (approximately thirty million years). Ceboidea, or platyrrhine monkeys, comprise a large number of genera and are found throughout central and South America as far south as Argentina.

Major types of New World monkeys include the following:

Alouatta, the howler monkey, has a prehensile tail and is the largest of the New World monkeys.

Aotus, the owl monkey, is the only nocturnal monkey.

Ateles, the spider monkey, has a prehensile tail.

Cacajao (closely related to the *Pithecia*) is a bright-crimson-faced small monkey with a long shaggy red coat.

Callicebus, a small form, lives in small social groups and defends territories.

Callithrichidae, or marmosets, are numerous, with at least two genera and many species.

Cebuella, or the pygmy marmosets, are the smallest of the New World monkeys.

Cebus is very common, the "organ grinder" monkey; it has a prehensile tail.

Lagothrix, the wooly monkey, has a prehensile tail.

Pithecia, the sakis, are short-tailed small forms.

Saguinus are the various kinds of tamarins.

Saimiri, the squirrel monkey, lives in large groups.

Because the New World forms are all arboreal and live in tropical forests, most species are very difficult to observe in the field. A few, such as the *Callicebus* (Mason 1968), the *Cebus* (Thorington 1967), and the spider monkeys, *Ateles* (Klein, personal communication), have been studied, and other studies are being planned or are underway.

The Old World monkeys, members of the family Cercopithecidae, are much better known, and many have been the subject of field studies during the last fifteen years. Morphologically, the African and Asian forms are all quadrupedal with long, narrow, deep trunks that are related to the basic adaptation of climbing by grasping (Schultz 1936). The single family of Old World monkeys has been divided into two subfamilies, the Cercopithecinae, and the Colobinae; each includes species that are primarily arboreal and others that spend the majority of their day on the ground. Visceral adaptations are the major basis for subdividing the family, and these, in turn, are related to diet, distribution, and habitat preferences. The two subfamilies of monkeys also have many behavioral differences.

The Colobinae are most numerous in Asia. In this subfamily, the common Indian langur (*Presbytis entellus*) is found in drier portions of both India and Ceylon, and spends more time on the ground than do any of the other Asian forms. Two species groups of *Presbytis* (*Trachypithecus* and *Presbytis,* Pocock 1934), and three genera (*Nasalis, Pygathrix,* and *Rhinopithecus,* Washburn 1944) comprise the Southeast Asian forms closely related to the Indian *Presbytis.* However, it is possible that these latter forms of Southeast Asia, with odd-shaped noses, belong in one genus rather than in three separate genera. In contrast to the great diversity in Colobinae in Asia, the African forms are contained in one genus, *Colobus*, with only a few species.

There are at least six major genera within the subfamily Cercopithecinae, including *Papio* (baboons), *Cercopithecus* (vervets, etc.), *Cercocebus* (mangabeys), *Theropithecus* (Gelada), *Erythrocebus* (patas) — all African in distribution; plus the Asian *Macaca* (macaques). The African baboons and the Asian macaques are similar enough in both morphology and behavior that they could be placed within one genus.

The African genus *Cercopithecus* contains many diverse forms with at least three major species groupings that live in a variety of habitats. Many forms within the genus are totally arboreal or at least spend the majority of their day in the trees. Others, such as the vervet, may spend a substantial portion of the day on the ground. Some genera, such as the gelada and the patas, are behaviorally and morphologically adapted to surviving in the open on the ground, sometimes a long distance from any trees large enough to offer safety from ground predators. Savanna baboons of the genus *Papio* also exhibit behavioral and morphological adaptations that enable them to spend their day a long distance from trees.

Two of the four apes are Asian and two are African. The African chimpanzee (*Pan*) and gorilla (*Gorilla*) are so similar in morphology and behavior and have such a recent evolutionary origin that some researchers suggest they be placed in a single genus (in 1963 Simpson suggested they be combined in *Pan*). The Asian apes include the orangutan (*Pongo*) and the gibbons, the latter being at least five species of small forms (*Hylobates*) and the large Siamang (*Symphalangus*). Considered as a group, the apes show striking differences in behavior, but all share many morphological features that separate them from the monkeys and align them more closely with man. Many anatomical features shared among apes and man relate to brachiation, originally an adaptation to feeding at the ends of branches. Not all living apes use this means of moving about nor do all feed exclusively in trees, but the basic morphological features of a brachiating ancestry characterize each one.

The African apes, the chimpanzee and the gorilla, are both knuckle-walkers. On a flat surface they elect to walk on all fours, placing their weight on the middle bone of the fingers. These apes are the only two that spend a substantial amount of time on the ground, but they have been classified as brachiators on the basis of their anatomical structure. Not until they were observed in the field was it understood that adult gorillas never brachiate, and adult chimpanzees seldom do, although young animals of both kinds of apes will brachiate.

Orangutans and gibbons rarely come to the ground; both are adapted very well to life in the trees. The orangutan's limbs are very mobile, capable of assuming and holding for long times postures that appear very uncomfortable to us. Gibbons are much less at home on the ground than are the African apes, and when a gibbon walks upright it does so with its long arms held out to the side or slightly above the head to balance its weight.

The morphological features and geographical distributions of living nonhuman primates are known in much greater detail than this very brief overview indicates. None of the early classifications of primates were based on behavior, since systematic field observations are of very recent origin. However, taxonomic status and general complexes of behavioral traits among the major subdivisions of monkeys and apes do correlate highly. It is abundantly clear that patterns of social behavior have been an integral part of the adaptation of each primate to the environment in which it has developed. The extent to which the many factors of the environment have affected, and continue to influence, forms of social behavior will be considered in the next section of this paper.

SOCIAL BEHAVIOR AND THE ENVIRONMENT

Only a very few years ago the list of field studies of monkeys and apes totaled a mere handful of types, and each of the primate species studied had been observed in only one location. On the basis of that limited knowledge, relatively little variability appeared within the behavioral repertoire of each species. Generalizations concerning behavior were simple, and they related to very few major kinds of social organization. New World monkeys were described as nonaggressive, in marked contrast to the strongly dominance-oriented aggressive Old World monkeys. Such a statement represented a very superficial contrast between the few kinds of monkeys that had been observed, including such New World forms as the howler monkey and the Old World savanna baboons. What appeared to be valid generalizations about primate behavior were, in fact, artifacts of the limited observation of a few species.

Soon, however, more field studies were undertaken and the list eventually grew to include restudies of species that had been observed earlier. But these restudies were of social groups living in different kinds of habitats from those of the original groups studied. The results were striking; they stimulated entirely new questions about primate behavior and about the range of adaptation in behavior complexes within a single species. For example, it was not until the rhesus monkeys of India were observed in both cities and forests that it became clear that troops behaved differently in the two locations. Whereas the city rhesus, crowded into small areas and harassed by man, were often highly territorial, forest rhesus spread over wider areas and intra- and intertroop relationships were far more relaxed. The frequency of aggression and wounding was much higher among the city monkeys, as one would expect from their stressful daily existence. In contrast, these events were far less common among the more peaceful forest troops.

East African vervet monkeys studied on Lolui Island in Lake Victoria, an ecologically rich area, and at Chobi in Uganda, an ecologically poor area, demonstrated marked differences in intertroop relations and in the behavior among the members of troops. On Lolui, territories were small, rigidly defined, and defended; the monkeys frequently scent-marked their area. Such was not the case at Chobi, where the vervets had more space and a widespread distribution of food items (Gartlan and Brain 1968). It was no longer a simple matter to describe the range of behaviors shown by all monkeys and apes; it became necessary to add many special conditions to nearly every general statement that had been made, and many of our early notions had to be discarded completely. Social behavior was neither as simple nor as uniform as early studies had led us to think. This is not to say that a single species would have different gestural or vocal repertoires, but that within a single species social organizations and the frequencies of gestures or calls would vary from one area to another depending on the environmental circumstances.

Most importantly, recent studies have posed a new set of questions about the effects of the environment on social structures and on individual patterns of behavior (Crook 1970, Jay 1968, Dolhinow in press). It has become apparent that variability both in behavior and in morphology is related to a large number of circumstances or contexts of life. Characteristics of the habitat are important factors that influence many aspects of primate behavior. A few examples of the relationships between habitat and social behavior will illustrate some significant correlations.

Patterns of social organization do not exist in a vacuum but are affected by many factors external (as well as internal) to the boundaries of the social group. Changes in a habitat will be reflected in the social group's activities, and, if the changes are pronounced or drastic, in the size and composition of the group as well. Studies in different habitats emphasize the ability of some species to adapt to a range of different circumstances of life. However, not all species are equally able to adjust to different habitats: some can survive only in a relatively narrow range of circumstances.

On a very simple level, primarily arboreal versus mainly ground-living forms exhibit substantial differences; a species of monkey or ape that normally spends most, if not all, of its time in the trees is much more reluctant to move, or is incapable of moving, over any distance of ground. That is, should forests change — should they be leveled by man, or decimated by drought or other natural causes — those species that habitually live in a specific type of forest may perish rather than move any distance into other forest areas. A break in the forest may prove to be an effective barrier to movement. In contrast, species that spend time on the ground, from only a few hours to most or all of the day, go longer distances in the open and, presumably, could travel into other areas should the need arise. Of course, such movements would not be accomplished overnight or even within a few weeks. Rather, this process can be thought of as a potential the species has to relocate over long periods of time as habitats change. The most widespread of primate species are, in general, those that spend a good deal of time on the ground. The exceptions are those that live in a continuous forest that extends for a long distance, thus providing an uninterrupted corridor of living space. Species such as the baboon are distributed almost continuously for over three thousand miles in Africa. The Indian rhesus monkey can survive in many habitats and is, as a result, also very widespread.

If a species' diet is specialized and depends upon only certain kinds of food, this too will determine how far the animals can travel and where they can live. The Indian langur monkey (Dolhinow in press, Jay 1965, Yoshiba 1968) is capable of digesting dry mature leaves, and its method of water metabolism (Bauchop and Martucci 1968) permits it to go without water for months at a time. Therefore the species can survive in dry areas during drought seasons — situations in which the rhesus macaque, that also lives in North India, cannot survive. In the Indian langur (and in other forms of Southeastern Asia langurs as well), this ability is based on important anatomical and physiological specializations. Similarly, fruit-eating apes and monkeys, or those that depend upon a high percentage of fruits and berries in their diet, are limited in the areas in which they can survive. Other specializations of diet may also influence the distribution of Old World primates.

The troop's social structure (that is, the organization of intratroop relationships including the social roles it encompasses) is related to the habitat in which the troop lives. For example, consider the set of features often characteristic of open savanna habitat. Food sources are generally widely dispersed and subject to seasonal fluctuations. Predators, including lions, leopards, cheetahs, wild dogs, and hyenas may be abundant. The troop that spends most of its days in the open in such a savanna may wander miles away from trees; some method of defense or patterns of avoidance must therefore be developed to minimize the potential threat from predators that are active during daylight hours. This defense has been accomplished in several ways by different species of monkeys.

Savanna baboon groups react to potential threat from predators by the actions of adult males and the responses of the rest of the troop (Hall and DeVore 1965). When a predator is sighted, adult males position themselves between the more defenseless troop members and the threat, forming a barrier the predator must overcome before attacking females and young. Since the adult males are large and strong, and have a very aggressive temperament, they provide a considerable deterrent to all but the largest of cats that might otherwise prey easily upon the young and female members of a troop. Moreover, each baboon serves as a possible sentry and is alert to danger so that any individual may give an alarm call that alerts all members of the troop.

The patas monkey as studied by Hall (1965) has developed other means of minimizing predation. These monkeys are exceedingly fast runners and do not wander far from the safety of trees, as savanna baboons typically do. The adult male patas spends a large part of his day acting as a sentry, and when a predator approaches, the patas immediately starts a noisy and very attention-drawing display during which he bounds about trees making a commotion. He then runs swiftly away from the rest of the group, leaving them to become very inconspicuously frozen in the tall grass. The male's diversionary tactics are most effective and serve to draw the predator's attention away from the females and young.

Most monkeys, however, are never far in the open, and when a predator threatens, each member of the social group responds to an alarm call by dashing quickly into nearby trees. A monkey troop that spends its days in the trees is not much threatened by ground living predators, although it must respond to threats of avian attack. The effects of predation on all nonhuman primates have probably been greatly underestimated. Schaller's study of the Indian tiger and leopard (Schaller 1967) revealed that 27 per cent of the feces of the leopard contained langur remains — a much larger percentage than had been expected on the basis of studies of the langur monkeys. Clearly, to measure the effect of predation on primate populations, it will be necessary to study the predators, not the primates.

The number and distribution of sleeping trees may also influence the troops' activities and daily routines. Nonhuman primates rarely sleep on the ground or on rocky cliffs. The gorilla (Schaller 1963) is a notable exception; it can sleep on the ground only because it is large enough for few predators to be seriously able to threaten an adult. Living as they do in dense tropical forests has also minimized predation on gorilla, since few large African cats can live in the same habitat.

A few kinds of Old World primates are found in very arid country, and survival in these areas has necessitated special adaptations. The hamadryas baboon (Kummer 1967b, 1968a, 1968b, 1968c) and the gelada monkey (Crook 1966) live in arid regions of Ethiopia. They are similar in having developed a basic social organization in which reproduction takes place consisting of a one-male unit led by an adult male that is responsible for several adult and/or immature females and their offspring.

Kummer's field studies of the hamadryas have provided excellent basic and experimental information on this species (Kummer 1968b, Kummer and Kurt 1963). The high arid plateaus of central Ethiopia provide a formidable environment for monkey survival, and the hamadryas has been able to succeed in living there by means of both morphological and social adaptations. Based on the older and more widespread patterns characteristic of the *Cynocephalus* baboons, the hamadryas has developed a basically one-male grouping system in which the females attached to each male follow him closely and seldom if ever leave his side. At night one-male units come together and move onto steep rugged cliffs that they will sleep on during the night. Although the hamadryas has no formal troop, in the same sense as a savanna baboon has, Kummer suggests that the regularity to the larger groupings on specific areas of the cliff might be in some ways analogous to the troop of other baboons. During the day, however, each one-male unit goes its own way and forages over considerable distances for the sparsely distributed items of food.

The hamadryas adult male is more than twice the size of the adult female, and the supreme dominance of each male within his group is clearly defined. Hostility or aggression among adult males is remarkably low, and through what must be a very complex system of adjustments, it has been possible for a system of social relationships to be built up among the one-male groups that results in a minimum of tension among them. The tremendous difference in size and strength between males and females, and the presence of only one adult male to each grouping, assures a minimum of competition among adults for a very limited amount of food, especially during the dry seasons. The formation of one-male groupings is, then, a response to several factors at least, including a pronounced scarcity of food items that are widely scattered. Kummer also suggests that the one-male groupings are related to predator pressure and the scarcity of appropriate sleeping places.

The amount of land over which any primate group moves during a year, its home range, is determined by a complex of factors that in turn also affect the size, composition, and social behavior of groups. Many different conditions prevail in different habitats. The savanna baboons are an example of a large social group that moves over miles in a relatively sparsely productive open area. If the food is widely dispersed, then a troop must move much further than is necessary in a dense forest where the food supply may be concentrated and rich. In the extreme of a harsh and unproductive habitat, large groups with many males might generate competition and aggression that would break down the social groupings. The open savanna or arid countryside is not the only area where food may be short. In a tropical forest habitat, little seasonal variability in the availability of food may be the cause of a chronic food shortage. The social structure of monkeys living in these areas may also be characterized by small one-male groups. One-male groups are not limited to only a single specific type of habitat, nor are multi-male groupings found in only specific areas. However, on the basis of available evidence it appears that each type of social group is related to conditions of the environment.

The availability of water as well as of food may influence the size of the home range of primate groups. In an area with a very limited or localized supply of water, troops will have to share access to the source. Some accommodation must be made for this, based on use at different times, in specific sequences, or communally. One group's controlling the supply could mean death for the others.

Several categorizations have been made of major types of social groupings among the nonhuman primates (see Table 1). The following are some of these major types:

1. One of the most common types of Old World social groups contains *several adult males and several adult females with young and adolescent or juvenile members.* These groups may be very large ones of more than a hundred, or small ones of less than ten. In general, they have a high degree of stability, and although members may be exchanged among adjacent troops, membership is maintained over a fairly long period of time. A group may actively reject the addition of new members from different groups. Examples of this type of group are found among savanna baboons (DeVore 1965, Hall and DeVore 1965), vervets (*Cercopithecus aethiops*) (Gartlan 1966, Gartlan and Brain 1968, Struhsaker 1967a, 1967b), and rhesus (*Macaca mulatta*) (Altmann 1962, 1965, Southwick 1962, Koford 1963a, Lindburg 1967, Neville 1966).

The species named above (savanna baboons, vervets, and rhesus) may or may not defend a territory, depending upon the circumstances of the

TABLE 1. GENERAL TYPES OF SOCIAL ORGANIZATION
AMONG SOME NONHUMAN PRIMATES

	Type 1 Adult males, females and young	*Type 2* One adult male, adult females and young	*Type 3* Mated pair and young	*Type 4* Local population with subgroupings
Apes	Gorilla		Gibbon	Chimpanzee Orangutan
New World Monkeys	Howler		Callicebus	
Old World Monkeys	Baboon Vervets Langurs Rhesus	Hamadryas Gelada Patas		

environment. In most of these species each social grouping lives within an undefended home range that may overlap substantially with adjacent home ranges. Other species characteristically have several adult male members, in addition to multiple adult females and young, that do normally defend their home ranges as territories. An example is the howler monkey of the New World (*Allouatta palliata*, Carpenter 1965).

2. A second major type of grouping, smaller than the first, is composed of *one adult male with several adult females and their young.* Two examples of this one-male grouping type have been cited above, the hamadryas baboon (*Papio hamadryas*, Kummer 1968b) and the gelada (*Theropithecus gelada*, Crook 1966). The patas monkey (*Erythrocebus patas*, Hall 1965) also lives in one-male groupings in Uganda. These monkeys occupy large home ranges and have little contact with other patas groups.

3. Another type of social grouping consists of a *mated pair with their offspring.* The callicebus monkey of the New World (*Callicebus moloch*, Mason 1968), and the gibbon (*Hylobates lar*, Carpenter 1940) are representative of this type. Both these primates defend territories and live in forests.

4. The fourth major type of social structure does not have clearly defined troops or social groupings like those above. In these species, living in forests or on the edges of forests and woodland savanna areas, local populations form subgroupings, the membership of which may shift over relatively short periods of time. Temporary gatherings of individuals are composed of animals according to age, sex, and reproductive activity. The Gombe chimpanzees' social structure represents this type, and Van Lawick-Goodall (1968a, 1968b) has described in detail the composition of chimpanzee subgroupings in this area.

In summary, the organization of social groups among primate species is related closely to conditions of the habitat. Field studies have recorded variability within a single widespread species living in different habitats, but it should be noted that the dimensions of variability within a species are organizational, including factors such as the size, composition, and ranges of social groups. Gestures or vocalizations and individual behavior patterns within a species do not vary appreciably, if at all. Although differences in the frequencies of certain types of gestures or interactions may be great, each monkey and ape share essentially the same social communication repertoire with every other animal in the same species. Kummer summarizes this phenomenon well when he states, "The field studies to date suggest that the patterns of social *behavior* of a species are related to the taxonomic position of the species. Social *organizations*, however, seem to appear here and there in the order Primates without apparent relationship to taxonomy or to patterns of social behavior" (Kummer 1967a:361 emphasis his).

MAJOR FEATURES OF
NONHUMAN PRIMATE SOCIAL BEHAVIOR

Many features of social behavior are common to all nonhuman primates. Life styles may vary according to the circumstances of the environment, and the details of interindividual relationships have many facets, but all monkeys and apes are faced with many of the same tasks and demands in their social life. Each individual must accommodate to life with others by learning the patterns of behavior that are essential to social adjustment and hence to survival. No primate lives alone during its period of infancy or juvenile development, and few are forced to live solitary lives thereafter. A social group is the normal context in which each animal spends the majority of its life and toward which, even when forced outside of a group, it orients many of its activities.

Each primate group has a location in space, designated as its home range; within this space, which may vary among different species from a few acres to many square miles, all events of life occur. Everything a group needs for survival is located within its home range, including food, water, and sleeping places. Home ranges are the result of continuing adjustments to the environment and to other groups of primates. In some instances groups may strive to maintain exclusive use of their range, in which case the area is referred to as a territory, but, more frequently, a group of monkeys or apes remains within its range and has little contact with other social groups. A meeting of groups seldom results in any violence. Rather, groups space themselves through habit and tradition, and the daily routines of each tend to keep them apart.

Each social group, in addition to having a location in space, has an organization that structures the behavior of each member regardless of age or sex. Individuals do not behave autonomously, and few actions occur without reference to others. Since an elaborate web of relationships exists among group members, what happens in one segment of the group often has immediate repercussions for many other members. Many nonhuman primate groups are relatively stable over time; membership remains constant, and few animals move from one group to another. By far the majority of animals that do move from one group to another are males, and the frequency with which this happens varies among different species and apparently within different populations of the same species. Normally, a tradition of relationships is built up over time and each group has a history of experiences shared by its members; what has happened in the past becomes part of the experiences of each animal. These experiences are important in daily interactions and make it unnecessary constantly to reestablish rankings or interaction patterns.

Since group organizational patterns are sensitive to change, social structures may be variable within the limits characteristic of a species.

Although a relatively conservative set of relations is established among group members, these patterns are responsive to many factors, both internal and external to the group. Animals mature, age, and die; thus it is necessary every so often for rankings to change. During these times challenges are made and animals change positions of power or leadership. Almost always, however, the changes that occur are consistent with the group's structure, and the results reestablish the organization as it was before the change. Although the occupants of various social roles may change, the roles normally remain constant.

An important part of social organization is the dominance hierarchy or structure of relations and leadership patterns among group members. Not all species have structures similar to the classical dominance hierarchies of some baboons and macaques, but each group has some set of relationships based on priorities in which certain individuals take precedence over others with respect to such items as food, estrous females, sleeping places, or other desired items in less abundance than will satisfy all group members. Often it is not meaningful to rank order the group adults, especially the adult females. Whereas males tend more often to rank themselves with respect to social activities and commodities, the ranking systems of adult females are much less clearly defined and often simply do not exist. The adult female may experience frequent minor changes of her status during the stages of her reproductive cycle, so that a specific ranking for her at any one time is relatively meaningless. More often than not, the most accurate way of describing female dominance is to divide up the females into very general categories of, for example, top, middle, and lower status, and not to attempt a specific numerical rank for each female.

Dominance itself, as a concept, is far more complex than as described in many early studies. It is much more than a total of wins and losses of a food item or a fight, and a male (or female) that ranks first on one measure may be far below on another. For example, leadership and success in food competition may not coincide. Among those species that usually live in small subgroupings of shifting membership, even though a larger local social unit may exist analogous to the typical troop, patterns of priority of access to food and space or to estrous females may be very vague or ambiguous.

Every species of nonhuman primate can be characterized by a set of behavior patterns, some of which are shared by many other species, others of which are not. Regardless of the constellation of behaviors that typifies a monkey or ape, by far the majority of behavioral items and the variations on each behavioral item or pattern must be acquired, and practiced, over time by each member of the species. Some behaviors are specific to one sex and not to the other, and, in addition, certain social roles may be distinguished by specific behaviors that are unique to that role (Benedict 1969). Thus it is possible that an individual primate in the course of its lifetime might not display a number of behaviors that nonetheless are characteristic of the species as a whole.

It is during the complex processes of an individual's maturation that behavior patterns are learned and practiced and that gradually each pattern assumes adult form and meaning in the matrix of social relationships of a troop. Both motor skills and social skills must be mastered and, to the extent that an individual becomes proficient at either or both, its future behavior and relationships will be affected. Early learning may depend to a great extent on the bonds between mother and infant (DeVore 1963, Jay 1962, 1963). This very close and intense relationship between the mother and her young is the most important and strongest social bond in the life of a primate. Seldom (if ever, among most species) is the "father" of any infant known. The social role of "father" is lacking. Instead, it is the mother that mediates for the infant and serves as its filter, at least during the infant's first few days or weeks, of all that goes on around the pair. Her status in the group, her social preferences, and her temperament are exceedingly important in determining the infant's early experiences.

It is predictable, then, that the mother's social position, or status, may have important implications for that of her offspring as it matures. This correlation varies greatly among different kinds of primates. In some, the mother is not associated with her young for many months and she severs all social ties with the young when the next infant is born, whereas in other primates the mother and her offspring may continue for years to have special relationships and many interactions. A male offspring, regardless of its mother's status, will sooner or later have to contest for social rank on its own, and only if the mother is extremely dominant during the years when the male's status is being determined, will her position have direct influence on his.

Influences of the mother's status on that of her offspring may be far more subtle, however, and may be important for many different primates. An infant with a very dominant, confident, or high-ranking mother will have a set of early experiences substantially different from those of another infant with a mother that is constantly being attacked and forced to behave in a subordinate and yielding manner. Since adult females vary considerably in terms of temperament, they will exhibit a concomitantly large range of variability in their quality of mothering. Very little research has concentrated on the effects of the mother's temperament on the development of her male and female offspring, although some attention has been drawn to those female rhesus macaques on Cayo Santiago[2] with

---

[2] Santiago is an island off the coast of Puerto Rico. In 1938 a colony of rhesus monkeys was established and since that time the monkeys have been studied by many investigators.

infants that did follow in their rather dominant footsteps (Koford 1963b, Sade 1965, 1966).

Obviously, not all patterns of behavior can be learned from the mother. A male must acquire and become skillful at activities that differ from those necessary to the female, and of course it works the other way around. A male may learn many qualities of dominance, aggression, or submission — to mention a few categories of behavior — from its mother without also learning to behave in a "feminine" manner. Many of these very broad categories of behavior are found across the boundaries of sex. In addition, a male may have many models within the social group from which it may learn the intricacies of adult male behaviors even though it may not practice them until later in development.

Most young primates spend many hours each day in play, thus utilizing an excellent way to practice both motor and social skills. Not all motor patterns nor all social behaviors are seen in play, but many are. Similarly, most patterns of behavior that are observed and practiced in play are not exclusive to the context of play. But play does provide an optimal context for practice, and, since most play groups are formed of young primates of approximately the same size and strength, it is a context in which the least harm is likely to come to the young individual from ignorance of social rules.

A short discussion can hardly hope to do justice to the variety of items of social behavior that are learned during development, nor can it even outline the major social relationships that will become important for the adult animal. In all social behavior, however, the system of communication of each species is a tremendously important factor. Every set of communication patterns for each species is complex, and few messages are sent that involve only one sensory modality. The normal context of social communication is a social group that has a history of relationships over time. Members know each other well, and their past experiences are very important in shaping the present and in determining the kinds of information passed among themselves. The majority of signals, perhaps, are passed or shared in a very subtle manner. An animal's posture, the quality of its movement, or the most nearly imperceptible of motions may be perceived instantly by others in the group and responded to in a way that is appropriate with their past experiences. A dominant animal does not need to send out strong signals to indicate irritation or anger; it will be heeded at a much less dramatic level. It may tense and lower its head a fraction of an inch, and that may be all it takes to alert other animals that it is watching. In contrast, the very low-ranking individual may have to exert great energy and display very strong gestures to produce so much as a flicker of response in another individual. The low status animal, in the presence of a high-ranking individual, may do as little as possible to avoid making the dominant animal take notice of its presence.

A great deal more information is shared by very subtle motions, by touches, or by glances, than was suspected in early studies. A monkey may place its hand momentarily on the back or side of another to signify that an interaction is finished. The significance of other gestures is not clear; for example a bonnet macaque may place its tail alongside the back of another (Simonds 1963, 1965) or a crab-eating macaque may wrap its tail around the side or limb of another member of the group. These gestures may be as much to reassure the one doing the touching as to communicate nearness, or some other affect, to the animal that is touched. Without some way of monitoring the internal reactions of one animal to another, one can only speculate as to the significance of these subtle gestures. With the development of more sophisticated telemetric devices it should be possible to measure internal physiological responses to social situations in a way never before possible (Delgado 1967). Many observers have been intrigued that some group members may sit close to a very exciting interaction and not appear to be involved or concerned in any way. It may well prove that the animal is indeed very much affected by what is going on about it, and that the experiences gained in this way are exceedingly important to the future behavior. At this point we can only suggest what is happening and wait for the techniques to be developed that will allow us to gather more data to answer more of our questions.

MONKEYS, APES, AND MAN

In their efforts to reconstruct the developments that occurred during the course of hominid evolution, anthropologists now rely upon as many sources of evidence as possible. This is a change from the early traditional methods that were limited primarily to comparative anatomical studies and to the archaeological and fossil record. The guidelines of time were the strata in which fossils and tools were found. To these indicators of geological time, modern chemical methods of dating have been added, and now it is possible to assign dates to fossils with a much greater degree of accuracy. As a result, concepts of time have changed vastly; with an understanding of the millions of years during which evolution has taken place, it is possible to reconstruct a much more meaningful picture of events in primate evolution.

Another dimension of information has been added to investigations of human evolution — the behavior of the living nonhuman primates (Washburn 1968b). Rather than content ourselves with speculations of early behavior inferred from fossil bones, we turn to living animals having the same or similar structures and investigate in detail the muscles, their relationships to features of bones, and the actions those structures make possible in life. Furthermore, we can describe and measure the importance of different motor patterns in the daily behavior of the individual primate — how much time the animal spends doing the variety of actions and activities its structure allows. It is possible to go even one step further and begin to investigate the complex relationships between an individual animal's form and the physical and social environment in which it lives. These relationships seldom can be detailed on the basis of what is known. Often new information leads to a more appropriate restatement of questions so that further investigations may be planned.

It is very important to base comparative studies on accurate understandings of the degrees of relatedness among the forms to be compared. Many different views exist as to which of the nonhuman primates is most closely related to man; the likely candidates have ranged from the tarsier, a prosimian, to the chimpanzee, an ape. According to measures of time, morphology, and behavior, the African apes are by far the closest to man, and each of these factors must be considered if clarification of events in man's history is the goal of investigation

Molecular information indicates a very recent divergence of the human lineage, the Hominidae, from that of the apes, the Pongidae (Goodman 1968, Sarich and Wilson 1967a, 1967b). According to these researchers the sequence of divergence among the Old World primates, from earliest to most recent is: monkeys, Asian apes, African apes, and last of all, man. Many morphological theories indicate man's closeness to the African apes. Washburn (1968a) suggests that man experienced a state of development during which he, like the chimpanzee and gorilla, was a knuckle-walker. What we take for granted as typical behavior and form for modern man did not evolve until very recent evolutionary time. Bipedalism, for example, did not appear in the hominid line until the *Australopithecus* forms that lived in late Pliocene and in Pleistocene times.

The important characteristics of man's head and brain developed long after the divergence of the hominid from the pongid lineages. Even after the development of bipedalism as an efficient form of locomotion, it was not until almost yesterday in evolutionary time that man reached a state of development in which his behavior included complex cultural traditions, skillful tool use and manufacture, and human language. Predicating all these last-named was the development of a large brain that enabled early man to perform the necessary tasks with skill and to develop complex social and cultural traditions that were to become the hallmark of modern man.

Keeping in mind the general sequence of developmental events in human history, and knowing the relative degrees of relatedness among the living primates, it is possible to assess the relative usefulness of the behavior of specific monkeys and apes in a reconstruction of human evolution. Some nonhuman primates are more appropriate than others as subjects of comparative studies that attempt to elucidate man's behavior, past and present. It is tempting to use the behavior of a monkey or an ape that appears, often in some very minor way, to be analogous to early man's condition. However, it is clear that behaviors of individuals and social groups can adjust to life in a specific location or under specific conditions in a number of ways. Merely because a baboon group can survive on an open savanna in certain ways does not mean that early man, who may have lived in a similar habitat, adjusted to life in even a remotely similar manner. The baboon social system is a vastly complex web of relationships within the troop based on a biology of substantial sexual dimorphism and social roles specific to the sexes. There are many fundamental biological differences between baboons and men, early or modern. To take bits or pieces of behavior patterns from much larger adaptive complexes and compare the items across the boundaries of taxa should be done only with great caution. When removed from the physical and social context, features of behavior or morphology may be incomparable even though they have superficial resemblances to patterns of other animals. Clearly, some topics are more relevant for comparative studies than are others.

Some of the major effects of environmental resources on the dispersion of individuals, the size of groups, and the means of obtaining sufficient quantities of food and water are better understood than ever before. Defense from predation in different kinds of habitats has also been investigated in recent field studies. How these problems are handled depends upon the basic type of social organization and the physical features of the species, facts that must be kept in mind when comparisons with early man are made. *Australopithecus* was not likely to have adjusted to environmental problems in the same manner as most of the living primates. For the latter, tools and hunting are not part of life, and the systems of communication and cooperation of living primates are not as developed as were those of early man.

The natures of social bonds among the primates, including man, have many features in common. However, here again, care must be exercised not to overstep the boundaries of probability when making comparisons. The most intense and long-lasting social bond among most of the monkeys and apes is that between a female and her offspring. In some species this bond lasts for years, well into the mature years of the offspring, and may be very important to the development of group status for the young. In other species, later behavior has almost no clear remnants from the mother-infant relationship. Superficial similarities between "family groupings" among certain of the monkeys and the gibbon and man's family structure must be considered carefully before analogies are made. The young gibbon is literally forced out of its natal group when it reaches sexual maturity and the roles of adult females and males are quite different from those of human adults. In this species and also in the arboreal *Callicebus* monkey, the differences among hominid behavior patterns are more significant than the similarities.

On the basis of present knowledge, the best candidate for comparison with early man relative to many aspects of social behavior is the chimpanzee. The chimpanzee is no closer to man than is any other nonhuman primate in many aspects of behavior, but, in general, if one needs to choose a subject for comparative study the most appropriate is the chimpanzee. Unless the gorilla turns out to be similar, there is no close second.

The chimpanzee is a slow-maturing primate that must learn a great deal of the behavior that is necessary for adult life. This in itself is not unique among the monkeys and apes, but characteristic chimpanzee behavior is far richer and more complex in both quantity and quality than that of other nonhuman primates. The mother-young relationship is exceedingly important and may last for many years, until long after the young have matured. Chimpanzee tool-making and use have been well documented and are found in more situations and for more purposes than is true of any other mammal except man. Hunting behavior has been observed on many occasions in the Gombe chimpanzee population, and the extent to which adult and subadult males cooperate in these ventures is unique among monkeys and apes. Sharing behavior is common and takes place among all ages and across the boundary of sex. In general, the communication system of the chimpanzee is the richest among all the nonhuman primates, permitting them to indicate very subtle nuances of reassurance, placation, aggression, and other aspects of social interaction. The chimpanzee communication system is not a precursor of human language, but it stands out among those of the other nonhuman primates as by far the most complex and subtle.

In summary, knowledge of the living primates, their behavior and ecological adaptations, is growing rapidly. From the great diversity of living primates major themes of behavior and adaptation are becoming apparent and it is now possible to associate types of social structures with differences in the environments in which the animals live. The nature of the adjustment between individual behavior patterns and the locations of life are becoming apparent. Researchers concerned with primate behavior are still a long way from understanding the processes by which these adjustments are achieved, but they are more aware, at least, of the general associations that exist.

Some general features of nonhuman primate social life have been sketched. It is apparent that some are far more appropriate than others for comparative analysis in the unraveling of human evolution. This is a point in primate studies where it is possible to investigate behavior experimentally both in the field and in the laboratory, and the results of explorations in both places will contribute the necessary data for both the reformulation of inquiries and the answering of some questions.

REFERENCES

Altmann, S. A.
  1962 "A Field Study of the Sociobiology of Rhesus Monkeys, *Macaca mulatta*," *Ann. N. Y. Acad. Sci.*, 102(2):338–435.
  1965 "Sociobiology of Rhesus Monkeys. II: Stochastics of Social Communication," *Journal of Theoretical Biology*, 8:490–522.
Bauchop, T. and R. W. Martucci
  1968 "Ruminant-like Digestion of the Langur Monkey," *Science*, 161:698–700.
Benedict, B.
  1969 "Role Analysis in Animals and Men," *Man*, 4(2):203–214.
Carpenter, C. R.
  1940 "A Field Study in Siam of the Behavior and Social Relations of the Gibbon, *Hylobates lar*," *Comp. Psychol. Monogr.*, 16(5):1–212.
  1965 "The Howlers of Barro Colorado Island," in *Primate Behavior: Field Studies of Monkeys and Apes* (I. DeVore, ed.). New York: Holt, Rinehart and Winston, Inc., pp. 250–291.
Clark, W. E. Le Gros
  1959 *The Antecedents of Man*. Chicago: Quadrangle Books.
Crook, J. H.
  1966 "Gelada Baboon Herd Structure and Movement: A Comparative Report," *Symp. Zool. Soc. Lond.*, 18:237–258.
  1970 "The Socio-ecology of Primates," in *Social Life in Animals and Man* (J. H. Crook, ed.). London: Academic Press.
DeVore, I.
  1963 "Mother-infant Relations in Free-ranging Baboons," in *Maternal Behavior in Mammals* (H. L. Rheingold, ed.), New York: Wiley, pp. 305–335.
  1965 *Primate Behavior: Field Studies of Monkeys and Apes*. (editor). New York: Holt, Rinehart and Winston, Inc.
Delgado, J. M. R.
  1967 "Brain Research and Behavioral Activity," *Endeavour*, 26(99):149–154.
Dolhinow, P. Jay
  in press "North Indian Langurs," in *Primate Patterns* (P.

Dolhinow, ed.). New York: Holt, Rinehart and Winston, Inc.

in press "Primate Patterns," in *Primate Patterns* (P. Dolhinow, ed.). New York: Holt, Rinehart and Winston, Inc.

Fiedler, W.
1956 "Übersicht über das System der Primates," in *Primatologia*, Vol. 1 (H. Hofer, A. H. Schultz and D. Stark, eds.). New York: S. Karger, pp. 1–266.

Gartlan, J. S.
1966 "Ecology and Behavior of the Vervet Monkey, Lolui Island, Lake Victoria, Uganda," unpublished doctoral thesis, Bristol University Library.

Gartlan, J. S. and C. K. Brain
1968 "Ecology and Social Variability in *Cercopithecus aethiops* and *C. mitis*," in *Primates: Studies in Adaptation and Variability* (P. C. Jay, ed.). New York: Holt, Rinehart and Winston, Inc., pp. 253–292.

Goodman, M.
1968 "Phylogeny and Taxonomy of the Catarrhine Primates from Immunodiffusion Data," in *Taxonomy and Phylogeny of Old World Primates with References to the Origin of Man* (B. Chiarelli, ed.). Turin: Rosenberg and Sellier, pp. 95–107.

Hall, K. R. L.
1965 "Behavior and Ecology of the Wild Patas Monkey, *Erythrocebus patas*, in Uganda," *J. Zool. Soc. Lond.*, 148:15–87.

Hall, K. R. L. and I. DeVore
1965 "Baboon Social Behavior," in *Primate Behavior: Field Studies of Monkeys and Apes* (I. DeVore, ed.). New York: Holt, Rinehart and Winston, Inc., pp. 53–110.

Jay, P. C.
1962 "Aspects of Maternal Behavior among Langurs," *Ann. N. Y. Acad. Sci.*, 102(2):468–476.

1963 "Mother-infant Relations in Langurs," in *Maternal Behavior in Mammals* (H. Rheingold, ed.). New York: Wiley, pp. 282–304.

1965 "The Common Langur of North India," in *Primate Behavior: Field Studies of Monkeys and Apes* (I. DeVore, ed.). New York: Holt, Rinehart and Winston, Inc., pp. 197–249.

1968 *Primates: Studies in Adaptation and Variability*. (Editor). New York: Holt, Rinehart and Winston, Inc.

Koford, C. B.
1963a "Group Relations in an Island Colony of Rhesus Monkeys," in *Primate Social Behavior* (C. H. South-

wick, ed.). Princeton: D. Van Nostrand, pp. 136–152.

1963b "Ranks of Mothers and Sons in Bands of Rhesus Monkeys," *Science*, 141:356–357.

Kummer, H.

1967a "Dimensions of a Comparative Biology of Primate Groups," *Amer. Jour. Phys. Anthro.* Vol. 27(3): 357–366.

1967b "Tripartite Relations in Hamadryas Baboons," in *Social Communication Among Primates* (S. A. Altmann, ed.). Chicago: University of Chicago Press, pp. 63–71.

1968a "Social Organization of Hamadryas Baboons: A Field Study," *Bibliotheca Primatologica*, 6:1–189.

1968b *Social Organization of Hamadryas Baboons*. Basel: S. Karger.

1968c "Two Variations in the Social Organization of Baboons," in *Primates: Studies in Adaptation and Variability* (P. C. Jay, ed.). New York: Holt, Rinehart and Winston, Inc., pp. 293–312.

Kummer, H. and F. Kurt

1963 "Social Units of a Free-living Population of Hamadryas Baboons," *Folia Primat.*, 1:4–19.

Lindburg, D. G.

1967 "A Field Study of the Reproductive Behavior of the Rhesus Monkey," unpublished doctoral thesis, University of California, Berkeley.

Mason, W. A.

1968 "Use of Space by Callicebus Groups," in *Primates: Studies in Adaptation and Variability* (P. C. Jay, ed.). New York: Holt, Rinehart and Winston, Inc., pp. 200–216.

Napier, J. and P. H. Napier

1967 *A Handbook of Living Primates*. London: Academic Press.

Neville, M.

1966 "A Study of the Free-ranging Behavior of Rhesus Monkeys," unpublished doctoral thesis, Harvard University.

Piveteau, J.

1957 *Traité de Paléontologie*, Tome VII (Primates, Paléontologie Humaine). Paris: Masson et Cie.

Pocock, R. I.

1934 "The Monkeys of the Genera *Pithecus (Presbytis)* and *Pygathrix* Found to the East of the Bay of Bengal," *Proceed. Zool. Soc. Lond.* 1934:895–961.

Sade, D. S.

1965 "Some Aspects of Parent-Offspring and Sibling Relations in a Group of Rhesus Monkeys, with a Discussion of Grooming," *Amer. J. Phys. Anthropol.*, 23:1–17.

1966 "Ontogeny of Social Relations in a Group of Free-ranging Rhesus Monkeys *(Macaca mulatta Zimmerman)*," unpublished doctoral thesis, University of California, Berkeley.

Sarich, V. and A. C. Wilson

1967a "An Immunological Time Scale for Hominid Evolution," *Science*, 158:1200–1203.

1967b "Rates of Albumin Evolution in Primates," *Proceedings of the National Academy of Sciences*, 58:142–148.

Schaller, G.

1963 *The Mountain Gorilla: Ecology and Behavior.* Chicago: The University of Chicago Press.

1967 *The Deer and the Tiger: A Study of Wildlife in India.* Chicago: University of Chicago Press.

Schultz, A. H.

1936 "Characters Common to Higher Primates and Characters Specific for Man," *Quarterly Review of Biology*, 11:259–283, 425–455.

Simonds, P. E.

1963 "Ecology of Macaques," unpublished doctoral thesis, University of California, Berkeley.

1965 "The Bonnet Macaque in South India," in *Primate Behavior: Field Studies of Monkeys and Apes* (I. DeVore, ed.). New York: Holt, Rinehart and Winston, Inc., pp. 175–196.

Simpson, G. G.

1945 "The Principles of Classification and a Classification of Mammals," *Bull. Am. Museum Nat. Hist.*, 85:1–350.

1949 *The Meaning of Evolution.* New Haven, Conn.: Yale Univ. Press.

1962 "Primate Taxonomy and Recent Studies of Nonhuman Primates," *Ann. N. Y. Acad. Sci.*, 102(2):497–514.

1963 "The Meaning of Taxonomic Statements," in *Classification and Human Evolution* (S. L. Washburn, ed.). Viking Fund Publications in Anthropology, No. 37, New York: Wenner-Gren Foundation, pp. 1–31.

Southwick, C.

1962 "Patterns of Intergroup Social Behavior in Primates with Special Reference to Rhesus and Howling Monkeys," *Ann. N. Y. Acad. Sci.*, 102(2):436–454.

Struhsaker, T. T.

1967a "Auditory Communication Among Vervet Monkeys *(Cercopithecus aethiops)*," in *Social Communication*

Among Primates (S. A. Altmann, ed.). Chicago: University of Chicago Press, pp. 281–324.

1967b   "Behavior of Vervet Monkeys (*Cercopithecus aethiops*)," *University of California Publications in Zoology*, 82:1–64.

Thorington, R. W.

1967   "Feeding and Activity of *Cebus* and *Saimiri* in a Colombian Forest," in *Progress in Primatology* (D. Stark, R. Schneider, H. J. Kuhn, eds.). Stuttgart: Gustav Fischer, pp. 180–184.

Van Lawick-Goodall, J.

1968a   "Expressive Movements and Communication in Chimpanzees," in *Primates: Studies in Adaptation and Variability* (P. C. Jay, ed.). New York: Holt, Rinehart and Winston, Inc., pp. 313–374.

1968b   "The Behavior of Free-living Chimpanzees in the Gombe Stream Reserve," *Animal Behavior Monographs*, Vol. I, Part 3:161–311.

Van Valen, L.

1965   "Treeshrews, Primates and Fossils," *Evolution*, 19:137–151.

Washburn, S. L.

1944   "The Genera of Malaysian Langurs," *Journal of Mammalogy*, 25(3):289–294.

1968a   "Speculations on the Problem of Man's Coming to the Ground," in *Changing Perspectives on Man* (B. Rothblatt, ed.). Chicago: University of Chicago Press, pp. 191–206.

1968b   *The Study of Human Evolution.* Condon Lectures, Oregon State System of Higher Education. Eugene, Oregon: University of Oregon Press.

Yoshiba, K.

1968   "Local and Intertroop Variability in Ecology and Social Behavior of Common Indian Langurs," in *Primates: Studies in Adaptation and Variability* (P. C. Jay, ed.). New York: Holt, Rinehart and Winston, pp. 217–242.

S. L. WASHBURN
PHYLLIS C. JAY
JANE B. LANCASTER

In the last five years the number of studies of free-ranging monkeys and apes, both in varieties of kinds observed and in studies of the same species living in different habitats, has greatly increased. Even the recent accumulation of information does not make it possible to resolve many questions raised only five years ago when this article was written. This paper, now in part an historical statement, represents a prediction of the feasibility and possible results of prolonged field observations with emphasis on specific aspects of behavior and social organization. The prediction of twice as many studies to come in the years following the publication of the paper was by far an underestimate.

Many of the problems cited as needing attention have been studied further. For example, much more is understood of the relationships between reproductive behavior patterns and the ecology of a species. With longer studies the effects of genealogical relationships upon the development of adult status and activities among some species are much better understood than when this article was written. Innovations in techniques of recording and filming have enabled the observer to record subtleties of behavior interactions. Social communication has been the subject of intensive research, and the addition of spectographic analysis of primate sounds as a routine in field studies has made it possible to be far more accurate than ever before in studying social interactions. The use of film in the study of gestural communication patterns is clarifying the development of accurate gestural repertoires in a way not possible when the observer had to depend upon only his own vision and power of recording. Subtleties of action and the complexity of multimodal interaction patterns are clear on film and tape, whereas they often were missed in early studies.

With long-term studies, social learning during early years can be followed by the recording of the development of adult patterns of behavior. Descriptive statements of ontogenetic sequences are less typological because more individuals have been observed, and the variability in behavior patterns is much clearer. The importance of a primate's early experience, already suggested by many researchers, is being documented by recent and ongoing studies. This importance is particularly well demonstrated by the study of the chimpanzee population in the Gombe.

Now that comparative studies of different nonhuman primate species in varying habitats are available, it is apparent that their usefulness in the understanding of the evolution of hominid patterns of behavior apparently depends upon many more factors than superficial similarities in single aspects of behavior. Far more critical use of nonhuman primate data will result in more accurate estimates of patterns of change during the course of human evolution.

As this article predicts, laboratory research is adding indispensable information to primate studies. Techniques such as those discussed by Delgado in "Brain Research and Behavioral Activity" provide new dimensions of investigation that will eventually be applied in field studies. Only with the combination of information obtained from controlled investigations in captive circumstances, and from field studies, will primate studies continue to progress.

15 Field Studies of Old World Monkeys and Apes

For many years there has been interest in the evolutionary roots of human behavior, and discussions of human evolution frequently include theories on the origin of human customs. In view of the old and widespread interest in the behavior of our nearest relatives, it is surprising

Reprinted from *Science*, vol. 150, pp. 1541–1547, December 17, 1965. Copyright 1965 by the American Association for the Advancement of Science.

how little systematic information was collected until very recently. At the time (1929) Yerkes and Yerkes collected data for their book on the great apes (1), no one had devoted even one continuous month to the systematic study of the behavior of an undisturbed, free-ranging nonhuman primate. Apparently scientists believed that the behavior of monkeys and apes was so stereotyped and simple that travelers' tales or the casual observations of hunters formed a reliable basis for scientific conclusions and social theorizing. As a part of the program of the Yale Laboratories of Comparative Psychology, Yerkes encouraged a series of field studies of the chimpanzee (2), the mountain gorilla (3), and the howling monkey (4). These first studies proved so difficult that Yerkes could write, in the introduction to Carpenter's study, "His is the first reasonably reliable working analysis of the constitution of social groups in the infra-human primates, and of the relations between the sexes and between mature and immature individuals for monkey or ape" (4, p. 4). Zuckerman, quite independently, had realized the importance of field observations and had combined some field work with physiology and the older literature to produce two very influential volumes (5). From this beginning, only Carpenter continued to make field studies of behavior, and his study of the gibbon (6) is the first successful study of the naturalistic behavior of a member of the family Pongidae. Hooton summarized (7) what was then known about the primates, particularly stressing the importance of behavior and the work of Carpenter and Zuckerman.

The war stopped field work, and no major studies were undertaken for some 15 years. Then, in the 1950's, investigators in Japan, England, France, Switzerland, and the United States independently started studies on the behavior of a wide variety of free-ranging primates. For the history of science it would be interesting to examine the reasons for this burst of parallel activity. Field studies were undertaken at more or less the same time, and publications start in the late 1950's and accelerate rapidly in the 1960's. This trend is still continuing and is well shown by the pattern of frequency of citations in a recent review by Hall (8). The review cites the papers of Bingham, Carpenter, Köhler (9), Nissen, Yerkes, and Zuckerman, but there are no references to additional field studies in the period 1941–1951, and most of the references are to papers appearing in 1960 or later.

The increased interest in primates, and particularly in the behavior of free-ranging primates, has given rise to several symposiums, and results of the new studies have been published almost as soon as they have been completed. Data from the recent field studies are included in volumes edited by Buettner-Janusch (10), Washburn (11), Napier and Barnicot (12), and, especially, DeVore (13). The volume edited by DeVore is devoted entirely to recent field studies and their evaluation. It includes accounts of the behavior of five kinds of monkeys, of chimpanzees, and of gorillas. Each chapter is by the person who did the field work, and in addition there are eight general chapters. Two new journals also are devoted to primates. *Primates*, published by the Japan Monkey Centre, is now in its 5th year, and *Folia Primatologica* has completed volume 3. Carpenter's field studies and general papers have been reprinted so that they are now easily available *(14)*. Southwick has published a collection of readings in primate social behavior *(15)*, and Eimerl and DeVore contributed a volume on the primates to the Life Nature Library *(16)*. Field studies have recently been reviewed by Jay *(17)*, and proceedings of a symposium organized and edited by Altmann *(18)*. This abundance of published material makes it hard to believe that only 2 years ago a course on primate social behavior was difficult to teach because of the lack of easily available, suitable reading material.

THE NEW FIELD STUDIES

Obviously, with so much new data a complete review is impossible, and readers wishing more information and bibliography are referred to Jay *(17)* and to the symposiums previously noted. Here we wish to direct attention to the nature of the recent field studies and to a few of their major contributions. Perhaps their greatest contribution is a demonstration that close, accurate observation for hundreds of hours is possible. Prior to Schaller's field work, reported in 1963 *(19)*, it was by no means clear that this kind of observation of gorillas would be possible; previous investigators had conducted very fragmentary observations, and Emlen and Schaller deserve great credit for the planning and execution of their study. A field study of the chimpanzee that seemed adequate in the 1930's now seems totally inadequate, when compared to Goodall's results *(20)*. Today a field study is planned to yield something of the order of 1000 hours of observations, and the observer is expected to be close to the animals and to recognize individuals. A few years ago observations of this length and quality were thought unnecessary, if not impossible.

The importance of studies in which groups are visited repeatedly and animals are recognized individually may be illustrated by the problems they make it possible to study. For example, during one season of the year chimpanzees "fish" for termites by breaking off sticks or stiff grasses and sticking the prepared implement into a termite hole *(21)*, and this whole complex of nest examination, tool preparation, and fishing is learned by the young chimpanzee. It can be seen at only one time of the year and can be appreciated only by an observer whose presence no longer disturbs the animals. Habituation to the observer is a slow and difficult process. Goodall reports *(20)* that after 8 months of observations she could approach to no closer than 50 meters of the chimpanzees and then only when they were in thick cover or up a tree; by 14 months she was able to get within 10 to 15 meters of them. The problem of tool use in nonhuman primates has been reviewed by Hall (22), but the essential point here is that the amount of throwing and object manipulation in the monkeys (Cercopithecidae) was greatly exaggerated in travelers' tales, which were uncritically accepted, and it took years of observation in a favorable locality to reveal the complexity of this kind of behavior in the chimpanzee (23).

PREDATION

Another example of the value of continued observations is in the study of deliberate hunting by baboons. In three seasons of field work and more than 1500 hours of observation DeVore had seen baboons catch and eat small mammals, but apparently almost by chance, when the baboon virtually stepped on something like a newborn antelope and then killed it (24, 25). But in 1965 DeVore saw repeated incidents of baboons surrounding, hunting, and killing small mammals (26).

The whole matter of predation on primates has been difficult to study. Rare events, such as an attack by an eagle (27) may be very important in the survival of primates, but such attacks are seldom observed, because the presence of the human observer disturbs either the predator or the prey. We think that the present deemphasis of the importance of predation on primates arises from these difficulties of observation and from the fact that even today most studies of free-ranging primates are made in areas where predators have been reduced or eliminated by man. Most predators are active at night, and there is still no adequate study of the nocturnal behavior of any monkey or ape. Predation probably can best be measured by studying the predators rather than the prey.

Recognition of individual animals is necessary for the study of many problems, from the first stages of the analysis of a social system to observations of social continuity or constancy of group membership; such observations are exceedingly difficult under most field conditions. For example, understanding of the dominance system implies repeated recognition of a number of animals under sufficiently various conditions so that the patterns of interaction become clear. Again, to be sure that a group has lost or gained a member, the observer must know the whole composition of the group.

Long-continued observations have proved to be important in many unexpected ways. For example, rhesus monkeys have been observed in several of their many very different habitats, and it has been found that young rhesus play more in cities than in some kinds of forest and play in the forest more at some seasons than at others. These differences are due in part to the amount of time which must be spent in getting food; the same forest troop may play more when fruits are available and hunger may be rapidly satisfied than at times of the year when the diet is composed to tiny seeds which take a long time to pick. Extracting the small seeds of sheesham pods during the months when rhesus troops spend most of their time in the sheesham trees takes many hours of the day (28). What might easily have been described in a short-term study as a species-specific difference of considerable magnitude turns out to be the result of seasonal and local variations in food source. It is essential to sample behavior in several habitats to gain an understanding of the flexibility of the built-in behavior patterns of a species, flexibility which precludes the need for development of new forms of genetically determined behavior to cope successfully with different habitats.

The long-term study in which many groups of a species are observed in different, contrasting localities, and in which at least some groups are known so well that most of the individuals can be recognized, will correct many false notions and will make valid generalizations possible. Although so far there have been only a few major investigations of this sort, some important generalizations seem possible.

ENVIRONMENT AND SOCIAL BEHAVIOR

Nowhere is the extent to which the behavior of a species is adaptable and responsive to local conditions more apparent than among groups of rhesus living in India. Rhesus occur naturally in such diverse environments as cities, villages, roadsides, cultivated fields, and many types of forest ranging to altitudes of over 2400 meters. Contact with man varies in these habitats from constant and close to rare and incidental.

Where rhesus groups are subjected to pressures of trapping, harassment, and high incidence of infectious disease, groups are tense and aggression is high. These pressures are found in areas where there is most contact and interaction with man, such as in cities and at places of pilgrimage. The animals are in generally poor physical condition, and numerous old and new wounds are evidence of a high rate of intragroup fighting. Tension among groups occupying adjacent areas of land is similarly high where there is insufficient space for normal movement and behavior, and where there may be intense competition for a limited supply of food and water. This is in sharp contrast to those groups living away from man where normal spacing among groups can be effected by the means evolved by the species. In the latter environments, such as forests, the rhesus are in excellent physical condition and what aggressive behavior occurs functions to maintain stable social groups and relationships among the members of the group; wounds are substantially fewer, and disease appears to be rare.

There has been considerable controversy in discussions of the relationships among social groups of the same species as to whether or not the geographical area occupied by a group should be called a territory or a home range. The point we wish to emphasize is that, within one species, populations living in different habitats may act quite differently toward neighboring groups. Populations may be capable of a wide variety of behavior patterns ranging from exclusive occupation of an area which may be defended against neighboring groups to a peaceful coexistence with conspecifics in which wide overlap in home ranges is tolerated. Because local populations of a species may maintain their ranges in different ways it is necessary to investigate all variations in group spacing in diverse habitats before attempting to describe characteristic behavior patterns for any species.

Not unexpectedly, population and group composition reflect these differences in habitat and stress. Groups living on the Gangetic plains, where trapping, harassment, and disease are important factors, are smaller, and the proportion of young members is also significantly smaller (28, 29). The long-term effects of pressures on different rhesus populations in northern and central India are now being investigated by a team of anthropologists of the National Center for Primate Biology.

A city presents a very different set of challenges to a rhesus group than does a forest. Often there are no trees to sleep in; living space must be shared with man and his domestic animals. Food is not available in the form common to other habitats, and monkeys may have to depend on their skill in stealing food from man. Often the food has been prepared by man for his own consumption, or it consists of fruits and vegetables pilfered from houses, shops, and streets. Garbage is picked through and edible portions are consumed. It is essential that the monkeys learn to differentiate between those humans who represent a real threat to their safety and those who are safe to approach. They must react quickly and learn to manipulate doors, gates, and other elements of the physical environment unique to their urban habitat. This is a tremendously different setting from that in which most rhesus live. City rhesus are more manipulative, more active, and often more aggressive than are forest rhesus. Clearly, the same species develops quite different learned habits in different environments.

ANNUAL REPRODUCTIVE CYCLE

The belief, which has been widely maintained, that there is no breeding season in monkeys and apes gave rise to the theory that the persistence throughout the year of groups, or highly organized troops, was due to continuous sexual attraction. The evidence for a breeding season has been reviewed by Lancaster and Lee (30) who found that in many species of monkeys there is a well-marked breeding season. For example, Mizuhara has presented data (31) on 545 births of Japanese macaques of Takasaki-yama. There were on the average approximately 90 births per year over six consecutive years. The average length of the birth season was 125 days, but it varied from 95 to 176 days. The majority of the births occurred in June and July. Copulations were most frequent in November to March and were not observed during the birth season, and in spite of this the highly organized group continues as a social unit throughout the year.

The birth season has been studied in other groups of Japanese macaques, and in general the situation is similar. There is no doubt that both mating and birth seasons are highly restricted in the Japanese macaque. The birth season is spring and summer, but its onset and duration vary considerably. If observations were limited and combined for the whole species, as they were in early studies, the birth season would appear to be much longer than in fact it is for an individual group, and it is the events within the local group, not averages of events for the species, that bear upon the role of sexual attraction in holding primate society together.

Under very different climatic conditions, in India, rhesus macaques also have a birth season, but copulations were observed in all months of the year, although probably not with equal frequency (29). Among rhesus on a small island off Puerto Rico births occur from January to June, and copulations are restricted to July–January (32). These data confirm the point that a birth season will be more sharply defined in a local group than in a species as a whole. There is a mating season among rhesus introduced on the island, but only a peak of mating in the same species in their native India (29). It is clear that survey data drawn from many groups over a wide area must be used with caution when the aim is to interpret the behavior of a single group. Since the birth season is an adaptation to local conditions, there is no reason to expect it to be the same over the entire geographical distribution of a species, and under laboratory conditions rhesus macaques breed throughout the year.

No data comparable to those for the macaques exist for other primates, and, since accurate determination of mating and birth seasons requires that reasonable numbers of animals be observed in different localities, really adequate data exist for only the Japanese macaque. However, Lancaster and Lee were able to assemble data on 14 species of monkeys and apes. They found that probably the most common situation is a birth peak, a time of year at which births tend to be concentrated, rather than sharply limited mating and birth seasons. This is highly adaptive for widely distributed species, for it allows the majority of births to occur at the optimum time for each locality while maintaining a widely variable basic pattern. The birth season may be a more effective adaptation to extreme climatic conditions. There may be a birth peak in the chimpanzee (20), and there may be none, in the mountain gorilla (19), but, since we have no more data than are necessary to clarify the reproductive pattern in a single species of macaque, we can conclude only that, while birth seasons are not present in either gorillas or chimpanzees, a peak is possible in chimpanzees, at least for those living near Lake Tanganyika.

Prior to the recent investigations there was a great deal of information on primate reproduction, and yet as late as 1960 it was still possible to maintain that there were no breeding seasons in primates and that this was the basis of primate society. Until recently the question of seasonality was raised without reference to a birth season as distinguished from a birth peak, or to a limited mating season as distinguished from matings throughout the year with a high frequency in a particular period.

FREQUENCY OF MATING

Obviously many more studies are needed, and one of the intriguing problems is the role of potency. Not only does the frequency of mating vary through the year, but also there appear to be enormous differences in potency between species that are reproducing at a normal rate. In nearly 500 hours of observation of gorillas, Schaller (19) saw only two matings, fewer than might be seen in a troop of baboons in almost any single morning. The redtail monkey (Cercopithecus ascanius) mates rarely (27), but the closely related vervet (Cercopithecus aethiops) does so frequently. To a considerable extent the observed differences are correlated with structure (33), such as size of testes, and all these species seem to be reproducing at an adequate and normal rate. There is no evidence that langurs (Presbytis entellus) are less successful breeders than rhesus, but the langurs copulate less frequently (34).

Now that more adequate data are becoming available, the social functions of sexual behavior should be reinvestigated. The dismissal of the theory that sexual attraction is *the* basis of primate society should open the way for a more careful study of the multiple functions of sexual behavior. The great differences among the primate species should provide data to prove or disprove new theories. In passing it might be noted that the human mating system without estrous cycles in the female and without marked seasonal variations is unique.

SYSTEMS OF MATING

Mating systems, like the presence or absence of seasonality in breeding and the frequency of copulation, are extremely variable in monkeys and apes. Eventually the relation of these variations to species adaptations will be understandable; at present it is most important to note that monkeys do not necessarily live either in harems or in promiscuous hordes as was once assumed. Restrictive mating patterns such as the stable and exclusive pair-bond formed between adult gibbons (6) and the harem system of the Hamadryas baboon *(35)* are comparatively rare. The most common mating pattern of monkeys and apes is promiscuity more or less influenced by dominance relationships. In species in which dominance relations are not constantly at issue, such as langurs *(34)*, chimpanzees *(20)*, or bonnet macaques *(36)*, matings appear to be relatively promiscuous and are often based on the personal inclination of the estrous female. When dominance relationships are constantly at issue, as in baboons *(37)*, Japanese macaques *(38)*, and rhesus macaques *(39, 40)*, sex often becomes one of the prerogatives of dominant rank. In such species dominant males tend to do a larger share of the mating than do more subordinate animals, but it is only in unusual situations that subordinate animals are barred from the mating system altogether. Mating systems probably support the general adaptation of the species to its environment. In most baboons and macaques the tendency for a few males to do much of the mating may be partly a by-product of natural selection for a hierarchy of adult males which dominates the troop so that in a dangerous terrestrial habitat external dangers will be met in an orderly way. Selection is not only for a male which can impregnate many females but it may also have favored a dominance-oriented social organization in which sexual activity has become one of the expressions of that dominance.

DOMINANCE RELATIONSHIPS

Long-term field studies of monkeys and apes in their natural habitats have emphasized that social relationships within a group are patterned and organized in very complex ways. There is no single "monkey pattern" or "ape pattern"; rather, there is great variability, both among different species and among different populations of the same species, in the organization and expression of social relationships. A difference in the relative dominance of individuals is one of the most common modes of social organization in monkey and ape societies. Dominance is not synonymous with aggression, and the way dominance is expressed varies greatly between species. In the gorilla, for example, dominance is most often expressed by extremely attenuated gestures and signals *(19)*; a gentle nudge from the dominant male is more than enough to elicit a submissive response from a subordinate, whereas, in baboons, chases, fights, and biting can be daily occurrences *(37)*. In many primates there is a tendency for the major age-sex classes to be ranked in a dominance order; for example, in baboons, macaques, and gorillas, adult males as a class are usually dominant over adult females, and females are dominant over young. This may not always be true, for in several species of macaques some females may outrank some adult males *(36)*, although groups dominated by a female (such as the Minoo-B troop of Japanese macaques) are extremely rare *(41)*. Dominance relationships may be quite unstructured, as in the chimpanzee *(20)*, where dominance is expressed in interactions between individuals but where these relationships are not organized into any sort of hierarchy. A much more common situation is one in which dominance relations, among males at least, are organized into linear hierarchies that are quite stable over time, as in baboons *(37)*, langurs *(34, 42)*, and macaques *(43, 44)*. Sometimes these dominance hierarchies are complicated by alliances among several males who back each other up very effectively *(37)* or even by an alliance between a male and a female *(36)*. Although dominance varies widely among monkeys and apes both in its form and function, it is certainly one of the most important axes of social organization to be found in primate societies.

GENEALOGICAL RELATIONSHIPS

Recognition of individual animals and repeated studies of the same groups have opened the way to the appreciation of other long-continuing social relationships in monkeys and apes which cannot be interpreted in terms of dominance alone. Long-term studies of free-ranging animals have been made on only two species of nonhuman primates, Japanese macaques, which have been studied since 1950 by members of the Japan Monkey Centre, and Indian rhesus macaques living free on Cayo Santiago, Puerto Rico, the island colony established by Carpenter in 1938. In these studies, when the genealogy of the animals has been known, it has been obvious that genetic relationships play a major role in determining the course and nature of social interactions *(41, 45–47)*. It becomes clear that bonds between mother and infant may persist into adult life to form a nucleus from which many other social bonds ramify. When the genealogy of individual animals is known, members of commonly observed subgroupings, such as a cluster of four or five animals grooming or resting together, are likely to be uterine kin. For example, members of a subgroup composed of several adult animals, both male and female, as well as juveniles and infants, may all be offspring of the same female *(47)*. These relations continue to be very important in adult life not only in relaxed affectional relationships but also in dominance interactions. Sade saw a female rhesus monkey divert the attack of a dominant male from her adult son and saw another adult female protect her juvenile half-sisters (paternity is not determinable in most monkey societies). There is a very high frequency of grooming between related animals, and many animals never seek grooming partners outside of their own genealogies.

It should be stressed that there is no information leading us to believe that these animals are either recognizing genetic relationships or responding to any sort of abstract concept of family. Rather these social relationships are determined by the necessarily close association of mother with newborn infant, which is extended through time and generations and which ramifies into close associations among siblings. We believe that this pattern of enduring social relations between a mother and her offspring will be found in other species of primates. Because of their dramatic character, the importance of dominance and aggression has been greatly exaggerated compared to that of continuing, positive, affectional relations between related animals as expressed by their sitting or feeding together, touching, and grooming. Much of this behavior can be observed easily in the field, but the extent to which it is in fact an expression of social genealogics has been demonstrated only in the studies cited above.

Positive, affectional relations are not limited to relatives. Male Japanese macaques may take care of young by forming special protective relationships with particular infants (48), but whether these males have any special relationship to the infants as either father or brother is uncertain, and the mating system is such that paternity cannot be known either to the observer or to the monkeys. MacRoberts (49) has recorded a very high frequency of care of infants by males in the Gibraltar macaque. In addition, he has demonstrated that these positive protective relations are very beneficial to the juvenile. Two juveniles which had no such close relationship were forced to be peripheral, were at a great disadvantage in feeding, and were groomed much less than other juveniles in the group.

The status of the adult can be conferred on closely associated young (frequently an offspring when the adult is female), and for this reason the young of dominant animals are more likely to be dominant. This inheritance of rank has been discussed by Imanishi (45) for the Japanese macaque and by Koford (46) for the rhesus. Sons of very dominant females seem to have a great advantage over other males both because their mothers are able to back them up successfully in social interactions and because they stay with their mothers near the other dominant animals at the center of the group. They may never go through the stage of being socially and physically peripheral to the group which is typical for young males of these species. A male cannot simply "inherit" high rank; he must also win this position through his own abilities, but his chances of so doing are greatly increased if he has had these early experiences of associating with and being supported by very dominant animals.

There could hardly be a greater contrast than that between the emerging picture of an orderly society, based heavily on affectionate or cooperative social actions and structured by stable dominance relationships, and the old notion of an unruly horde of monkeys dominated by a tyrant. The 19th-century social evolutionists attributed less order to the societies of primitive man than is now known to exist in the societies of monkeys and apes living today.

COMMUNICATION

Research on the communication systems of monkeys and apes through 1962 has been most ably summarized and interpreted by Marler (52). Most of the data represent work by field observers who were primarily interested in social structure, and the signals, and their meanings, used to implement and facilitate social interactions were more or less taken for granted. Only in the last year or so have communication systems themselves been the object of careful study and analysis (see, for example, 18). Marler has emphasized both the extraordinary complexity of the communication systems of primates and the heavy dependence of these systems on composite signals (50). Most frequently it is not a single signal that passes between two animals but a signal complex composed of auditory, visual, tactile, and, more rarely, olfactory signals.

Communication in some monkey species is based on a system of intergrading signals, whereas in others much more use is made of highly discrete signals. For example, most vervet sounds (described by Struhsaker, 51) are of the discrete type, there being some 36 different sounds that are comparatively distinct both to the human ear and when analyzed by a sound spectrograph. In contrast, Rowell and Hinde have analyzed the sounds of the rhesus monkey (52) and found that of 13 harsh noises, 9 belonged to a single intergrading subsystem expressing agonistic emotions.

As more and more study is done on primates it will probably be shown that their communication systems tend to be of mixed form in that both graded and discrete signals are used depending on the relative efficiency of one or the other form in serving a specific function. In concert this use of both discrete and intergrading signals and of composites from several sensory modes produces a rich potential for the expression of very slight but significant changes in the intensity and nature of mood in the signaling animal. Marler has emphasized (50) that, except for calls warning of danger, the communication system is little applied to events outside the group. Communication systems in monkeys and apes are highly evolved in their capacity to express motivation of individuals and to facilitate social relationships. Without this ability to express mood, monkeys and apes would not be able to engage in the subtle and complicated social interactions that are a major feature of their adaptations.

SOCIAL LEARNING

Harlow and Harlow's experiments (53) show the importance of learning in the development of social life; however, monkeys and apes are so constituted that, except in the laboratory, social learning is inevitable. They adapt by their social life, and the group provides the context of affection, protection, and stability in which learning occurs. No one factor can explain the importance of social behavior, because society is a major adaptive mechanism with many functions, but one of the most important of these functions is the provision of a rich and protected social context in which young mature. Field observations, although mainly observations of the results of learning rather than of the process itself, provide necessary clues as to the nature of the integration of relevant developmental and social factors. These factors can then be estimated and defined for subsequent intensive controlled research in a laboratory or colony.

It has become clear that, although learning has great importance in the normal development of nearly all phases of primate behavior, it is not a generalized ability; animals are able to learn some things with great ease and other things only with the greatest difficulty. Learning is part of the adaptive pattern of a species and can be understood only when it is seen as the process of acquiring skills and attitudes that are of evolutionary significance to a species when living in the environment to which it is adapted.

There are important biological limitations which vary from species to species and which do not reflect differences in intelligence so much as differences in specializations. For example, Goodall (21) has observed young chimpanzees learning to fish for termites both by their observation of older chimpanzees and by practice. It takes time for the chimpanzee to become proficient with these tools, and many mistakes are made. Chimpanzees are not the only primates that like termites, and Goodall has observed baboons sitting near chimpanzees watching and waiting while the latter are getting termites. The baboons are just as eager as the chimpanzees to eat termites but are unable to learn how to fish for termites for themselves.

It is likely that there are important variables among groups of a single species that make it possible for the acquisition of new patterns of behavior or the expression of basic learned species patterns to vary from group to group and from one habitat to another. For example, the nature of the integration and operation of a social unit vary in the extent to which it depends on the personalities of individuals in the group — this is another dimension of our understanding of how social behavior may affect species survival. Particularly aggressive adult males can make the behavior of their groups relative to that of adjacent groups with less assertive males substantially different. For example, a group with very aggressive males can control a larger geographic area than is occupied by a group with much less aggressive males. The tenor of life within a group may be tenser or more relaxed depending on personalities of adults in the group.

Imprinting has traditionally been distinguished from other learning processes by the fact that in imprinting the young animal will learn to follow, to be social (54), without an external or immediate reward (55).

However, among monkeys and apes, simply being with other animals is a reward, and learning is reinforced by the affectional, attentive, supportive social context of the group (56). Butler was the first to use the sight of another monkey as a reward in psychological experiments (57). The field worker sees sick and practically disabled animals making great efforts to stay with their group. Among ground-living forms, animals that have lost or broken limbs or are so sick that they collapse as soon as the group stops moving, all walk along as the troop moves. Instances of wounded rhesus macaques' moving into langur groups after the rhesus have left or been forced out of their own group have been recorded. Clearly, it is essential for the young monkey or ape to mature in a social setting in which it learns appropriate skills and relationships during early years and in which it continues to learn during adulthood. "Where the individual primate is, in temporary isolation, learning a task without reference to any other member of its species, the learning is not normal" (58).

FUTURE PRIMATE STUDIES

At present many long-term studies are in process and major films are being edited (Goodall on chimpanzee and DeVore on baboon). There will be about twice as many major accounts available in 2 years as there are now. Since it is now clear that detailed descriptive studies of undisturbed free-ranging primates can be made, and since available data show that there are substantial differences in the behavior of the different species, more species should be investigated. So far studies have concentrated for the most part on the larger ground-living forms which are easier to study. There is no study of *Cercocebus*, little on *Colobus* (59), and nothing on the numerous langurs (*Presbytis*) of southeast Asia. New World monkeys have been investigated very little, and there are numerous genera that have not been the subjects of a major field study. Also, since local variation is important, forms such as the chimpanzee and gorilla should be studied in more and contrasting localities.

Once the general characteristics of the behaviors of several species are known, then interest can shift to topics such as detailed ecology, birth, infant behavior, peer groups, affectionate behaviors, sex, or dominance, to mention only a few. The behavior of a whole species is a large problem, and description has to be at a very general level when the goal is a first general statement. A problem-oriented study permits choice of species and elaboration of techniques. A further advantage of the problem-oriented approach is that it allows the close coordination of the field work with experimental work in the laboratory. Fortunately, no division has developed between those doing the field work and those involved in the experimental analysis of behavior. Many scientists have done both controlled experiments and field studies. The interplay between naturalistic observation and controlled experiment is the essential key to the understanding of behavior *(60)*. The character of the natural adaptation of the species and the dimensions of the society can be determined only in the field. Many topics, such as geographic range, food, predation, group size, aggression, and the like, can be seen only under field conditions. But the mechanisms of the observed behavior can be determined only in the laboratory, and this is the more complicated task. The relation of a field study to scientific understanding is like the relation of the observation that a man walks or runs to the whole analysis of locomotion. The field worker lists what the animals eat, but this gives no understanding of nutrition. The kinds of interactions may be charted in the field, but their interpretation requires the laboratory. Field workers saw hours devoted to play, but it was Harlow's experiments that showed how essential this activity was to the development of behavior. As the field studies develop it is to be hoped that they will maintain a close relation to controlled experiment. It is most fortunate that the present studies are being carried on by anthropologists, psychologists, and zoologists. An understanding of behavior is most likely to come from the bringing together of the methods and interests of many sciences, and we hope that the field studies remain a part of general behavioral science and do not become independent as workers and problems become more and more numerous.

Even now, in their preliminary state, the field studies can offer some conclusions that might be pondered by students in the multiplicity of departments now dividing up the study of human behavior. Behavior is profoundly influenced by the biology of the species, and problems of perception, emotion, aggression, and many others cannot be divorced from the biology of the actors in the social system. Early learning is important, and an understanding of the preschool years is essential to an understanding of behavior. Play is tremendously important, and a species that wastes the emotions and energies of its young by divorcing play from education has forfeited its evolutionary heritage — the biological motivation of learning. Social behavior is relatively simple compared to the biological mechanisms that make the behavior possible. Ultimately a science of human behavior must include both biological and social factors, and there is no more reason to separate the study of human behavior into many compartments than there would be to separate the field studies from the intellectual enrichment coming from the laboratory.

REFERENCES

1. R. M. Yerkes and A. W. Yerkes, *The Great Apes, A Study of Anthropoid Life* (New Haven: Yale Univ. Press, 1929).
2. H. W. Nissen, "A Field Study of the Chimpanzee," *Comp. Psychol. Monogr. No. 8* (1931).

3. H. C. Bingham, "Gorillas in a Native Habitat," *Carnegie Inst. Wash. Publ. No. 426* (1932).

4. C. R. Carpenter, "A Field Study of the Behavior and Social Relations of Howling Monkeys," *Comp. Psych. Monogr. No. 10* (1934).

5. S. Zuckerman, *The Social Life of Monkeys and Apes* (London: Routledge and Kegan Paul, 1932); *Functional Affinities and Man, Monkeys and Apes* (London: Routledge and Kegan Paul, 1933).

6. C. R. Carpenter, "A Field Study in Siam of the Behavior and Social Relations of the Gibbon, *Hylobates lar.*," *Comp. Psychol. Monogr. No. 16* (1940).

7. E. A. Hooton, *Man's Poor Relations* (Garden City, N.Y.: Doubleday, 1942).

8. K. R. L. Hall, *Proc. Zool. Soc. London 14*:265 (1965).

9. W. Köhler, *The Mentality of Apes* (New York: Harcourt Brace, 1925).

10. J. Buettner-Janusch, ed., "The Relatives of Man," *Ann. N.Y. Acad. Sci. 102*:181–514 (1962); J. Buettner-Janusch, ed., *Evolutionary and Genetic Biology of Primates* (New York: Academic Press, 1963–1964).

11. S. L. Washburn, ed., *Classification and Human Evolution*, Viking Fund Publications in Anthropology No. 37 (Aldine, New York, 1963).

12. J. Napier and N. Barnicot, eds., "The Primates," *Symp. Zool. Soc. London No. 10* (1963).

13. I. DeVore, ed. *Primate Behavior: Field Studies of Monkeys and Apes* (New York: Holt, Rinehart and Winston, 1965).

14. C. R. Carpenter, *Naturalistic Behavior of Nonhuman Primates* (University Park: Pennsylvania State Univ. Press, 1964).

15. C. H. Southwick, ed., *Primate Social Behavior* (Princeton: Van Nostrand, 1963).

16. S. Eimerl and I. DeVore, *The Primates* (New York: Time, Inc., 1965).

17. P. Jay, in *Behavior of Nonhuman Primates*, A. M. Schrier, H. F. Harlow, F. Stollnitz, eds. (New York: Academic Press, 1965), pp. 525–591.

18. S. A. Altmann, ed., "Social Communication among Primates" (Chicago: Univ. of Chicago Press, 1967).

19. G. Schaller, *The Mountain Gorilla: Ecology and Behavior* (Chicago: Univ. of Chicago Press, 1963).

20. J. Goodall, *Primate Behavior: Field Studies of Monkeys and Apes*, I. DeVore, ed. (New York: Holt, Rinehart and Winston, 1965), pp. 425–473.

21. ———, *Nature 201*:1264 (1964).

22. K. R. L. Hall, *Current Anthropol. 4*(5):479 (1963).

23. J. B. Lancaster, "Chimpanzee Tool Use," paper presented at Southwestern Anthropological Association annual meeting, Los Angeles, Calif. (Apr. 1965).

24. I. DeVore and K. R. L. Hall, in *Primate Behavior: Field Studies of Monkeys and Apes* (New York: Holt, Rinehart and Winston, 1965), pp. 20–52.

25. "Baboon Behavior," motion picture produced by I. DeVore and S. L. Washburn, University Extension, Univ. of California, Berkeley (1961).

26. I. DeVore, personal communication (1965).

27. A. J. Haddow, *Proc. Zool. Soc. London* 122 (II):297 (1952).

28. P. Jay and D. Lindburg, "The Indian Primate Ecology Project (September 1964–June 1965)," unpublished manuscript.

29. C. H. Southwick, M. A. Beg, M. R. Siddiqi, *Ecology* 42:538 (1961); *ibid.*, p. 698.

30. J. B. Lancaster and R. B. Lee, in *Primate Behavior: Field Studies of Monkeys and Apes*, I. DeVore, ed. (New York: Holt, Rinehart and Winston, 1965), pp. 486–513.

31. M. Mizuhara, personal communication (1965), quoted by Lancaster and Lee *(30)*.

32. C. B. Koford, in *Primate Behavior: Field Studies of Monkeys and Apes*, I. DeVore, ed. (New York: Holt, Rinehart and Winston, 1965), pp. 160–174.

33. A. H. Schultz, *Anat. Rec.* 72:387 (1938).

34. P. Jay in *Primate Behavior: Field Studies of Monkeys and Apes*, I. DeVore, ed. (New York: Holt, Rinehart and Winston, 1965), pp. 197–249.

35. H. Kummer and F. Kurt, *Folia Primatologica* 1.4 (1963).

36. P. E. Simonds, in *Primate Behavior: Field Studies of Monkeys and Apes*, I. DeVore, ed. (New York: Holt, Rinehart and Winston, 1965), pp. 175–196.

37. K. R. L. Hall and I. DeVore, in *Primate Behavior: Field Studies of Monkeys and Apes*, I. DeVore, ed. (New York: Holt, Rinehart and Winston, 1965), pp. 53–110.

38. K. Tokuda, *Primates* 3:1 (1961–62).

39. C. H. Conaway and C. B. Koford, *J. Mammal.* 45:577 (1965).

40. C. Southwick, in *Primate Behavior: Field Studies of Monkeys and Apes*, I. DeVore, ed. (New York: Holt, Rinehart and Winston, 1965), pp. 111–159.

41. M. Yamada, *Primates* 4:43 (1963).

42. S. Ripley, in "Social Communication among Primates," S. Altmann, ed. (Chicago: Univ. of Chicago Press, 1967).

43. S. A. Altmann, *Ann. N.Y. Acad. Sci.* 102:338 (1962).

44. J. Itani, R. Tokuda, Y. Furuya, K. Kano, Y. Shin, *Primates* 4:1 (1963).
45. K. Imanishi, *Current Anthropol.* 1:393 (1960).
46. C. B. Koford, *Science* 141:356 (1963).
47. D. S. Sade, *Am. J. Phys. Anthropol.* 23:1 (1965).
48. J. Itani, *Primates* 4:1 (1959).
49. M. MacRoberts, "Gibraltar macaques," paper presented at Southwestern Anthropological Association annual meeting, Los Angeles, Calif. (Apr. 1965).
50. P. Marler, in *Primate Behavior: Field Studies of Monkeys and Apes,* I. DeVore, ed. (New York: Holt, Rinehart, and Winston, 1965), pp. 544–584.
51. T. T. Struhsaker, in "Social Communication among Primates," S. A. Altmann, ed. (Chicago: Univ. of Chicago Press, 1967).
52. T. E. Rowell and R. A. Hinde, *Proc. Zool. Soc. London* 138:279 (1962); T. E. Rowell, *Symp. Zool. Soc. London* 8:91 (1962).
53. H. F. Harlow and M. K. Harlow, in *Behavior of Nonhuman Primates,* A. M. Schrier, H. F. Harlow, F. Stollnitz, eds. (New York: Academic Press, 1965), vol. 2, pp. 287–334.
54. N. E. Collias, in *Roots of Behavior,* E. L. Bliss, ed. (New York: Harper, 1962), pp. 264–273.
55. W. Sluckin, *Imprinting and Early Learning* (Chicago: Aldine, 1965).
56. K. R. L. Hall, *Brit. J. Psychol.* 54:201 (1963).
57. R. A. Butler, *J. Exp. Psychol.* 48:19 (1954).
58. K. R. L. Hall, unpublished manuscript.
59. W. Ulrich, *Zool. Garten* 25:305 (1961).
60. W. A. Mason, in *Primate Behavior: Field Studies of Monkeys and Apes,* I. DeVore, ed. (New York: Holt, Rinehart and Winston, 1965), pp. 514–543.

HANS KUMMER

*In this article Kummer likens a primate social group, at some
levels of organization, to an organism. He thus makes one of the
earliest statements on types of integration characteristic of
primate groups, and emphasizes what he terms the "motivational
and organizational raw materials" upon and from which groups
are structured and operate. A social group is a complex and
integrated structure that is responsive to the environment and to
pressures from within the group itself. A group's form or
structure, then, is strongly affected by the broad social and
ecological context within which it developed over time and by
the circumstances in which it operates on a day-to-day basis.
Each individual animal has a place in the web of interactions that
structure group life into a functionally meaningful network of
relationships.*

*Kummer begins by looking at the individual group member
and continues on to group norms of behavior. In so doing he
reaches the conclusion that individual patterns of social
behaviors, that is, the stereotyped or regular items of behavior
that each individual exhibits, are related to the general taxonomic
position of the species. In contrast, social organizations, or the
structures of groups, are less directly correlated with the
taxonomic relationships of groups or with the specific patterns
of behavior characteristic of the members of a species. In his own
words, "Improbable as it sounds, social behavior as we have so
far described it cannot be the cause of differences in social
organization." This major conclusion is in basic agreement with
the more recent work of many other researchers concerned with
primate behavior.*

*Kummer acknowledges that the analogy between a primate
social group and an organism breaks down when the discussion
turns to the ontogeny of new groupings. To illustrate how similar
social structures may have developed in very different kinds of
primates, he suggests that the appearance of one-male units, for
example, may represent convergent group evolution based on
different behaviors and on differing motivational elements.
Although this has not been demonstrated with any certainty, it
appears to be a likely hypothesis.*

*By asking what the motivational elements are that lead to or are
important in shaping different general types of social groupings
among nonhuman primates, Kummer is seeking a re-evaluation*

of common elements of behavior in terms that have not previously characterized the thinking of those who study the primates. He is asking the investigator to set aside, for the moment, the traditional boundaries imposed by taxonomic divisions and to look further — to the environment, both social and ecological, in which groups actually live and to which they have had to adapt in order to survive.

16 Dimensions of a Comparative Biology of Primate Groups

Eight years have now passed since field studies on primate behavior became the active concern of a group of anthropologists in this country, and the broader anthropological audience may rightly ask what this group has done and where they are heading. . . . This paper, therefore, is not a review of facts but an attempt to familiarize the morphologist and physiologist with the special nature of our task in the field.

Let us first ask why we seek our subjects in their native habitats. Every biologist knows that a living system should be grown and studied in as many different environments as possible. No single environment reveals all the phenotypic modifications of which a genotype is capable. Captive animals may develop adaptive behavior patterns that are never observed in their wild conspecifics, and vice versa. It follows that there is nothing basically superior or sacred about studying animals in their natural habitat. Any controversy about a general superiority of either laboratory or field studies is pointless if we agree that our ultimate aim is not a description of one single modification, but an idea of the full genetic potential of our species.[1] A particular environment is a good or a bad choice only in relation to the questions we ask.

From *American Journal of Physical Anthropology*, Vol. 27, pp. 357–366. Reprinted by permission of the Wistar Institute of Anatomy and Biology, Philadelphia, and the author.
[1] For a discussion of the relationship of field and laboratory work, see Menzel ('67).

The biologist interested in primate behavior has two reasons for going to the field. The first is his interest in behavior as a means of survival. Behavior can become adaptive in a particular environment either because its genetic substrate was selected by this or a similar environment or because the environment evokes adaptive modifications from the genetic substrate of the present generation. The highest degree of adaptiveness will generally be found in an environment that shaped both the genotypes and the modifications of the genetic substrate of the animals studied. For a given population, this environment is most likely the one in which it presently occurs.

The second reason for field studies is the need to observe *group* behavior. We may without difficulty buy individuals for our laboratory studies, but as yet no dealer sells us an entire group as he found it in the wild. We may have the courage to assemble the system which we are going to study, but before we do so we should learn as much as possible about these fragile structures in their native habitat. For this second reason, the study of social groups may be considered the typical task of field work on primates. The study of social groups will also be the frame of this discussion.

As a first approximation, a social group can be approached as merely another living system, as a form of compound organism which appeared late in phylogeny and in which the metazoan individual is no longer the whole but a part. The organism analogy at one time played its heuristic role in the study of social insects. We shall use it here because it permits us to start out from familiar biological dimensions. We shall ask the questions that every biologist asks when he faces a new kind of organism, namely those concerning the anatomy, the physiology, the ontogeny, the ecology, and the evolution of the "group organism." In answering each of these questions, we shall arrive at a point where the analogy with the organism no longer holds and where the vertebrate group as a form of life reveals its own characteristics. To the biologist working in other fields, these points will best demonstrate the problems of studies on primate societies.

The primate species of the open country of East and South Africa serve as examples throughout this paper. Their social organizations show two basic types of groups in various combinations: the multi-male group, in which several adult males live with a number of females and their offspring, and the one-male group, in which females and young are associated with only one male. The multi-male group is typical of the savanna baboons (*Papio anubis, P. cynocephalus, P. ursinus*). In these groups, each male potentially has access to each female (Hall and DeVore, '65). The patas monkeys (*Erythrocebus patas*) of Uganda represent the other extreme; their organizational units are one-male groups which live far apart from each other (Hall, '65). Between these two extremes there are two species that show a combination of the two types of groups. In *Papio hamadryas*, the "desert baboon" of Ethiopia, a number of one-male groups together form a larger association, the "band," which travels and fights as a unit. The band resembles the multi-male group of the savanna baboons except that each female is the exclusive partner of one and only one male (Kummer, '67). A similar two-level organization is found in the gelada baboons (*Theropithecus gelada*) of the Ethiopian highlands. But the gelada one-male groups are more independent of each other; they separate when food is scarce; and, although they join to form large troops, there is no evidence that several one-male groups form a stable well-organized association with the pattern of the hamadryas band (Crook, '66).

GROUP ANATOMY

Like an amoeba, a group constantly changes its shape in space, but certain arrangements of the members of the group occur more frequently than others. Some of them hit the eye immediately. In baboons and macaques, females tend to hold the center of the group with a few dominant males, whereas younger males are more peripheral. This general arrangement, however, can be modified according to the situation. In a troop of geladas walking along the edge of a vertical cliff, the females walk close to the edge, shielded only on the farther side by a belt of large males. When two one-male groups of hamadryas baboons forage in the savanna, their females will form a line between the males. But if the two males start to threaten each other, each set of females swings outward to line up behind its respective male and away from the other group. The obvious advantage of flexible anatomy is that the group can cope with certain situations simply by altering its shape.

The exact quantitative analysis of a group's spacing pattern is rather difficult. My own preliminary attempts have failed because the animals under experimental conditions did not keep one particular arrangement for more than seconds or minutes. Maps of spatial arrangements of hamadryas baboons in the field nevertheless showed that certain simple characteristics survive most changes in formation. For example, the animals of a particular sex-age class are usually surrounded by neighbors of a typical sex-age distribution, and this reveals much about the affinities between the classes.

Although we know so little yet about the spatial dimensions of groups, the question "What is a group?" is in practice answered most often and with reasonable success on the basis of a spatial criterion. In general, a spatial aggregation of primates that travel and rest together and at the same time avoid the proximity of other such aggregations is, at closer inspection, also a functional and reproductive unit.

GROUP PHYSIOLOGY

The members of a group, like the cells of an organism, exchange signals that affect the activity as well as the development of the members that receive them. The effect is a more or less coordinated activity of the group as a whole. From what has been said about the loose spatial structure of the group, it is obvious that group physiology faces a particular task in merely maintaining the group's identity within the population. The individual primate, unlike the metazoan cell, can physically leave the body of the group and survive on his own, at least for some time. In addition, since he is not biochemically earmarked as a stranger, he can enter another group and become its member. Why, then, are certain primate groups as stable in membership as we have found them in the field? What is the "immunological" process by which the stranger is recognized and rejected? Here again, we know next to nothing. One might hypothesize that the members of each group share certain behavioral or morphological traits by which they are recognized, and this may most likely be true in species where the groups respond to each other with "territorial" calls. The alternative is that primates know the members of their group as individuals and recognize a stranger by exclusion, as an unfamiliar individual.

Beyond the necessity of differentiating between strangers and group members, the closed group must have mechanisms of actual inclusion and exclusion if it is to maintain its integrity. Some members of the same species must attract or tolerate each other while avoiding or chasing away others. Groups of savanna baboons avoid each other, and occasional strangers lingering about the group are chased away, although with persistence they may finally enter the group. A patas male spotting another male near his own group will simply chase the stranger away. The integrity of the group is in these cases maintained by the use of distance as an isolating agent. This widespread and relatively primitive technique, however, is obviously replaced by others in species such as the gelada or the hamadryas, where several small groups join to form larger social units without losing their identity. Although the one-male groups of a hamadryas band travel and rest so close together that it can take hours to tell the groups apart, the members of each one-male group mate and groom only among themselves. The spatial proximity of these groups does not destroy their isolation where social interactions are involved. In hamadryas, the mechanisms that maintain this segregation are not the same for females and males. By themselves, the females do not refrain from interacting with other band members, and they actually manage to do so when their male is not watching. Their isolation is imposed on them by the male, who threatens and even bites them when they move too far away from him or when they try to mate or groom with members of other one-male groups. The male hamadryas, in contrast, refrains from mating or grooming with outsiders for reasons not apparent to an external observer. Even a male to whom other animals submit in other contexts will not interact with the females of subordinate males. Of the nature of this inhibition we know nothing except that it is probably limited to the members of the same band: one-male groups artificially transplanted into a distant area are attacked by the local males, and their females are distributed among the resident males without any fighting among the new "owners." Such experimental transplantations may soon teach us more about the mechanisms of exclusion and the permeability of group boundaries.

A closed primate group not only maintains its composition but also travels as a closed body, in a coordinated fashion. How do its members determine the direction of their common travel? In a gorilla group, the members attend to and follow their leader, the single silver-backed male (Schaller, '63). But in a large hamadryas troop ready for departure from a resting place there are several such old males, and the younger males, in addition, reveal clear directional intentions of their own. The ultimate direction is determined by a process in which younger males walk away from the troop in the direction of their choice, thus forming troop "pseudopods" in various directions. The troop, however, does not follow them until an older male accepts one of the proposed directions by walking toward one of the pseudopods. At this signal, the younger males in the pseudopod start out in the indicated direction, and the troop follows with the older males in the rear. In this case, the functioning order reveals two male "roles": the role of initiative, typical of younger males, and the role of decision, taken in turn by one of the older males of the troop.

Functioning orders of vertebrate groups are most frequently described by the term "dominance." In its classical definition, a dominance order is the relatively stable sequence in which the animals of an established group have access to an "incentive," such as a piece of food or a desired social partner. The emphasis that this concept puts on the competitive aspect of group life betrays its origin, the laboratory In the captive group, competition is indeed a prominent feature of social order, more so, it seems, than in the wild. Field studies show that group function is based on a number of additional orders, which have little to do with sequences of access. Drawing again on the hamadryas data, we find that the number of females belonging to a male (a classical criterion of dominance) is not correlated with his influence on the troop's travel direction: younger males have more females than older males, but it is the older males that determine where the troop will go. The dominance concept, often used so broadly as to be ambiguous and misleading, must be complemented by other concepts. Among the social "roles" (*cf.* Bernstein and Sharpe, '66), which may or may not be correlated with classical dominance, the following may be mentioned:

(1) *Leadership* can be provisionally defined as the probability with which an animal's movements in space are taken over by others. The hamadryas example shows that leadership must not be correlated with classical dominance.

(2) The role of *protection* may or may not rest with the dominant animal. The spatial arrangement of baboon troops suggests that the less dominant males on the troop's periphery may be more active in encounters with humans and predators.

(3) An animal may be so persistent in asserting his *exclusive access* to a particular partner that the latter becomes his social "property." The hamadryas male achieves this by interfering with his females' interactions with all other males. In a comparable way, baboon mothers are more possessive about their infants than are the mothers of langurs. Logically, this exclusiveness is the extreme expression of dominance. However, since even a mother or a male of otherwise low dominance status can establish and assert the exclusive access to a particular partner, the phenomenon of exclusiveness must be distinguished from the dominance concept and be investigated as a separate aspect of a group's functioning order.

In short, a dominant primate may be the leader or protector of his group as well as the exclusive owner of his females, but correlations between roles cannot be taken for granted. On the other hand, classical dominance can be correlated with apparently unrelated behavioral traits. In a zoo colony of hamadryas baboons, the four adult females stirred during sleep at night with frequencies that conformed exactly with their dominance order. The most dominant female stirred most rarely, the most subordinate most frequently (Kummer, '56). When the dominance order was rearranged, the frequencies of sleeping movements changed accordingly.

In all these aspects of a group's functioning order, a basic contrast to the functioning order of an organism is apparent. In a developing metazoan organism, the parts gradually differentiate as to structure and function, and at a certain stage of development this differentiation of a part becomes irreversible. The functional role of a part is then determined for the rest of the organism's life. In contrast, the only roles in a primate group that are irrevocably prescribed by morphological and functional differentiation are those of the two sexes. Within the sexes, the roles of the dominant animal, of the leader, or of the peripheral defender are not the permanent roles of clearly differentiated castes. The individual qualities of a dominant animal, for example, occur on a continuous scale throughout a group, and the actual role taken by an individual therefore depends on where his qualities place him in his particular group. The low-ranking male of this year can become the high-ranking male of next year since the relevant qualities change with age; changing alliances in the group add to the lability of role distribution. Even the roles of the two sexes are not exclusively differentiated. One female in a captive hamadryas colony showed complete male herding behavior toward the other females of her group, and the most dominant female of each of our captive gelada groups adopted male roles toward the rest of each group's females. In comparison with the tissues of an organism, the members of a vertebrate group are so similarly equipped that the distribution of roles is never quite stable, and distribution is often achieved with difficulty. In the case of dominance, the ultimate decision may only be reached by overt, aggressive competition. It is this competition for roles among similarly equipped parts in which the functioning order of the vertebrate group most clearly differs from the physiology of organisms. Human history has seen many attempts to abandon this competitive order and violent struggles to reestablish it.

CAUSES OF DIFFERENCES IN GROUP TYPE

In this section we are concerned only with the immediate causes of group organization. The question is not: why did this species evolve its present social organization? Instead, we ask, of what kind are the *immediate* motivational or behavioral causes which, in a given generation, bring about monogamous groups in one species, polygynous groups in another, and multi-male groups in still another?

Our first attempt to answer these questions consists of a close look at the social behavior of the individual group member. It has become a tradition, inherited from ethology, that a preliminary field study should include a catalogue of the gestural and vocal signals exchanged by the individuals of the respective species. In studying the signals used among the members of a species we may have hoped to discover some key signals that have a direct effect on the composition of the group. If we had any such hopes, they have failed so far. From the very similar behavioral catalogues of *Papio anubis* and *P. hamadryas* nobody could predict that anubis baboons live in basically promiscuous groups, whereas hamadryas are organized in bands composed of polygynous one-male groups. The behavior that one would expect to be an exclusive hamadryas pattern is the male's particular bite on the nape of the female's neck. This bite brings straying females back to their male and thus is the enforcer of group cohesion. But even this pattern is common to both species. The anubis baboons simply do not use it to herd females. Our captive gelada males also bit their females on the neck, but without relating this action to the female's being too far away. On the other hand, the behavioral repertoires of patas monkeys and geladas are very different, although they both are organized in one-male groups. The field studies to date suggest that the patterns of social *behavior* of a species are related to the taxonomic position of the species. Social *organizations*, however, seem to appear here and there in the order Primates without apparent relationship to taxonomy or to patterns of social behavior. Improbable as it sounds, social behavior as we have so far described it cannot be the cause of differences in social organization. We obviously must separate the two phenomena more clearly in our research than we have done so far. We must also expect to find that apparently similar, convergent organizations in distant species have different causes.

One reason for our failure to explain various types of social organizations is obvious. In the field as in the laboratory, social behavior has almost exclusively been studied on dyads, i.e., on interactions of only two animals. But to study the exclusion of a stranger from a group or the mechanisms responsible for the formation of a monogamous pair, one has to analyze the interactions of at least three animals. If this is done, the causes of differences in type of group may be found to be different affinities among sex-age classes and active interferences of one class with the interactions among two other classes. A comparison of the species forming one-male groups may give us a glimpse of the kind of causal factors we may find. The patas monkeys of Uganda and a population of Hanuman langurs near Dharwar in India (Sugiyama, '66) both live in groups of one adult male and a number of females. Apparently, the adult males of these populations do not tolerate one another in the same group. Surprisingly, however, these populations also include groups of several males without females. This suggests that there is an attraction among the males but that it breaks down in the presence of females. An observation by Sugiyama confirms this hypothesis for the langur. He has sometimes seen an all-male langur group that cooperates in expelling the single male of a one-male group and takes over its females. Immediately after that, however, the new males fight each other until one of them has expelled all the others and becomes the sole leader of the female group. In contrast with these species, the one-male groups of hamadryas and gelada baboons live together in large troops. Here, the attraction among the males seems to outweigh the disruptive effect of the females, but this effect is nevertheless apparent: hamadryas males who have no females often sit close to each other and groom each other, but those who have females keep farther apart and are never seen to groom each other. Our unpublished experiments on captive geladas have shown that the bond between two males regresses to an earlier, more hostile stage as soon as females are added: grooming disappears and aggressive behavior is resumed. Observations of the four species mentioned suggest that there are at least two causal factors determining their social organization: the degree of attraction among adult males and the degree of its reduction in the presence of females. The organizational differences between langurs, patas, geladas, and hamadryas may be an effect of different ratios of these two factors. This interpretation admittedly lacks nothing in crudeness, but it can be experimentally tested, and it seems at least to aim at the kind of phenomena that will ultimately lead to an understanding of the causes of social organizations.

GROUP ONTOGENY

We would certainly understand more about what causes various kinds of groups if we could study their development. But here, unfortunately, the organism analogy seems to fail right away. The ontogeny of an organism is the result of an ordered sequence of gene actions which initiate developmental steps and create temporary states in which the organism is especially sensitive to certain developmental stimuli. In contrast, groups appear to have no distinct life cycle; they do not go through an irreversible ageing process. Potentially the group's capacity to regenerate appears unlimited.

There is, however, a sort of "false exception." A group may be organized around one key animal whose death it cannot survive. In the extreme case, the composition and organization of the group may be so strongly affected by the key individual that the group itself assumes a life cycle, which is the effect of the behavioral ontogeny of that one critical member.

The hamadryas one-male group presents such a case. Subadult hamadryas males have a tendency to "kidnap" and mother infants and young juveniles temporarily. Single infants and juveniles that we released into hamadryas troops were adopted by single, young adult males, who behaved as typical hamadryas mothers. Left to themselves, such young adults will eventually adopt a one-year-old female of their own troop. Thus, the typical one-male group of a young adult male consists of himself and one sexually immature female. There is no overt sexual behavior in these initial groups; instead, the male handles and carries his female as if he were her mother. A number of intermediate stages between this immature form and the groups of old males suggests that the young female eventually becomes the male's sexual consort. Toward the male's early prime, the number of his females increases, for he probably adopts one or two more juvenile females and takes over adult females from older males. During early prime, the male's herding behavior is most intense, and the group's spatial cohesion is strongest. As the male approaches his late prime, however, he becomes more tolerant. His females may now stray away from him as far as 40 meters, and even then the male is unlikely to threaten them. Accordingly, the group of the ageing male decreases in size, but at the same time he becomes more influential in matters of band and troop movements. This influence can still be found in old males who have lost or given up all their females.

This development shows first that certain roles in a primate group may be specifically attributed to certain age classes, even within the time span of adulthood. Secondly, it suggests a hypothesis about the causation of the hamadryas social system: the adult hamadryas female remains a life-long follower of a particular male *because* she was so early in life adopted, mothered, and restricted by a single adult male. Whereas her mother would soon have released her from control, the male who adopted her will keep "maternal" control over her until she is fully adult. Thus, the hamadryas female never develops the independent social habits of female anubis baboons.

A strong "parental" motivation of the males may be only one way by which a species develops a system of one-male groups. Neither Crook ('66) nor Hall ('65) has found evidence of the hamadryas solution in their gelada and patas populations. Since one-male groups appeared independently in one species of each of four genera, it would not be a surprise if they arrived at their similar organizations by different pathways and by exploitation of different behavioral and motivational raw materials. These one-male units would then be typical examples of convergence.

ENVIRONMENTAL MODIFICATIONS OF GROUP STRUCTURE

When Zuckerman ('32) formulated his theory of primate social organization, he appeared to assume that all higher primates were organized in the same basic grouping pattern. Later, Carpenter's ('64) work and the field studies of the last decade suggested that each primate species has its own organization. Only the most recent studies, in which a species was observed in various parts of its distributional range, have shown that there is also a considerable intraspecific variability of social life (e.g., Gartlan and Brain, '68). Unless we assume that these intraspecific variations are genetical, we may interpret them as modifications induced by the particular physical environments. The issue could be settled experimentally by transferring random samples of the same population into different habitats where they could then be studied for at least two generations. The rhesus population introduced by Carpenter and other workers to several islands off Puerto Rico offers research opportunities in this direction, although the value must decrease with every generation that is subjected to the particular selective factors of the new environment before the comparisons are made. Modifications induced by the *social* environment can be more easily studied. It would be sufficient to raise, for example, anubis baboons in a hamadryas troop to explore the capacity of anubis to be modified toward hamadryas group life.

Another opportunity for evaluating the modifying effects of environment, although unsatisfactory, is the study of colonies established in zoological gardens and laboratory enclosures. Since these artificial environments differ in nearly all variables from the original habitat of the transferred animals, they serve merely as a test of the resistance of a social organization to a drastic, general change. Furthermore, captive groups are usually composed of individuals that have not grown up together in the same wild group. Instead of growing into an existing group, they have to build one with unfamiliar partners. If the new organization turns out to be different from that of the original population, it will not be possible to attribute the change to any particular environmental factor. But if the original grouping pattern reappears and survives into the next generation, we may assume that it is highly resistant to a wide range of environmental changes. Some species indeed have shown this stability. A colony of geladas, imported from the wild as subadults, formed one-male groups within ten days after being admitted to the 100 by 400 foot enclosure of the Delta Center. Zuckerman ('32) found that the hamadryas colonies of three different zoos were organized in one-male groups (Kummer and Kurt, '65), and the hamadryas baboons of the Sukhumi research station in Russia show the same pattern even after several generations in captivity (Bowden, '66).

Studies of groups under changed environments can, however, produce results that are more interesting than a mere demonstration of organizational stability. The hamadryas colony of the Zurich Zoo regularly displayed a behavior pattern that we never observed in wild hamadryas troops. In this pattern, called "protected threat," an animal enlists the support of a stronger individual against his opponent by a specific set of gestures. Surprisingly, the protected threat is not found in wild hamadryas, but wild anubis baboons (DeVore, '62) and rhesus monkeys (Altmann, '62) show it. This and parallel examples support the assumption (probable already on theoretical grounds) that the genetic potential of a species for social behavior and organization is broader than the overt behavior observed in the wild. Parts of the repertoire of a species must be latent, and among these latent behaviors there may be some that are overt in related species. An investigation into these latent repertoires would certainly add to our understanding of comparative social life in primates.

In interpreting the effects of a change in environment on social structure, one has to consider a possibility that can be disregarded in analogous studies on single organisms, namely the transmission of non-genetical information from one generation to the next by means of "tradition." The work at the Japanese Monkey Centre on the spreading of food habits within a group is too well known to be reviewed here. What we must realize, however, is that traditions of group life (i.e., social behavior appearing in younger animals as an enduring response to behavior of their elders) might counteract modifying effects of the physical, non-social environment. Geladas may form one-male groups in captivity because they have been socialized to do so as juveniles in the wild, and their captive-born offspring might be socialized in the same way. Only a partial reduction of the socialization process could reveal the modifications of the physical environment within one generation.

EVOLUTION AND ADAPTIVE FUNCTIONS
OF TYPES OF GROUPS

A social organization must have an evolutionary history if it is determined by genes. As we just observed, however, we have as yet no idea of the extent to which a social organization is genetically determined. We know that skeletal and many biochemical characters are under relatively precise genetic control, and we may therefore attribute changes in them during evolution to changes of genotypes. But if we find that two related species differ in their grouping patterns, we cannot decide whether the difference was caused by a change in the constituents of the gene pool or by a modification of the expression of the genotype. It is uncertain whether hamadryas baboon behavior is merely an overt display of an environmental modification which the savanna baboons would show as well if they were subjected to the hamadryas environment or whether the hamadryas organization is the result of an evolutionary change. The latter appears more likely because both the savanna baboons and the hamadryas baboons maintain their type of group in captivity, but the answer must wait for the appropriate experiments.

Regardless of the degree to which modifications and mutations contribute to a particular organization, we should eventually investigate the adaptive functions of the organization in various types of habitat. The question of adaptation has been the foremost concern of the anthropologists studying primates in the field, and therefore I should like to illustrate the kinds of speculations that we may derive from the available preliminary studies.

All three African monkey species that have been found to organize themselves in one-male groups are highly terrestrial, and all live in open habitats where food is sparse and where sleeping trees are scarce or unsafe. Since widely scattered food resources are better exploited by small groups than by large troops, independent one-male groups of the patas type may be an adaptation to the distribution of food supply. In accordance with this hypothesis, Crook ('66) found that geladas live in isolated one-male groups in areas where food is scarce. In richer areas, the one-male groups join to form large troops.

The density and quality of sleeping lairs for the night seem to be the second major factor determining the organization of the open-country species. The best sleeping trees in the habitats of patas monkeys are small and offer little protection against predators. Patas monkeys reduce the risk of predation by dispersal at nightfall: each tree is occupied by only one individual. In a hamadryas habitat, the best sleeping lairs are vertical cliffs. These cliffs, however, are often far apart, and therefore the baboons must form large sleeping parties at night. The hamadryas thus have to cope with two contradictory ecological factors; they form small foraging groups of four to eight animals during the day, but at night they congregate by hundreds on the few available cliffs. No single type of group can satisfy these contrasting needs. Accordingly, the hamadryas has developed a unique multi-level organization, in which small one-male groups, without losing their identity, are organized in large troops or sleeping parties. This interpretation does not explain the intermediate level of hamadryas organization, the band. The similarity of the band to the multi-male group of savanna baboons has already been mentioned. If, as is likely, the hamadryas has evolved from savanna baboons as a specialist of the semidesert, the hamadryas band is probably the surviving homologue of the savanna baboon group. By splitting the original group into small foraging one-male groups for the day and by developing an intergroup tolerance at night, the hamadryas may have arrived at his present three-level stage of organization which permits reversible fusion and fission according to conditions.

CONCLUSION

By subjecting the primate group to the standard questions of biological research, we have tried to point out to the biologist working in other fields some of the special characters of the group organism. The flexibility of a group's anatomy permits the group to assume various shapes, each of which may be adaptive in a special situation. On the other hand, this loose structure leaves the group with the constant task of maintaining its identity, i.e., attracting its members and excluding strangers. The functioning order of the group is further marked by the minimal morphological and functional differentiation of its members. Assumption of some of the roles or functions within the group are therefore subject to competition from a number of similarly equipped individuals. The distribution of roles has only temporary stability, for the established order is for some time recognized rather than challenged by the group members.

The immediate causes of a particular social organization apparently are not related to the repertoire of social signals but probably to the relative strength of affinities among sex-age classes and to the degree to which relationships among certain classes are tolerated or prevented by other animals in the group. The example of hamadryas baboons suggests that phylogenetically old motivations, such as maternal motivations, may assume new functions in group life. Groups in general appear to lack a genetically programmed life cycle except when they are focused on the life cycle of one key individual.

What can a comparative science of primate social organization contribute to anthropology? It may show us the repertoire of motivations and organizational elements present in the order Primates: it may show us what forms of societies have evolved on the basis of this raw material; and it may show us what kinds of inhibitions and functional readjustments of phylogenetically old motivations could lead to the types of societies presently found in nonhuman primates. What, for instance, are the motivational syndromes that can produce monogamous groups or purely male groups? Is primate monogamy, for instance, always based on the same constellation of motivational factors, regardless of whether it appears in the gibbon or in the South American *Callicebus*, or are there several ways in which primates can realize the monogamous pattern? The answers to such questions would establish a body of comparative theory and data against which the specific solutions found by human societies could be evaluated. Which factors of the group-building repertoire does man share with other primates and in which has he specialized? In short, where in the order Primates is man to be placed on the basis of the specific factors underlying social organizations?

A second group of questions concerns the modifiability of social organization. We have seen that a species may in captivity reveal organizational elements that it does not show in the wild but which are found in closely related species under natural conditions. Such observations suggest that a species has a repertoire of social organizations which is only partly realized in any single environment. How large is this latent repertoire? Man may serve as an example. His technical capacities have allowed him to occupy an enormous variety of physical environments, and this variety probably brought out at some epoch and in some place all social modifications of which he is capable. The question of tremendous practical importance is: to how many and to what new kinds of environments can man yet respond with adaptive social organizations without changing his present gene pool? Under what conditions does this capacity to modify fail, and which elements of social behavior and organization are most likely to fail under a particular condition? No nonhuman primate has had man's enormous technical ability to adapt to a large variety of habitats. Each species is more or less confined to one type of habitat, which in turn produces social organizations that vary little within each species. The full genetic potential of such species would only come to the fore if they were experimentally exposed to other environments. The results would not only reveal much more about the evolution of social life than we can presently know, but they could also yield some answers on the critical limits of our own social adaptability.

REFERENCES

Altmann, S.
    1962   "A Field Study of the Socio-Biology of Rhesus Monkeys, *Macaca Mulatta*," *Ann. N. Y. Acad. Sci* 102:338–345.

Bernstein, I. S. and L. G. Sharpe
  1966 "Social Roles in a Rhesus Monkey Group," *Behaviour*
       26:91–104.
Bowden, D.
  1966 "Primate Behavioral Research in the USSR — The
       Sukhumi Medico-Biological Station," *Folia Primat.*
       4:346–360.
Carpenter, C. R.
  1964 *Naturalistic Behavior of Nonhuman Primates.* University Park: Pennsylvania State University Press.
Crook, J.
  1966 "Gelada Baboon Herd Structure and Movement. A
       Comparative Report," *Symp. Zool. Soc. Lond.* 18:237–258.
DeVore, I.
  1962 "The Social Behavior and Organization of Baboon
       Troops." Ph.D. Thesis, Department of Anthropology,
       University of Chicago.
Gartlan, J. S. and C. K. Brain
  1968 "Ecology and Social Variability in *Cercopithecus
       Aethiops* and *C. Mitis*," in *Primates: Studies in Adaptation and Variability* (P. Jay, ed.). New York: Holt,
       Rinehart and Winston.
Hall, K. R. L.
  1965 "Behaviour and Ecology of the Wild Patas Monkey,
       Erythrocebus Patas, in Uganda," *J. Zool.* 148:15–87.
Hall, K. R. L. and I. DeVore
  1965 "Baboon Social Behavior," in *Primate Behavior* (I.
       DeVore, ed.). New York: Holt, Rinehart and Winston.
Kummer, H.
  1956 "Rangkriterien bei Mantelpavianen (Criteria of Dominance in Hamadryas Baboons)," *Revue Suisse de Zool.*
       63:288–297.
  1967 "Social Organization of Hamadryas Baboons," *Bibl.
       Primatol.* 6. Basel: Karger.
Kummer, H. and F. Kurt
  1965 "A Comparison of Social Behavior in Captive and Wild
       Hamadryas Baboons," in *The Baboon in Medical Research* (H. Vagtborg, ed.). Austin: University of Texas
       Press.
Menzel, E. W.
  1967 "Naturalistic and Experimental Research on Primates,"
       Human Development 10:170–186.
Schaller, G. B.
  1963 *The Mountain Gorilla.* Chicago: University of Chicago
       Press.

Sugiyama, Y.
   1966   "An Artificial Social Change in a Hanuman Langur
          Troop *(Presbytis Entellus),*" *Primates* 7:41–72.
Zuckerman, S.
   1932   *The Social Life of Monkeys and Apes.* London: Kegan
          Paul.

JOSÉ M. R. DELGADO

The experimental investigation of the brain by triggering activity
with radio stimulation opened new vistas in the study of
intracerebral mechanisms and behavior patterns. The results of
these experiments have changed many early ideas concerning the
workings of the brain, and, in addition, have had tremendous
implications for man in modern medicine and the control of
certain behavior pathologies. As Delgado states, these
investigations and techniques "bring the investigation of the
mind further into the domain of experimental science."

Only with recent technical advances has it been possible to
control fine stimulations of different parts of the brain with
precision, and to do so without restricting the movement of the
subject or requiring external leads from the subject to the
apparatus of stimulation. Because it is now possible to test man
and animals in an unrestricted, more natural social situation, it
has become clear that when the result of stimulation is motor
activity, the stimulated subjects direct the activity appropriately
within their surroundings. Depending upon the nature of the
stimulation, the subjects respond to three-dimensional space and
to the individuals around them.

This article discusses only a fraction of the applications and
complexities of brain radio stimulation, but a natural extension
of the results of Delgado's and his associates' work, among other
benefits, will enable the investigator of social interactions to
seek through experiments answers to far more detailed questions
concerning the motivation and nature of observed behaviors
than have ever before been possible. Newly designed telemetric
devices that can be monitored and controlled remotely, in
addition to the apparatus for radio stimulation of the brain, not
only will allow the inhibition or stimulation of specific behaviors
in the subject, but will also permit the monitoring in detail of
many physiological reactions to what is happening around the
subject in as complex a setting as the investigator wishes to
design. This combination of the stimulation of specific behaviors
and the recording of reactivity to stimuli from outside the
organism will produce critical information that has been totally
unavailable. Students of behavior have had to speculate upon the
internal mediation of the external context of daily life. They have
always had to guess rather than know, for example, the internal
reactions of individuals when they did not display the common
externally observable patterns of reaction indicating their
involvement in what was happening around them.

324

*Although Delgado does not discuss other areas of research,
the implications of radio stimulation and internal monitoring of
physiological responses may well revolutionize the study of
primate behavior. The ability to stimulate many specific kinds of
motor patterns and interactions experimentally will make it
possible to test behavior units, social relationships, learning
situations, and a myriad of other aspects of daily existence
throughout development and maturity. Expected patterns of
interaction may be manipulated to test the reactions of subjects
to unexpected actions, to challenges, or to refusals to interact.
Dominance relationships may be manipulated at will so that their
development, maintenance, and importance to the individual
and to the social group may be investigated. Qualities of
mothering and of early experience may be altered according to
design in order to investigate details of how and why a young
primate learns — from which other animals, and in what
contexts. Eventually it may be possible to use these techniques in
the field where the complex behavior of free-ranging animals
can be investigated.*

17 Brain Research and Behavioural Activity

During most of the nineteenth century, the possibility of
exciting the spinal cord and brain stem by other than physiological stimuli
was violently debated, and the excitability of the brain was completely
denied. This concept changed after G. Fritsch and E. Hitzig (1870)
pioneered experiments on anaesthetized dogs, exposing the cerebral cortex
and applying galvanic stimulation. Excitation of the posterior part of the
brain failed to give observable results, but stimulation of the fore-brain
induced movements in the contralateral portion of the body; if the intensity
was too great, generalized convulsions appeared. Clinical studies by Paul
Broca (1824–1880) showed the anatomical localization of speech areas.

Reprinted from *Endeavor*, vol. 26, no. 99, pp. 149–154 by permission of Imperial
Chemical Industries, Ltd., London.

This led to wide interest in the possibility of correlating cerebral structure with function, using either regional ablation or electrical stimulation. For many years experiments were limited to heavily sedated animals. Textbooks of cerebral physiology described pathways, reflexes, postures, and movements, but more abstract functions such as behaviour, consciousness, and memory were considered beyond the limits of physiology. At the same time, psychologists dealt with non-physical stimuli and responses and were reluctant to study neuronal phenomena. Only now is the gap between these two approaches beginning to be bridged.

One solution to the problem of exploring the awake brain was to introduce fine wires into a selected point in the central nervous system under anaesthesia, and then to study the results of stimulation one or two days later when the animal had fully recovered. J. R. Ewald (1898) pioneered this method in 1898, and W. R. Hess (1932) used it more extensively to explore the hypothalamus and other cerebral areas in unanaesthetized cats. In a series of brilliant experiments which won him a Nobel prize in 1949 (with A. E. Moniz), Hess demonstrated that autonomic functions, posture, equilibrium, movements, sleep, fear, and rage may be influenced by electrical stimulation of specific cerebral structures. For the first time it was shown that "psychological" manifestations like aggression can be induced by electrically stimulating the brain. These findings were well received in the scientific world, but did not significantly affect philosophical thinking. Nevertheless, they were as important in their day as the nineteenth-century demonstration that the contraction of a frog muscle did not depend on circulating spirits and could be physically controlled.

For two decades, implantation of electrodes in the brain attracted limited interest among biologists, but in the 1950s there was a great expansion of the new disciplines of psychosurgery, psychosomatic medicine, psychopharmacology, and physiological psychology. Many investigators realized the great potential of intracerebral explorations for the study of neural mechanisms related to behavioural activities in awake animals. New techniques were developed and refined. Electrodes were no longer inserted freehand, but according to stereotaxic co-ordinates with the aid of micromanipulators. Three dimensional anatomical maps of the brain were prepared for rats, cats, dogs, monkeys, chimpanzees, and man. The use of aseptic precautions, biologically inert materials, acrylic cements, and stainless steel anchorages permitted long-term implantation of electrodes, which in some cases were left in the brain for several years without signs of functional disturbance.

Stimulation and the recording of resulting cerebral activity required connecting wires, which limited the freedom of experimental animals. These were a serious obstacle when monkeys were used, because of their destructive skills, and made the method unsuitable for long-term stimulation or for the study of group activities. Several remote-controlled methods were therefore developed (see bibliography in Delgado, 1963a), but practical solutions to many technical problems were not found until transistors and other microminiature devices were available. Such instrumentation now permits simultaneous stimulation of, and recording from, the brain through two or more channels, using units weighing less than 60 grams. In this way it is possible to record and stimulate the activity of cerebral structures during the performance of virtually unrestricted individual and social activities.

ELECTRODES IN THE HUMAN BRAIN

As experience accumulated from animal experimentation, it was natural that several investigators considered implanting electrodes inside the human brain. In some cases of drug-resistant epilepsy, for example, it was imperative to explore the subcortical regions in depth in order to detect the regions affected by abnormal discharges so as to guide surgical treatment. Patients with intractable pain, anxiety neurosis, involuntary movements, and other disabilities could also benefit from the cerebral explorations conducted without the confinement and stress of the operating theatre. The introduction of needles and catheters into the brain was already a well-known and relatively safe procedure used by many neurosurgeons, and as the electrodes used for implantation had a smaller diameter, their introduction did not appear to involve any greater risks.

These assumptions have already been substantiated in hundreds of patients in the United States, Britain, Japan, and other countries, who have had intracerebral electrodes implanted continuously for weeks or months. At first sight, leaving wires inside the brain would seem uncomfortable or dangerous, but in reality the patients have suffered no ill effects and have not been concerned by the presence of the leads. Indeed, the use of electrodes represents a more conservative approach than the destruction of portions of the brain, which may now be regarded as necessary in the treatment of special cases of pain or involuntary movements. In some cases, long-term electrical stimulations may obviate the need irrevocably to destroy cerebral tissue by surgical operation.

Therapeutic stimulation of the human brain is paralleled by the present trend to maintain essential physiological mechanisms by electric instrumentation. The clinical success of cardiac pacemakers is well known, and many patients are alive today only because the contraction of their hearts is maintained by artificial electrical stimulation. Paralysed limbs have similarly been activated by programmed stimulators. In patients with permanent spinal block, urination may be induced by electrical activation of the bladder, thus avoiding the need for repeated catheterizations. The uniqueness of cerebral stimulation is that we can influence not only bodily functions such as gastric secretion but "psychic" activities, including memory and fear. Behavioural and mental activities are no longer unreachable, and the underlying neurophysiological mechanisms are being brought within the domain of experimental scrutiny.

MOTOR RESPONSES

In all mammals, including man, electrical stimulation of the parietal cortex induces contraction of the muscles of the opposite side of the body. This fact, discovered nearly 100 years ago, was dramatized in many textbooks with a drawing of an homunculus lying upside down in the cerebral cortex and supposedly in charge of motor performance. Today, this primitive conception has been replaced by a far more sophisticated one. Motor responses have been elicited by electrical stimulation of the motor cortex, and also of various basal parts of the brain.

Some of the evoked responses were simple contractions of a small group of muscles, resulting in flexion of a finger or extension of a limb. However, much subtler effects were often noted, especially when unrestricted animals were tested. Electrical stimulation of the brain was shown to be able to reproduce behavioural responses with a coordination and purpose indistinguishable from voluntary activity. In the cat, for example, excitation of the cortex of the cruciate sulcus evoked flexions of the contralateral hindlimb (Figure 1). The animal lowered the anterior part of its body and raised its pelvis and tail, adopting a posture enabling it to balance its weight on three legs. The evoked effect was constant if the experimental situation was kept constant, but the response was modified if the animal was subjected to sensory stimulation. If, during stimulation, the experimenter extended his hand, the cat lowered its head and rubbed it against the hand, seeking to be petted (Figure 1b). This showed that such brain stimulation of motor areas was not producing emotional disturbances inhibiting spontaneous behaviour. It also showed that spontaneous and evoked behaviour influence each other, because the evoked flexion of the hindlimb increased when the head of the cat was raised by the experimenter (Figure 1c). Motor responses evoked by stimulation of other areas of the brain (Figure 2) could be usefully directed by the animal. For example, when licking was elicited by excitation of the cortex hidden in the sulcus presylvius, activation of tongue and mouth consistently occurred and the animal looked around for something appropriate to lick, such as a bowl of milk or the experimenter's hand.

These findings have been confirmed in studies performed with monkeys in an established colony. In these animals, five seconds of stimulation of the rostral part of the left red nucleus in the base of the brain produced the following sequence of effects: interruption of existing activities, change in facial expression, turning to the right, standing up on two feet, walking with erect posture around the cage (Figure 3), climbing the wall, and then descending to the floor. Immediately after stimulation, the monkey vocalized once or twice, stood on all fours with a threatening attitude, opened its

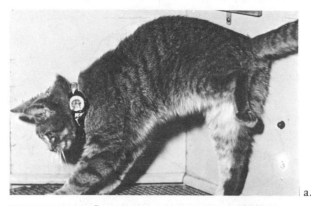

a.

b.

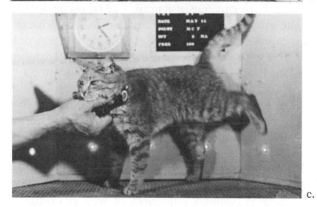

c.

FIGURE 1

(a) Electrical stimulation of the right motor cortex elicited flexion of the left hindlimb, with perfect postural adaptation and without emotional disturbance. (b) During motor cortex stimulation the animal was as friendly as usual. Because its head was lowered during petting, the evoked leg lifting was greater. (c) Evoked leg movement was modified if the cat's head was raised (Delgado 1964).

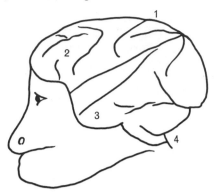

FIGURE 2   DIAGRAM OF THE BRAIN

1. The motor cortex extends over the lateral surface of the brain and also within some of its folds (in the cat, some of these areas are located more rostrally within the sulcus cruciatus and sulcus presylvius). Its stimulation evoked a wide variety of movements.

2. The septal area is located in the depth of the frontal lobe. Its stimulation inhibits aggressive behaviour.

3. The amygdala is in the depth of the temporal lobe. The stimulation of some of its points seems to be pleasant to monkeys.

4. Stimulation of the tectal area and central grey, located in the depth of the posterior part of the brain, may induce fear.

mouth, flattened both ears, raised its tail, looked menacingly at a particular monkey in the group, and then resumed normal activities. This complex sequence was repeated as many times as stimulation was delivered, and in one monkey the evoked effects continued even after more than 20,000 stimulations had been applied, each for five seconds once a minute, over a period of two weeks. These responses were not just a stereotyped contraction of muscles, but were well organized and adapted to changing circumstances. The general sequence of events was always maintained, although the details varied according to the initial posture, proximity of other animals, and other factors. This is not an isolated observation: a great variety of motor responses has been obtained by brain stimulation in awake animals, including many of the movements observed during spontaneous behaviour, as well as complex sequences of well co-ordinated activities.

TRIGGERING OF PHYSIOLOGICAL MECHANISMS

The performance of even such a simple motor act as leg flexion requires a precise and progressive contraction of several muscles, determined by the processing of a large number of messages coming from joints and muscle spindles and integrated with a vast amount of informa-

FIGURE 3

The first three pictures show the effect of radio stimulation in the red nucleus. Well-organized sequential behaviour was induced, the monkey rising and walking round the cage on two feet. The fourth picture shows the effect of stimulation of a point located 3 mm away from the previous one: yawning was induced, demonstrating the specificity of brain stimulation.

tion stored in the central nervous system. The complexity of the neurophysiological events is naturally far greater during the performance of sequential behaviour, and the physiological mechanisms involved in spontaneous motility must be highly sophisticated. In contrast, electrical stimulation of the brain of the kind we have been considering is very simple and depends on a train of pulses applied — without modulation, without code, and without feedback — to a group of neurons which by chance are located within the artificially created electrical field.

How can we explain this contradiction of the observed responses? When considering whether a simple electrical stimulus could be the cause of the many events of behavioural responses, we may ask whether the finger of the officer who pushes a button to launch a man into orbit is responsible for the complexity of the machinery or for the subsequent sequence of events. In this case, the finger is only the trigger of an already programmed series of events; similarly, the electrical stimulus applied to the brain is the trigger of the sequence of motor responses. It is sufficient to assume that the stimulus initiates a chain reaction in which the final effect depends on the functional properties of the activated structures rather than on the initial stimulation.

Behaviour requires a sequence of motor acts typical, within a range of variability, for each behavioural category. Suppose, for example, that we offer a banana to a monkey. His first response is one of orientation, looking at and recognizing the meaning of the object presented. Then, if the animal is hungry and unafraid, there is an approaching response, walking a few steps and extending the paw to reach for the food. The sequence culminates with the cleaning, licking, biting, chewing, and swallowing of the food. The sequences of acts are linked to each other in the behavioural pattern of food intake, but none of them is exclusively alimentary. Thus the monkey may orient his attention in response to many different stimuli; may use its limbs for other purposes; may swallow because it is anxious; may bite during a fight; and so on. Each one of these behavioural fragments probably has anatomical and functional representation inside the brain. According to a theory of fragmental organization of behaviour that I have proposed (1964), the motor performance of each fragment depends on a set of cerebral structures that may be modified and simplified by usage. The co-ordination of the fragments in time and space which is necessary for organized performance of a complete behavioural sequence depends on a different set of cerebral structures. Motor fragments related to specific behavioural categories, like food intake, have a functional affinity and form a natural sequence. The kinetic formulae are stored in the brain and may be activated by voluntary drives or by electrical stimulation at a particular rate; whatever the triggering mechanism, the subsequent series of events is the same. The immense complexity of voluntary behaviour reflects the vast and unknown complexity of past experience, modulating mechanisms, and present perceptions.

AGGRESSIVE BEHAVIOUR

In his original studies, Hess (1932) observed that, during electrical stimulation of the grey matter around the central cavity of the brain, cats responded as if threatened by a dog; that is with dilation of the pupils, flattening of the ears, growling, and so on. Similar offensive-defensive responses have been described by several authors (see bibliography in Delgado 1964). There is convincing evidence that in both cats and monkeys well-organized aggressive behaviour may be evoked by stimulation of the amygdala, posteroventral nucleus of the thalamus, tectal area, central grey, and other cerebral structures. That one animal can be electrically driven to fight another has been well established (Delgado 1955). In these studies, when a small cat was placed on a testing stage in the company of a larger one, they enjoyed perfectly friendly relations until the smaller cat was stimulated in the mid-brain area. Immediately it started growling, unsheathed its claws, and launched an attack against the larger animal, which retaliated. The fight continued as long as stimulation was applied, and ended as soon as stimulation ceased. These experiments were always of short duration and no animal was hurt, but repetition of the stimulations created mistrust between the two animals, which watched each other with hostility.

Similar studies have been repeated in colonies of several cats. When one of them was radio-stimulated in the mid-brain area, it started prowling around looking for fights with other animals, avoiding the most powerful. It was clear that while brain stimulation created a state of increased aggressiveness, the stimulated cat directed its hostility intelligently. Stimulation created a state of hostility, but the subsequent behavioural performance depended on individual characteristics, including learned skills and previous experiences.

Similar experiments have been performed in monkey colonies, where radio stimulation of the posteroventral nucleus of the thalamus or of the central grey matter increased the aggressiveness of the stimulated animal, inducing well-directed attacks against unfriendly members of the group. In some cases the aggressive behaviour induced by cerebral stimulation was self-directed and the animal looked enraged, biting its own arms, legs, and body, but without drawing blood. In the example illustrated in Figure 4, it was interesting to observe that the mother monkey bit herself but was careful not to harm her baby. However, the instinctive maternal attitude of hugging the little monkey, which is so constant in these animals, was lost for several minutes after repeated stimulation of the mid-brain.

BEHAVIOURAL INHIBITION

Behaviour depends not only on activation of some motor mechanisms but on inhibition of many other unrelated responses. To act is

a.

b.

FIGURE 4

(a) Female monkey wearing a three-channel radio stimulator (not active) round her neck. (b) and (c) Radio stimulation of the mesencephalon induces self-directed aggressive behaviour. The monkey bit her own hand, but did not harm the baby. (d) After several stimulations, mother and baby confronted each other without the usual affection, and then the mother lay down and ignored the baby (e). (Unpublished experiments, performed in collaboration with Dr. Diego Mir.)

c.

d.

c.

to choose one motor pattern from among the many available possibilities, and, as we are well aware, inhibitions are continuously suppressing inappropriate or socially unacceptable activities. The education of children is largely based on inculcating patterns of behaviour, teaching them what to do and what to suppress. It is therefore logical to suppose that the brain may have powerful inhibitory areas that can be identified experimentally.

Inhibition of behaviour normally triggered by electrical stimulation of the brain has been demonstrated by several investigators. The effects include induction of sleep; complete and sudden arrest of existing activities which can immobilize an animal in the position in which it was caught at the onset of the stimulation, as if a moving picture had been halted. There may be specific inhibition of a particular response (Delgado 1964). Normally ferocious animals like monkeys or bulls have been tamed by electrical stimulation of some points in the basal ganglia (Delgado 1965).

If a rhesus monkey was confronted with the experimenter's hand or a glove, its natural reaction was violently aggressive. Stimulation of some points in the caudate nucleus inhibited this aggressive reaction without evoking generalized inhibition or loss of muscular tonus; it was possible to touch the animal and even put a finger in its mouth (Figure 5). When a monkey was one of a colony, its basic reaction to a threat was similar, but stimulation of some appropriate points would pacify it. So reliable was the effect that continuous stimulation of this nature was often used to aid in catching a monkey inside the colony cage, because although it remained oriented and alert it hardly resisted capture. Similarly, the aggressiveness of the "boss" monkey in a colony could be controlled; indeed, another monkey in the colony could learn how to operate the switch controlling the stimulating circuit (Delgado 1963b).

STIMULATION OF THE HUMAN BRAIN

During therapeutic implantation of electrodes in the human brain, repeated electrical explorations are necessary to determine local excitability and the functional characteristics of the cerebral areas to be treated. These procedures provide important information for both the clinical evaluation of patients and the understanding of neuronal mechanisms related to behaviour. In our studies, spontaneous conversations between patients and a therapist were tape-recorded while, at undisclosed moments, different intracerebral points were intermittently stimulated. The interviews were later transcribed, divided into two-minute blocks, and analysed to determine their ideological and emotional content, possible changes following brain stimulation, and the statistical significance of the evoked phenomena. The investigations showed that both subtle and obvious changes in mental activity can be induced by simple electrical stimulation of the brain. For example, in a subject who was speaking an

a.

b.

FIGURE 5

Natural aggressiveness of the monkey shown in (a) was inhibited
by electrical stimulation of the caudate nucleus (Delgado 1964),
as demonstrated in (b). The monkey was not sleepy, atonic, or
adynamic.

average of eight words per minute, stimulation of the temporal lobe increased his rate to 44 words per minute. As the patient's conversation increased, his friendly remarks were also augmented, to about nine times more than during the control period, that is, more than *pro rata*. These results were reliable and highly specific for only a single point of stimulation located in the second temporal convolution. In other cases, excitation deep in the frontal lobes caused a block in the thinking processes. The patients were oriented and could obey the doctor's instructions, but were unable to reply to questions or even to utter a single word.

Electrical stimulation of the human brain has evoked a variety of other mental phenomena, including vivid recollection of the past; sensations of fear and threats of unknown danger; feelings of pleasure and happiness, accompanied by laughter and humorous remarks; perception of words and phrases; intuitions that the present had already been experienced in the past; and the hearing of pleasing melodies. These findings are of considerable scientific interest, and may well lead to new progress in the difficult task of treating mental illness. In addition, they demonstrate that mental functions can be influenced by physical means, bringing the investigation of the mind further into the domain of experimental science.

Clearly, the clinical approach must be made cautiously, but progress will certainly be facilitated by new developments in methodology. At present, it is necessary to use leads connected to the depth of the brain, but we are already investigating the possibility of transferring inductive energy through the skin, in order to develop multichannel stimulators so small that they can be permanently implanted underneath the scalp. Such instruments would be able to stimulate on command several predetermined areas of the brain, and to telemeter information about local electrical activity, in completely unrestrained individuals. The dual link would be capable of computing signals and of feeding back appropriate radio stimulation to selected cerebral structures.

Such instrumental control to gain information from, and to act upon, neuronal activity may have important medical applications. These are already beginning to be explored in patients with epilepsy, intractable pain, and involuntary movements, and also in the as yet little understood field of mental illness.

REFERENCES

Delgado, J. M. R.
    1955   *J. Neurophysiol.* 18:261.
    1963a   In *Bio-Telemetry* (L. Slater, ed.). New York: Pergamon Press, p. 231.
    1963b   *Science* 141:161.

1964 In *International Review of Neurobiology,* Vol. 6 (C. C. Pfeiffer and J. R. Smythies, eds.). New York: Academic Press, p. 349.

1965 "Evolution of Physical Control of the Brain," James Arthur Lecture on the Evolution of the Human Brain, Amer. Mus. Nat. Hist., New York.

Ewald, J. R.
1898 *Berl. klin. Wschr.* 35:689.

Fritsch, G. and E. Hitzig
1870 *Arch. Anat. Physiol.* 37:300.

Hess, W. R.
1932 "Beitrage zur Physiologie d. Hirnstammes. I. Die Methodik der lokalisierten Reizung und Ausschaltung subkortikaler Hirnabschnitte." Leipzig: Georg Thieme.

V
HUMAN
BEHAVIOR:
TOOLS
AND
HUNTING

JANE B. LANCASTER

*This article is an excellent example of conclusions achieved by
combining the results of investigation in many disciplines to
reconstruct the evolution of hominid behavior patterns. Modern
estimates of geological time, an ever increasing number of
fossils, and recent studies of the living nonhuman primates all
contribute essential information that makes clearer the sequence
of events in man's early stages of development. The earliest part
of the Pleistocene, the time during which small-brained, bipedal
hominids made and used very crude stone tools, is now known
to have lasted four times as long as all subsequent periods. It is
apparent from this that for several million years, before the
appearance of the genus* Homo, *hominid tool-using behavior
changed very little. The presence of tools did not lead to a rapid
increase in cultural complexity.*

*Tool use is based on a constellation of behaviors, as is hunting
(discussed in "The Evolution of Hunting"). The ability to handle
and produce stone tools and to learn the behavior patterns
needed to include them in daily life, was already a part of*
Australopithecus *heritage. Even at this rudimentary level, early
man had already far surpassed the abilities of any other primate.
If one inspects the tool use of living chimpanzees, it requires
little imagination to credit far more complex usage and
manufacture to early Pleistocene hunters. Surely* Australopithecus
*must have learned the behaviors of tool use in much the same
way as the young chimpanzee does: by long and patient
observation of the behavior of older individuals with which the
young has close ties and to which it pays careful attention.*

*Considering hominid abilities — some of which are shared
with other primates, and particularly with the African apes —
Lancaster concludes that a crucial difference between the tools
of the nonhuman and the human primate lies in the skill with
which they are made and used. The vast increase in complexity
that marks the Middle Pleistocene tool traditions is based on the
increasingly complex and larger brains of the men living at that
time. It was only with the addition of substantial skill in tool
making, made possible in turn by the biology of the makers, that
the rich and variable patterns that are characteristic of the genus*
Homo *developed.*

342

18   On the Evolution of
Tool-Using Behavior

This paper directs attention to the theoretical importance of recent discoveries and observations — especially those in primate field studies — to the interpretation of the fossil record. It is intended not as a review but simply as a discussion of the implications of recent developments.

TIME AND THE NEW METHODS OF DATING

The estimate of the amount of time occupied by the Pleistocene has steadily increased. In 1932 Keith thought that the Pleistocene might have lasted 200,000 years and the Pliocene an additional 250,000. Then for a long time the Pleistocene was estimated at one million years and the Pliocene ten times that long (Zeuner 1959). According to that view, the Pleistocene was divided into two approximately equal parts: the first 500,000 years contained at least some very simple tool traditions, but these were of uncertain date and duration; the second 500,000 years spanned three glacials and contained all the tools of the Acheulian and later tool-making traditions. With the advent of potassium-argon dating, now partly supported by the fission-track method, radiometric dates rather than relative estimates could be given for these two parts of the Pleistocene (Butzer 1964, Evernden and Curtis 1965, Fleischer *et al.* 1965). The dates and duration of the last part of the Pleistocene have not been greatly altered but the early part has been radically extended in time. The new radiometric dating suggests well over two million years ago as a probable date for the Pliocene-Pleistocene boundary, but keeps 700,000–500,000 B.P. as likely for the onset of the First Interglacial period (Table 1). Two million years ago, according to Evernden and Curtis (1965), is a minimal estimate for the start of the Pleistocene and it may well have begun more than three million years ago. Estimates of the extent of the Lower Pleistocene, especially of the earliest part, the Villafranchian, have been the most radically affected by radiometric dating. The Villafranchian, which was once considered a relatively brief period preliminary to the major events and time spans of the Pleistocene, is now seen as lasting perhaps 2.5 million years and comprising three quarters of the total length of the Pleistocene.

While the radiometric chronology of the late Tertiary and Pleistocene stratigraphic unit is not finally settled, it is very clear that the time spans

"On the Evolution of Tool-Using Behavior" by Jane B. Lancaster is reproduced by permission of the American Anthropological Association from the *American Anthropologist*: Vol. 70 (1968), pp. 56–66.

TABLE 1. CHRONOLOGY OF THE PLEISTOCENE[a]

Upper	Third Interglacial (Eemian)	100,000 B.P.	
Middle	Second Interglacial (Holstein)	255,000 B.P. or more	
	First Interglacial (Cromerian)	700,000–500,000 B.P. 1,000,000 B.P.	Acheulian and later traditions
Lower	Villafranchian (Early Villafranchian?)	2,000,000 B.P. 3,000,000–2,500,000 B.P. ???	Oldowan tools

[a] After Butzer 1964, Evernden and Curtis 1965.

involved in the early stages of the Pleistocene have been seriously underestimated in the past. Geophysical age determinations indicate the need for a radical revision in our conception of the rate of development of tool-using abilities and techniques and in our understanding of the interrelation of tool types to the biology of their makers. At Olduvai Gorge, chopping tools, trimmed and utilized flakes, polyhedral "flaked" stones, and other utilized stones are found near the base of Bed I in layers dated between 1.9 and 1.75 million years (Evernden and Curtis 1965, M. D. Leakey 1966). From these same stratigraphic levels fossils of two distinct hominid forms have been recovered. Regardless of the ultimate classification of the hominid forms found in Bed I, there are none with large brains. Tobias' most generous estimate for the cranial capacity of the juvenile parietal fragments is still only 725 cc. His more conservative estimate is 670 cc. (Tobias 1964).

The Oldowan industries from Bed I are at present the oldest radiometrically dated stone artifacts, but they need not necessarily represent the very beginning of stone flaking traditions, which we can expect to extend to perhaps a quarter to a half million years earlier. At Olduvai these industries persisted into the time of deposition of the lower part of Bed II, while in upper Bed I early handaxe industries occur.[1] The age of the transition from Oldowan to Acheulian has not been directly determined at Olduvai[2] but archeological and faunal correlations can be made with other strata for which geophysical data indicate an age of between 700,000 and 500,000 B.P. (Isaac 1965). The elementary stone techniques and poorly standardized tool-making tradition of the Oldowan appears in East Africa to have lasted

[1] The early handaxe industries are designated Lower or Early Acheulian, the term Chellean having been abandoned by workers in many parts of Africa (Biberson 1961, Mason 1962, Leakey and Leakey 1965).

[2] There is only a single sample from Olduvai for which dates ranging from 500,000–300,000 B.P. have been published (Hay 1963, Evernden and Curtis 1965).

at least one million years and quite probably for more than double that time with little change or advance in their manufacture or in the biology of their makers. We can assign a time span for Oldowan tools from probably earlier than 2,000,000 B.P. up to 500,000 B.P., the time when the first hand-axe cultures and the remains of larger-brained men classified as *Homo erectus* began to appear. The only possible makers of the Oldowan tools are small-brained forms (*Australopithecus*, in the broad sense).

There is reason to think that Oldowan tools were used for much longer than the 1.5 million years that passed between the lowest levels of Bed I and the beginning of the European First Interglacial period. Tools similar to the Oldowan may also date from the same or an earlier period at other African sites, such as Laetolil, Omo, Kanam, Ain Hanech, and elsewhere (Cooke 1963). Furthermore, the small incisors and canines of *Australopithecus* suggest that members of this genus had been using tools for a very long period of time and that the use of tools had almost entirely relieved their dentition of the functions of food getting and self protection. An estimate of two million years of tool use prior to handaxe cultures and *Homo erectus* is undoubtedly conservative. This would mean that the stage of human evolution in which small-brained men used pebble tools and walked bipedally lasted at least four times as long as have all the subsequent stages. The early part of the evolution of stone tools and of man must have proceeded at a rate very different from the later stages and advances must have come very much more slowly.

To summarize to this point, the archeological discoveries from Bed I in Olduvai Gorge and the advent of new dating techniques have radically altered our conceptions of the duration of the early, primitive stages of tool using and tool making. The natural assumption has always been that tool use was so highly adaptive that once it had been firmly established as part of the normal behavior of the species the pace of evolution quickened immediately. Advances were assumed to have come in rapid succession as the brain, tool-making techniques, and cultural traditions interacted in a mutually stimulating feedback relationship. Events of the past, however, apparently did *not* move this rapidly, at least not in the beginning.

TOOL USE BY THE AFRICAN APES

In the same years that discoveries at Olduvai Gorge and advances in the techniques of radiometric dating were being made, field workers were making new efforts to study the behavior of contemporary monkeys and apes in their natural habitats. Most of these modern field studies report very little object-manipulation in nonhuman primates except that directly involved in feeding activity (Hall 1963b, Menzel 1966). In feeding, nonhuman primates will turn over rocks, probe fingers into holes, and pull off bark or shells in search of food, but even here they are only manipulating objects and not using tools. In contrast to the findings of field workers on other primate species, Goodall (1964) has found that tool use in the chimpanzee is an important behavior pattern. Goodall (1962, 1963, 1965) over a period of six years has observed the behavior of a single population of approximately 60 free-ranging chimpanzees in the Gombe Stream Reserve in Tanzania. There can be little doubt now that tool-using performances by chimpanzees excel those reported for all other animals except man in both variety and complexity. They are also very close to man in many other measures: anatomy of the body, serum proteins, chromosome number and form, and dentition. Therefore it is not surprising that chimpanzees are closest to man in some aspects of behavior as well.

It may well be that further observations on the behavior of gorillas in the wild will produce evidence of tool-using behavior paralleling the performances of the chimpanzees. Schaller (1963) with 500 hours of observations of the behavior of the mountain gorilla reported that he never saw gorillas use or show interest in objects except vegetation for nest building and for throwing in aggressive display. The aggressive display of the gorilla is a highly stereotyped sequence of behavior patterns that usually includes the throwing and tossing of vegetation just before a running charge (Emlen 1962, Schaller 1963). Many of the same elements, including the throwing of vegetation followed by a charge, constitute the most essential parts of the chimpanzee aggressive display. At least in this one context both species show a strong tendency to manipulate and throw objects. It should be noted that what appear to be species differences in behavior between chimpanzees and gorillas may in part merely reflect Goodall's unique long-term observations; in the first year of her study she only saw one kind of tool use, termiting. Moreover, there may have been important ecological differences between the two study areas. Schaller worked in a region of lush evergreen vegetation of herbs and vines, where rocks, sticks, and other hard objects were rare. Food plants were abundant and everywhere at hand. The feeding pattern of the gorillas was simply a leisurely grazing through the lush vegetation. In contrast, the Gombe Stream Reserve includes valleys of dense gallery forests and higher points of open woodland and grassy slopes where wood and stone are readily available materials. Food items are often seasonal, concentrated, and hard to get. The chimpanzees make an effort to locate and to gather their food; this is exactly the sort of situation where tool use in food getting might be likely to appear. Finally, the behavior of young gorillas in captivity is very similar to that of young chimpanzees in their interest in and manipulation of objects (Schenkel 1964, Glickman and Sroges 1966). In captivity both chimpanzees and gorillas spontaneously learn to throw dirt and food with considerable accuracy at visitors.

Goodall's most remarkable observations of chimpanzee tool use are of the use of twigs and grass blades for "fishing" ants or termites out of their nests. She has collected more than 1000 of these tools and on over a hundred occasions has observed actual termiting. Chimpanzees are very efficient in getting the termites. The animal takes a piece of twig and puts it in the termite hole where the insects seize the end of the stick with their mandibles. The chimpanzee then takes it from the hole and leisurely eats the termites that are clinging to the tip. Not only do the chimpanzees use these twigs very effectively as tools but they also will frequently improve the bit of twig or grass before using it. The animal will break off a piece of vine or a twig and prepare it by stripping away any side branch or leaf that might get in the way and by breaking it to the appropriate length, which differs by a foot or more for anting as opposed to termiting. There is much individual variation in the skill and care with which a tool is made. Some animals will take nearly anything at hand; others will search carefully for just the right piece and then spend some time in preparing it. A few prepare a little pile of stems before starting to termite and some make the twig even before a nest is found. Goodall saw one male carry a termiting twig in his mouth for more than half a mile while he went from nest to nest looking for one that was ready to work.

The actual grip used to hold the twig for termiting is standardized among adults who hold it between the thumb and the side of the bent index finger (Goodall, personal communication). Infants who have not fully mastered the adult technique may grip the tool using only four fingers and not using the thumb at all. Chimpanzees are ambidextrous in their termiting; all animals can use either hand although there may be some individual preference for one hand over the other (Goodall, personal communication). This absence of handedness may be indicative of the limitations that the chimpanzee's brain places on its ability to develop highly skilled tool use. By human standards these termiting movements and other kinds of tool-using behavior in chimpanzees always appear clumsy, like the use of tools by a human child. Tool use is learned by the chimpanzee, improves with practice, but never develops the deftness either of human skill or of highly stereotyped innate motor patterns.

Goodall was fortunate enough to observe a one-and-a-half-year-old female in the process of learning how to use the termiting twig. The infant's technique was imperfect. She made tools that were too short to more than just enter the hole; the longest was only two inches whereas the adults always use 6- to 12-inch twigs. The infant's motor patterns were imperfectly coordinated and sometimes she would jerk the twig out of the hole so quickly that the termites were knocked off. Her attention span was very short as well; she would termite for a few minutes and then break off to play. In contrast, adults often work with great concentration for more than an hour without stopping. Goodall also observed that young animals try to termite out of season in what may have been a form of play activity. She is convinced that much of the ability to termite is learned by young animals by observing the adult technique and then practicing it. She often saw infants intently watching an adult termiting and then, when the adult had moved off leaving the twig or grass blade by the nest, the infant would pick up the abandoned tool and try termiting too.

Chimpanzees are not the only primates that like termites, and Goodall has seen baboons near chimpanzees while they are at work. Baboons are eager to eat termites, but they have never been observed trying to fish for termites themselves. The baboons do occasionally watch the chimpanzees termiting but not as intently as do young chimpanzees who will peer at working adults for minutes at a time (Goodall, personal communication).

Termiting is a seasonal activity, coming just before the termites begin their nuptial flights, which occur about eight times for each termite heap over a period of four months or more during the rainy season. During most of the year the termites are protected by a concrete-like shell that covers their nests, but for the flights the workers tunnel out to the surface. After each flight, the holes are sealed over until the next. Chimpanzees are able to scratch off the thin covering at the end of the tunnel and thus, by using the fishing technique, are able to eat termites throughout the entire season. Birds, monkeys, and other animals can feast on the termites only during the actual flights. The simple technique of fishing for termites assures the chimpanzees of a protein-rich diet for several months out of every year without competition from other species, and the inability of the baboons to imitate the chimpanzee behavior robs them of the extra protein.

Termiting is only one example of tool use by chimpanzees. Goodall saw them make sponges for dipping water out of crevices and boles of trees that were too small to let them put their faces down to the water. They would take a handful of leaves, chew them slightly, dip the wad into the water and then suck it. Goodall tried the same thing and found it seven to eight times more efficient than the technique used by many nonhuman primates of dipping the hand or fingers into water and letting the water drip into the mouth. Besides using leaves as sponges for drinking water, chimpanzees use them to wipe water or dirt from the body or sticky substances from the fingers. This use of objects to groom the body is more unusual than it seems. Although some species of bird are known to rub ants in their feathers as a part of grooming and elephants sometimes use objects to scratch themselves, man is the only animal reported to habitually use objects in grooming (Hall 1963b).

One other way in which chimpanzees use objects as tools is in aggressive display (Kortlandt and Kooij 1963, Goodall 1964). This behavior is particularly interesting because it suggests that tools for defense may have been developed just as early in man's history as tools for foodgetting. Random throwing of objects — anything that comes to hand such as stones, sticks or other vegetation — is a common element in the excited displays of many primates, and chimpanzees are no exception (Hall 1963b). They tend to throw things when meeting other groups after a separation or when being annoyed by baboons (and probably by predators, Kortlandt and Kooij 1963). Sometimes an animal will even take some care in aiming the object; instead of just tossing it into the air, he will throw it toward the animal at which the display is aimed. Goodall saw chimpanzees aim and throw stones, both overhand and underhand, at baboons and at humans as part of such a sequence of aggressive display. This behavior pattern is significant because, as Washburn (1963b) has pointed out, it suggests the possible first steps in the evolution of weapons. If an animal is displaying to intimidate an aggressor, object throwing as a part of that display is effective whether he hits the other animal or not. If the total display is not intimidating enough, the chimpanzee is still able to flee or to fight with his canines. It is easy to imagine how the ability to develop skill in aimed throwing of sticks and rocks could gradually evolve until it became so effective that the creature need no longer rely on his canines. Only then would the selective pressure on large canines be relaxed and a behavior pattern, defense with weapons, could ultimately replace the behavioral and morphological pattern of defense by fighting with canines.

These examples of tool use in chimpanzees, when taken together, provide a good starting place for answering questions about how and why tools were used by man's earliest ancestors. It is true that some birds and other mammals use tools, but in any one tool-using species there is likely to be only one kind of tool. There is no nonprimate that uses such disparate objects as termiting twigs, leaf sponges, and stone projectiles. And, conversely, in the chimpanzee there is no single, highly evolved, stereotyped sequence of movements of the sort common in other vertebrate tool users such as the deft twist of a cactus spine used by finches to dig grubs from bark or even the much more complex but still relatively stereotyped patterns of nest building found in many mammals. In the chimpanzee there is a far more generalized tendency to manipulate objects and to use them in many different situations. And, if Goodall is correct, these different ways to use tools constitute a tradition based on biology but transmitted from adults to young by observational learning and practice.

Chimpanzees use tools in an impressive number of different situations, when they are compared with the rest of the animal kingdom in this respect (Hall, 1963b). By far the most common types of tool use in vertebrates are in feeding behavior or in preparation of nests or dens. The use of objects in self-grooming is almost unknown in animals and in aggressive displays it has been observed only in monkeys, apes, and man. Goodall's single population of chimpanzees performed more complex kinds of tool use, and in a wider variety of situations, than has been observed for any other animal; that is true even though tool use is a very small part of their behavior repertoire and is a comparatively rare event. This small group of apes over a period of a few years was seen to use tools in agonistic display, in aimed throwing, in a variety of food-getting situations, in drinking, and in self-grooming. Perhaps the making of nests or sleeping platforms should be included in this list too, since it is very similar to these other forms of tool use in that objects are manipulated and modified to perform some important activity better — in this case the nest is a tool for sleeping.

CHIMPANZEE LEARNING OF TOOL-USING TRADITIONS

It would be interesting to know why chimpanzees seem to be able to learn the use of objects more readily than do many other primates. There are important biological limitations on learning abilities that vary from species to species and do not reflect differences in intelligence so much as differences in specialization. Hall (1963b) has argued that in themselves tool-using performances give no indication of relative intelligence. A finch that uses a cactus spine to extract grubs is no more intelligent than other finches; the species has simply evolved a behavioral pattern rather than a morphological pattern to aid in its feeding. Nevertheless, chimpanzees do have large brains and the great apes have a much longer maturation period than do other nonhuman primates; certainly both these characteristics are related to greater learning abilities.

Undoubtedly there are many factors that contribute to the ontogeny of such an important adaptive pattern as the use of objects as tools. Schiller (1957) and more recently Chance (1960) have emphasized the importance of certain motor patterns occurring in the tool-using performances of captive chimpanzees that appear to be largely determined by heredity and that require only the opportunity for play for their perfection. For example, the tendency to manipulate sticks, to lick the ends, and to poke them into any available hole are responses that occur over and over again in captive chimpanzees. These responses are not necessarily organized into the efficient use of sticks to probe for objects but they probably form the basis of complex motor patterns such as termiting.

Certain kinds of human-like tool use such as overhand and underhand throwing are easier for an ape than for a monkey. The anatomy of the shoulder girdle of man and the apes enables them to throw or toss objects using powerful movements, something which is much more awkward and difficult for a quadrupedal monkey (Washburn and Jay 1967). In contrast, differences between chimpanzees and monkeys in manipulative abilities of the hands are based not so much on anatomical differences in the forelimbs as on the brain and the ability to learn different kinds of object manipulations. The hands of monkeys and apes are equally suited to picking up a stick and making poking or scratching movements with it but differences in the brain make these much more likely behavior patterns for the chimpanzee.

Another factor, one that may be just as important in tool use as genetic tendencies toward motor patterns, is the degree to which chimpanzees can learn by observing the activities of other animals. Hall (1963a) has emphasized that observational learning is rarer in nonhuman primates than one might expect and that the ability to learn in this way varies tremendously according to the task to be learned and the context in which this learning takes place. Monkeys and apes seem to have greater abilities in this direction than do most other mammals, and Hall has suggested that these abilities are most often demonstrated when the animals are in the relaxed, protected atmosphere of a social group formed of animals linked by close affectional bonds. This is a situation that is common in the natural environment of monkeys and apes, but it is rarely duplicated in the laboratory. Monkeys and apes learn emotional attitudes, such as fear of particular objects or situations, with great ease from other group members as might be expected in animals for which group life is an important adaptive mechanism (Hamburg 1963).

Other, more complex kinds of observational learning in monkeys and apes are much more rare. Frequently the activities of one animal will stimulate another animal to do the same thing, but this sort of social facilitation is often merely a matter of a focusing of the attention of the second animal on a stimulus that then elicits a parallel response. For example, Hall (1963a) reported an experiment in which a young baboon, raised in captivity, was released near a wild troop. The young animal had been fed the diet of a pet and was unfamiliar with the wild foods of the area in which it was released. It learned how to dig for bulbs and roots by watching the other animals closely and then going over and digging beside them, but, as Hall emphasized, it did not learn how to dig, but rather where and for what to dig. The ability to mimic a novel motor pattern demonstrated by another animal has not conclusively been shown for any nonhuman primate except the chimpanzee. Studies of captive chimpanzees (Köhler 1925, Yerkes and Yerkes 1929, Hayes and Hayes 1952) point toward their considerable abilities in all the forms of observational learning mentioned above, ranging from the simpler kinds of attention focusing to something that must be genuine imitation of novel motor patterns. It is likely, then, that both these factors — the existence of simple hereditary motor acts that form the basis of more complex motor patterns of tool use and the ease with which one chimpanzee can learn by observing the activities of another chimpanzee — play important roles in the development of tool-using traditions within local populations of chimpanzees.

Tool-using behavior by chimpanzees is remarkable in the multiplicity of forms it takes, but it is very different from human use of tools in degree if not in kind. Chimpanzees, like men, both use and make tools, but man's brain is highly evolved and highly specialized to learn many different skilled uses of objects. For a species to depend on tool use as a way of life — for obtaining food and for defense — such tool use must be skillful. A spear has to be thrown just as skillfully as a baboon wields its canines in fighting, or the behavior pattern could never replace the morphological pattern in agonistic situations. Skill is a matter of evolutionary changes in the brain that do not fossilize. There are really only two indirect lines of evidence of skill from the past: (1) relative brain size of the tool makers and (2) the tools themselves, in the techniques by which they were made and in the complexity and specializations of the tool assemblages. The specializations of modern man's brain that allow him to learn many different skilled uses of tools may have come relatively late in the history of tool use, perhaps not until *Homo erectus*, when the rate of change in tool traditions became so rapid and when a major increase in cranial capacity occurred. The slow pace of evolution in tools and in their makers before that time may well reflect a lack of ability to use them skillfully.

The tool-using behavior of chimpanzees suggests the kind of ape ancestor that might be postulated for the origin of the hominid line — an ape that used tools for many different reasons and in many different ways, no matter how insignificant the tool, like leaf sponges, or how undramatic, like termiting twigs, or inefficient, like a clumsily swung stick. The more kinds of tools this ape used the more likely his ancestral role, because it would have been the accumulated influence of many reasons for using tools and many ways of using them that would have taken selective pressure off the specific situation, the specific tool, and the specific movement. Selective pressure was put on a hand that could use many tools skillfully and on a brain capable of learning these skills. Natural selection would then have acted upon a broader category of behavior, one involving the brain, the hand, many objects, and a wide variety of social and ecological situations and problems. The evolution of skilled tool using marks a major change from the kind of tool use that is incidental to the life of a chimpanzee to the kind that is absolutely essential for survival of the human individual.

PROBLEMS OF INTERPRETATION
IN THE EVOLUTION OF TOOL USE

Chimpanzee tool-using behavior raises the question of how many millions of years of this sort of casual tool use and object manipulation by apes has existed. It also raises the problem of whether the ancestors of chimpanzees and man used tools before their separation or whether tool use evolved independently in the two species. Any reconstruction of evolutionary events can be guarded against the possibility of parallelism and convergence only by an evaluation of the degree of similarity between two species in as many different and unrelated systems as possible. The greater the number of similarities that can be found, in as many unrelated biological systems as possible, the higher the chances that one is dealing with true genetic affinities between special and not superficial similarities due to parallel evolution. A large number of such similarities between two species also suggests a shallow time depth of separation in which minor and random differences have not had a chance to accumulate.

Anatomical affinities between man and the apes have long been recognized both in dentition (Clark 1962) and in the anatomy of the shoulder girdle (Grand 1964, Washburn 1963a). Washburn (1963a) noted that similarities between man and apes in the shoulder girdle involve fine details in a series of highly specialized modifications of the shoulder, elbow, and wrist joints. The full complement of these modifications was not present in the apes of the Miocene and may not have been established until the Miocene-Pliocene border, perhaps 3 million years ago. Washburn argued that man is likely to have separated from the African apes sometime in the early Pliocene, perhaps several million years after the establishment of a modern shoulder girdle in the family Pongidae.

The number of similarities between man and the great apes is extremely impressive. Besides the affinities in dentition and the anatomy of the shoulder girdle mentioned above, man is closer to the great apes than to any other animal in susceptibility to special kinds of viral disease (Hsiung, Black, and Henderson 1941), in blood groups (Franks 1963), and in the glands of the axilla, the form of the hair follicles, the chemicals found at the ends of nerves, and many other details of the skin (Montagna and Ellis 1963).

The African apes are often specifically cited as being the most similar to man and the orangutan has never been mentioned as being closer to man than are the African apes. In respect to chromosome number and form, the chimpanzee is almost identical to man with only one extra set of arocentric chromosomes (Klinger *et al.* 1963, Chiarelli 1962). Dunn (1966) compared the internal parasites of man and apes and found that man and the African apes shared in common a much greater number of species of parasites, especially the host-specific ones, than do the Asiatic apes and man. Man living in the tropical forests of Southeast Asia shares many more species of helminths with African apes than with the Asiatic apes who are living in the same forest. Thus even when sharing his habitat with the Asiatic apes, man carries the internal parasites of the African apes. Goodman (1963) came to the conclusion that man and the African apes are so similar in their serum proteins that *Pan* and *Gorilla* should be classified in the Hominidae,

TABLE 2. CHRONOLOGY OF THE EVOLUTION OF
TOOL-USING BEHAVIOR

Geological Time Divisions	Radiometric Age Estimates	Tool-Using Species of Primates	Types of Tool-Using Traditions
Pleistocene	700,000–500,000 B.P.	Homo erectus (1 species only)	Handaxe and later traditions
	2,000,000 B.P.	Australopithecus (more than 1 species)	Oldowan industries
Pliocene		Pongid and Hominid (many species)	Unskilled, ape tool use (hypothetical)
	13,000,000 B.P.		

whereas *Pongo* should be left in the Pongidae. Other workers on primate hemoglobins (Zuckerkandl 1963, Buettner-Janusch and Buettner-Janusch 1964, Hafleigh and Williams 1966) agree on the close affinities between man and the African apes as opposed to the Asiatic apes but do not take such an extreme taxonomic position. Sarich (1966) in a quantitative assessment of differences among the apes and man in serum albumins and gamma globulin found that man was very similar to the African apes and much less closely related to the Asiatic apes. The order of magnitude of these differences suggested a separation between man and the African apes going back perhaps 8 million years and a common ancestor for all modern apes and man coming from the Miocene-Pliocene border. There is no reason to think that all the different biological systems mentioned above are either genetically or functionally linked. Thus, an evolutionary change in one of these systems should not necessarily involve corresponding changes in the others. So many similarities between these systems can only be interpreted as reflecting close genetic relationships between man and the African apes, a relationship in which the time of separation is small enough that minor or random differences have not had a chance to accumulate.

The lack of divergence in many different systems strongly supports the idea of an end of the Miocene or early Pliocene (but no earlier) division between man and the African apes, somewhere on the order of 10 million years ago. If this is so, then it may be worth considering the possibility that casual, unskilled tool use might have been typical of many species of apes during the Pliocene. It should be remembered that the late Miocene and early Pliocene represent a time when apes were abundant, diverse, and widely spread over much of the Old World (Simons 1963a, 1963b). Fossil apes have been found in Europe, Africa, India, and China — a much larger geographical distribution than that of the modern apes, which live only in restricted areas of Africa and Southeast Asia (Simons and Pilbeam 1965). The number of different forms of apes was also much greater than today. From a single site, Ruisinga Island in Lake Victoria, there are at least two species from the genus *Dryopithecus* as well as one or more species of gibbonlike apes. The modern apes are only remnants, survivors of a time when the family was highly successful and diverse. Table 2 suggests that a kind of unskilled ape tool use continued without major changes for millions of years and has continued down to the present in one or more of the surviving, descendant species of ape.

The onset of the Pleistocene witnessed the emergence of perhaps one or more forms of bipedal hominid that, although possessing relatively small brains, had come to rely on tool use for much of their food getting and defense. Clearly, specializations in the hand and especially the thumb (Napier 1962), the reduction in the canines and incisors (Robinson 1963), and bipedalism (Napier 1964), all point toward the importance of tools to their way of life. Both the small brains and the tools themselves suggest a lack of skill in the way these tools were made and used. These hominids of the Early Pleistocene should not be thought of as merely forms transitional to man. They were highly successful, judging by their wide geographic distribution, and they lasted without major changes in either anatomy or tool traditions for a long time, perhaps 2.5 million years. Then, about half a million years ago, a rapid rate of evolutionary development in brain size and complexity of tool assemblages seems to have begun. This later period is associated with the emergence of a single species of tool user, *Homo erectus*, dominating much of the Old World. Remnant species of ape also survived but with quite restricted geographic distribution. Perhaps a new efficiency in the skilled use of tools effectively closed the niche to competition. It probably left no room within the broad niche created by tools for separate species to develop specialized applications. Any possibility for different kinds of tool users — perhaps an open savanna, a woodland, and a forest form (a possibility that may have been realized in *Australopithecus* during the Early Pleistocene) — disappeared and a single species of Hominid, using various tool traditions, spread across the Old World. The increase of efficiency and skill with which tools were used, a trend that probably began in the early Pliocene, may well have been associated with a gradual decrease in the number of primate species able to command a portion of the niche open to tool users. At an early, inefficient stage many species may have tried using tools with variable degrees of success but, as skill and efficiency increased, the competition between tool-using species also increased and the possibility of many forms sharing the niche disappeared.

SUMMARY

Our conceptions of the conditions under which tools first evolved have been radically altered by recent archeological discoveries, new methods of dating, and primate field studies. All point toward a single conclusion — that in itself tool use does not cause a major change in the history of a species. Man is not the only primate to use tools and probably many species of ape have in time past used tools to some degree. The new radiometric dating by potassium-argon and fission-track methods indicates that the Early Pleistocene lasted for at least 2.5 million years and that during that time small-brained men used simple tools with little change or advance. The rapid acceleration of cultural advances, once traditionally thought to be a natural consequence of tools of any sort, came late in the history of tool use and was probably associated with specializations in the human brain that allowed the skilled use of many different kinds of tools. This evolutionary advance occurred in only one genus and species, *Homo erectus,* that preempted the entire niche once open to a number of different kinds of tool users. As Oakley (1954) argued some years ago, it is the skill with which man uses his tools that best reflects man's specializations for a human way of life.

REFERENCES

Biberson, P.
   1961   Le Paléolithique Inférieur du Maroc Atlantique. Pub. Serv. Antiquités Maroc, Mem. 17.
Buettner-Janusch, J. and V. Buettner-Janusch
   1964   "Hemoglobins of Primates," in *Evolutionary and Genetic Biology of Primates,* Vol. II (J. Buettner-Janusch, ed.). New York: Academic Press.
Butzer, K. W.
   1964   *Environment and Archeology: An Introduction to Pleistocene Geography.* Chicago: Aldine.
Chance, M. R. A.
   1960   "Kohler's Chimpanzees — How Did they Perform?" *Man* 60:130–135.
Chiarelli, B.
   1962   "Comparative Morphometric Analysis of Primate Chromosomes. I. The Chromosomes of Anthropoid Apes and of Man," *Caryologia* 15:99–121.
Clark, W. E. L.
   1962   *The Antecedents of Man,* 2nd Ed. Edinburgh University Press.
Cooke, H. B. S.
   1963   "Pleistocene Mammal Faunas of Africa With Particular Reference to Southern Africa," in *African Ecology and*

Human Evolution (F. C. Howell and F. Bourlière, eds.). Viking Fund Publications in Anthropology No. 36.

Dunn, F. L.
1966 "Patterns of Parasitism in Primates: Phylogenetic and Ecological Interpretations, with Particular Reference to the Hominoidea," *Folia Primatologia* 4:329–345.

Emlen, J. T.
1962 "The Display of the Gorilla," *Proceedings, American Philosophical Society* 106:516–519.

Evernden, J. F. and G. H. Curtis
1965 "Potassium-argon Dating of Late Cenozoic Rocks in East Africa and Italy," *Current Anthropology* 6:343–385.

Fleischer, R. L., L. S. B. Leakey, P. B. Price, and R. M. Walker
1965 "Fission Track Dating of Bed I, Olduvai Gorge," *Science* 148:72–74.

Franks, D.
1963 "The Blood Groups of the Primates," in *The Primates* (J. Napier and N. A. Barnicot, eds.). *Symposium, Zoological Society of London* 10:221–250.

Glickman, S. E. and R. W. Sroges
1966 "Curiosity in Zoo Animals," *Behaviour* 26:151–188.

Goodall, J. M.
1962 "Nest Building Behavior in the Free Ranging Chimpanzee," *Annals, New York Academy of Science* 102:455–467.

1963 "Feeding Behaviour of Wild Chimpanzees," *Symposium, Zoological Society of London* 10:39–48.

1964 "Tool-Using and Aimed Throwing in a Community of Free-Living Chimpanzees," *Nature* 201:1264–1266.

1965 "Chimpanzees of the Gombe Stream Reserve," in *Primate Behavior: Field Studies of Monkeys and Apes* (I. DeVore, ed.). New York: Holt, Rinehart, pp. 425–473.

Goodman, M.
1963 "Serological Analysis of the Phyletic Relationships of Recent Hominoids," *Human Biology* 35:377–436.

Grand, T. I.
1964 "The Functional Anatomy of the Shoulder of the Chimpanzee." Doctoral Dissertation, University of California, Berkeley.

Hafleigh, A. S. and C. A. Williams, Jr.
1966 "Antigenic Correspondence of Serum Albumins among the Primates," *Science* 151:1530–1535.

Hall, K. R. L.
1963a "Observational Learning in Monkeys and Apes," *British Journal of Psychology* 54, 3:201–226.

1963b "Tool-Using Performances as Indicators of Behavioral Adaptability," *Current Anthropology* 4:479–494.

Hamburg, D. A.
1963 "Emotions in the Perspective of Human Evolution," in *Expression of the Emotions in Man* (P. H. Knapp, ed.). New York: International Universities Press.

Hay, R. L.
1963 "Stratigraphy of Beds I through IV, Olduvai Gorge, Tanganyika," *Science* 139:829–833.

Hayes, K. J. and C. Hayes
1952. "Imitation in a Home-Raised Chimpanzee," *Journal of Comparative and Physiological Psychology* 45:450–459.

Hsiung, G. D., F. L. Black, and J. R. Henderson
1964 "Susceptibility of Primates to Viruses in Relation to Taxonomic Classification," in *Evolutionary and Genetic Biology of Primates*, Vol. II (J. Buettner-Janusch, ed.). New York: Academic Press.

Isaac, G.
1965 "The Stratigraphy of the Peninj Beds and the Provenance of the Natron Australopithecine Mandible," *Quaternaria* 7:101–130.

Keith, A.
1932 *The Antiquity of Man*, Vol. I. Philadelphia: Lippincott.

Klinger, H. P., J. L. Namerton, D. Mutton, and E. M. Lang
1963 "The Chromosomes of the Hominoidea," in *Classification and Human Evolution* (S. L. Washburn, ed.). Viking Fund Publications in Anthropology No. 37.

Kohler, W.
1925 *The Mentality of Apes*. New York: Harcourt Brace.

Kortlandt, A. and M. Kooij
1963 "Protohominid Behaviour in Primates," in *The Primates* (J. Napier and N. A. Barnicot, eds.). *Symposium, Zoological Society of London* 10:61–88.

Leakey, M. D.
1966 "A Review of the Oldowan Culture from Olduvai Gorge, Tanzania," *Nature* 210:462–466.

Leakey, L. S. B.
1965 *Olduvai Gorge 1951–1961: A Preliminary Report on the Geology and Fauna*, Vol. I. Cambridge University Press.

Leakey, L. S. B. and M. D. Leakey
1965 Personal communication quoted in G. Isaac, "The Stratigraphy of the Peninj Beds and the Provenance of the Natron Australopithecine Mandible," *Quaternaria* 7:118.

Mason, R.
1962 *Prehistory of the Transvaal.* Witwatersrand: Witwatersrand University Press.

Menzel, E. W., Jr.
1966 "Responsiveness to Objects of Free-Ranging Japanese Monkeys," *Behaviour* 26:130–150.

Montagna, W. and R. A. Ellis
1963 "New Approaches to the Study of the Skin of Primates," in *Evolutionary and Genetic Biology of Primates,* Vol. 1 (J. Buettner-Janusch, ed.). New York: Academic Press.

Napier, J. R.
1962 "Fossil Hand Bones from Olduvai Gorge," *Nature* 196: 409–411.
1964 "The Evolution of Bipedal Walking in the Hominids," *Archives de Biologie* 75:Supplement:673–708.

Oakley, K. P.
1954 "Skill as a Human Possession," in *A History of Technology,* Vol. I (C. Singer, E. J. Holmyard, and A. R. Hall, eds.). Oxford: Clarendon Press.

Robinson, J. T.
1963 "Adaptive Radiation in the Australopithecines and the Origin of Man," in *African Ecology and Human Evolution* (F. C. Howell and F. Bourlière, eds.). Viking Publications in Anthropology No. 36.

Sarich, V.
1966 "Quantitative Immunochemistry and the Evolution of the Anthropoidea." Paper presented at the 35th Annual Meeting of the American Association of Physical Anthropologists, April 4–6, 1966, Berkeley, California. Abstracted in *American Journal of Physical Anthropology* 25:208.

Schaller, G.
1963 *The Mountain Gorilla: Ecology and Behavior.* Chicago: University of Chicago Press.

Schenkel, R.
1964 "Zur Ontogenese des Verhaltens bie Gorilla and Mensch," *Zeitschrift fur Morphologie und Anthropologie* 54:233–259.

Schiller, P. H.
1957 "Innate Motor Action as a Basis of Learning," in *Instinctive Behavior* (C. H. Schiller, ed.). New York: International Universities Press.

Simons, E. L.
1963 "A Critical Reappraisal of Tertiary Primates," in *Evolutionary and Genetic Biology of Primates,* Vol. I (J. Buettner-Janusch, ed.). New York: Academic Press.

1963b   "Some Fallacies in the Study of Hominid Phylogeny,"
         Science 141:879–889.
Simons, E. L. and D. R. Pilbeam
    1965   "Preliminary Revision of the Dryopithecinae Pongidae,
            Anthropoidae," *Folia Primatologia* 3:81–152.
Tobias, P. V.
    1963   "Cranial Capacity of *Zinjanthropus* and other Austra-
            lopithecines," *Nature* 197:743–746.
    1964   "The Olduvai Bed I Hominine with Special Reference
            to Its Cranial Capacity," *Nature* 202:3–4.
Washburn, S. L.
    1963   "Behavior and Human Evolution," in *Classification
            and Human Evolution* (S. L. Washburn, ed.). Viking
            Fund Publications in Anthropology No. 37.
    1963b   "Comment," *Current Anthropology* 4:492.
Washburn, S. L. and P. Jay
    1967   "More on Tool Use among Primates," *Current
            Anthropology* 8:253–254.
Yerkes, R. M. and A. W. Yerkes
    1929   *The Great Apes.* New Haven: Yale University Press.
Zeuner, F. E.
    1959   *The Pleistocene Period: Its Climate, Chronology, and
            Faunal Successions.* London: Hutchinson and Co.
Zuckerkandl, E.
    1963   "Perspectives in Molecular Anthropology," in *Classifi-
            cation and Human Evolution* (S. L. Washburn, ed.).
            Viking Fund Publications in Anthropology No. 37.

K. R. L. HALL

*This chapter presents a new approach to an old problem: the
interpretation of tool-using among animals. The list of animals
other than primates that use some form of tool is a rather long
one, and the tendency has been to include every animal
regardless of the function or nature of its tool. Whereas tool use
has traditionally been regarded as a measure of the intelligence
of a species, Hall set aside this bias and looked instead at the
species' performance in a larger ecological and behavioral
context. Rather than describe the similarities among different
types of tool usage, he sought the function of each act. On the
basis of these functions, he scrutinized the important differences
in the application of each object.*

*Tools are used by different kinds of animals in three basic
contexts: 1) agonistic, 2) feeding, and 3) display, nest building,
and body care. Hall indicated that primates seldom used tools in
feeding, although since the time he wrote, field studies of some
New World monkeys and additional information from the
chimpanzee studies in the Gombe have reported that a
substantial amount of object use is directed toward obtaining
food. It is important, however, that Hall was correct in noting
that the first category, the use of tools in agonistic interactions,
occurs only among primates. In general, most animals known to
use tools use only one kind in a relatively stereotyped manner
that varies little among the members of the species. After
surveying the major examples of tool use among other animals,
Hall emphatically concludes that "tool-using as such, and even
tool making, taken outside of the total behavioral context in
which it occurs, is not a criterion of adaptability that should be
assigned any special weighting."*

*Tool-use by animals other than primates occurs in highly
specialized ecological settings and does not appear to lend more
or less selective advantage to the animal using them than is
provided by alternative forms of adaptation. Hall made this
apparent because he used data that were fully documented and
examples that were from free-ranging animals rather than from
the massive amount of anecdotal stories of the behaviors of
captive animals.*

*Hall suggests that the "emotional" use of tool objects by
monkeys and apes, as during aggressive interactions, offers clues
as to the origins of similar uses of tools in human phylogeny.
Many anthropologists concur with this theory. It has been skill*

362

rather than simple use that has characterized the use of tools among hominids and particularly for Homo. *Although all primates have hands and feet adapted for grasping and manipulating objects, only a very small proportion of primate species have used tools. Most examples of so-called tool-using among the nonhuman primates are examples of the use of convenient objects rather than tool-use in the sense Hall has described it. However, it is most likely that, in addition to the display function of objects and the use of objects for economic purposes, their crucial importance to man lies in his having had a long history of handling them. Adding up very small increments of ability over a long period of time has been a long slow process. The displays and feeding situations in which chimpanzees use tools suggest the situations in which small changes in skill and ability were rewarded and led to an increase in over-all skillful use for the species. We can measure the results of this long usage by the archeological record of man's development.*

19 Tool-Using Performances as Indicators of Behavioral Adaptability

INTRODUCTION

The use by an animal of an object or of another living organism as a means of achieving an advantage has been commonly regarded by comparative psychologists as an indication of intelligent adaptability. The mediating object is required by definition to be something extraneous to the bodily equipment of the animal, and its use allows the animal to extend the range of its movements or to increase their efficiency.

Reprinted with permission from *Current Anthropology,* Vol. 4, No. 5, pp. 479–494, December 1963. Comment on this article by R. J. Andrew, C. R. Carpenter, Radomir Chiak, Harry F. Harlow, Gordon W. Hewes, Harry J. Jerison, Arthur J. Riopelle, J. P. Scott, S. L. Washburn, J. S. Weiner, and a reply by K. R. L. Hall are included in the original article in Current Anthropology, Vol 4, No. 5, December 1963.

Phrases like "functional extension" have been applied to such performances, whose crucial characteristic is manipulation of something in the environment, in appetitive or aversive behavior or, much more rarely, as part of an instinctive display or nesting operation.

Many problems arise as to the origin, in ontogeny and phylogeny, of such performances. It is rarely clear whether a performance is characteristic of a species, or whether individual variations due to local ecological conditions modify it. Nor is it clear whether a performance, once it has occurred in an individual given or in a group of animals, can be transmitted to form a "tradition," in the sense of a habit learned and retained, or whether the more likely evolutionary process is selection, on the basis of the advantage of the performance; in the latter case, the learning is a matter of trial-and-error application of the tendency, comparable to the way in which any number of inherited tendencies may be ecologically employed. Thorpe (1951, 1956) has examined much of the evidence along these lines, with particular reference to birds. In the present paper it is intended to carry the analysis into the realm of nonhuman primate behavior; some of the well-authenticated studies of other animals will be cited to give the necessary comparative perspective.

On evaluating performances as falling inside or outside the category of tool-using, it will be evident that they vary greatly in their flexibility and apparent behavioral complexity. All performances are conventionally excluded if they involve simply applying a "primary" object, for example, food, to a "secondary" object, such as a rock. Thus, the snail-breaking by thrushes or the dropping of shells by gulls or crows onto a hard surface can be excluded. Included can be performances as manifestly unlike as the carrying of actinians in the claws of crabs and the enlisting of aid among chimpanzees in the cooperative solving of problems beyond the ability of a single chimpanzee, or the inducement of one chimpanzee by another, through food-begging or threat, to bring it food.

TOOL-USING OTHER THAN FOR DEFENSE OR FOOD-SEEKING

The classic example of tool-using in insects, that of the solitary wasp, *Ammophila urnaria*, was reported by Peckham and Peckham (1898); to be sure, Williston (1892) had already made similar observations on another species. In each instance, the act consisted of holding a small pebble in the mandibles and using it as a hammer to pound dirt into the nest burrow. The Peckhams commented: "We are claiming a great deal for *Ammophila* when we say that she improvised a tool and made intelligent use of it, for such actions are rare even among higher mammals. . . ." (p. 223). Whether this is to be counted as an "individual" achievement rather than characteristic of a species is not certain, and the problem is not, at this level, of importance except in the way it parallels the situation in "higher"animals. So unexpected and interesting were these observations to the early comparative psychologists that they tended to jump to the conclusion that "intelligent purpose" and "perception of the relation of means to an end" (Morgan, 1900) were involved, while McDougall (1923) was somewhat more lyrical, saying:

> Are we then to regard each of these two wasps as a lively *bahnbrechende* genius, leading their species onward to the use of tools; individual sports comparable to the man, or ape, who first took a stone in his hand to crack a nut and so foreshadowed the genius of Nasmyth? I see no other plausible interpretation of the facts. [p. 91]

The best known and most reliably reported instance of tool-using among birds occurs in the Satin bower-bird, *Ptilonorhynchus violaceus*. This species was said by Chisholm (1954) to use a "tool," such as small wads of bark, to aid in the painting of the inside walls of its bower. He commented:

> . . . it had been supposed that these served the office of a brush, but it is now thought more probable that each one acts as a cork, or stopper, to prevent the paint oozing from the tip of the mandibles while the bird is plastering the walls of the bower with the sides of the bill. [p. 381]

Marshall's study (1960) provides the behavioral context of these performances in the Satin bower-bird species, as well as a very full description of them:

> . . . many, but not all, adult males begin to plaster their bower with a thick, black, tacky material made from a mixture of charcoal compounded with saliva. With a bark wad held between the tips of the beak, the plaster is forced between the mandibles and so transferred to the inside sticks of the bower. [p. 207]

A similar kind of behavior is reported of some male members of the genus *Chlamydera*: painting their bowers with dry grass mixed with saliva. These performances occur during displays which serve partly to attract females to the display grounds, partly to repel other males, so that pair-formation can occur: "Remarkable as they are, the bowers and display paraphernalia of bower-birds are no more than an extension of the territorial and display impulses to be found in other birds" (p. 208), and the whole performance of bower-construction and painting is interpreted by him as the outcome of a "displaced nesting-drive," the male taking no part in nest-building or incubation. Marshall commented that bower birds are no more intelligent than other highly developed passerine species, and there is, indeed, no valid reason for supposing they might be simply on the grounds that an elementary act, definable as tool-use, is incorporated into the display. The *rarity* of any such performance among birds or other animals in such a context suggests that it is a special case of behavioral adaptation which has no particular significance in the evolution of "intelligent" tool-using.

Seemingly the only instance in this miscellaneous category known in mammals is that of the Burmese elephant, which, according to Williams (1950), picks up a long stick with its trunk to scratch its body. Although in captivity monkeys and apes are known to cover themselves with sacking or other materials, apparently as protection from cold or wet, no such instances are known from field studies.

TOOL-USING AS PART OF AGONISTIC BEHAVIOR

Not a single authenticated instance of tool-using as an element in agonistic behavior is known in animals other than that of the monkeys and apes which use a tool in repelling predators or intruders. According to Duerden (1905), the carrying of actinians by the crab *Melia tessellata* may have protective function. The crab travels with the actinians expanded and directed forward, sometimes waving them from side to side; when irritated, it moves its chelipeds toward the source of irritation, thereby placing the actinians in what may be considered the most favorable aggressive or defensive attitudes. It is possible, however, that this function is secondary and incidental, for the crab reacts in the same way whether it is carrying the actinians (as food-getting "instruments") or not.

In considering such evidence as there is of the "agonistic" use of objects by monkeys and apes, trying to analyze the observations in terms of function and context of the act, we should first examine reports on wild animals, in which no training by or imitation of human beings is presumably involved. Some of the sources of information (Table 1) are personal observations of trained field-workers, others, those of naturalists and hunters (Wallace; Merfield and Miller; Hingston), and the rest, of unknown source. The two major field studies of baboons (DeVore 1962, etc.; Hall 1962a and b, etc.) include no observations of agonistic object-use. In both of these studies, the investigator's objective was to study the baboons without disturbing them by his presence, and hence, the very situations most likely to elicit agonistic behavior in a group usually were lacking. The unexpected presence of parties of travelers or soldiers in baboon country may produce great agitation in the animals, eliciting a more intensive reaction.

In analyzing the function and context of these "primitive instrumental acts" (Carpenter 1934), we shall need to refer chiefly to the few studies in which sufficient detail of observation is available. In general, it is implicit in most early reports that the animals roll stones or drop or throw branches and other objects *with intent* to hit or drive away intruders. Aim or purpose in the act is assumed, and hence the whole act is usually thought of as intelligent or learned rather than instinctive or emotional. Lacking detailed and careful observation, one alternative was that these happenings are the "accidental" result of some agonistic behavior pattern characteristic of the species. Thus, excited macaques may dislodge stones in scrambling up a slope away from an intruder, or members of an arboreal species may chance to break off branches while making threatening gestures. Zuckerman (1932) inclined to the view that the many instances of this sort of behavior could be explained as the more or less accidental outcome of emotional displays, and thus did not need to assume the animal's perception of a relationship between such acts and the possible consequence of driving away an intruder.

This explanation seems correctly to emphasize the emotional origin of such acts but probably incorrectly assumes that animals noted for their learning ability would not readily carry out the emotional gesture with a very elementary directedness rather than in a supposedly random fashion.

Analysis of two sets of observations may help to clear the way for a critical evaluation of the status of the behavior involved. Carpenter (1935) describes the reactions to man of red spider monkeys in Panama as including the following: (1) barking; (2) frequently, approach; (3) in trees within 40 to 50 feet of the observer, shaking of the branches associated, almost invariably, vigorous scratching; and (4) "breaking off and dropping of branches...close...to the observer." "This behavior cannot be described as throwing, although the animal may cause the object to fall away from the perpendicular by a sharp twist of its body or a swinging circular movement of its powerful tail." Sometimes the dropping is delayed for a few seconds, as an observer approaches; feces and urine are also dropped. All are "instrumental acts" carried out with reference to objectives.

This account indicates that: (1) the approach of the monkeys is an aggressive action; (2) the vigorous scratching represents a displacement activity, which is known experimentally to occur in agitated monkeys that, because of caging, are unable to act out their escape or aggressive tendencies more directly (Hall 1962c); (3) shaking of the branches probably represents a redirection of the aggressive tendency; (4) breaking off and dropping the branches would seem to be a natural carryover of the aggressive movements, no new type of movement being involved; (5) the delay in dropping and the imparting of direction to the branches is "purposive" or "instrumental" in the elementary sense that the consequence of this

TABLE 1. SOME SOURCES OF EVIDENCE ON THE
AGONISTIC USE OF OBJECTS BY MONKEYS
AND APES IN THE WILD

Species genus	Author	Behavior and situation recorded
Gorilla	Merfield and Miller (1956)	When hunted, tearing off branches and flinging in direction of hunters below, "after peering about to locate them accurately"
	Schaller (1963)	Various forms of throwing of branches in agonistic display; not reported to be directed at source of disturbance
Orang-utan	Wallace (1902)	Throwing down of branches and heavy fruits in direction of intruder
	Schaller (1961)	Breaking off and hurling branches in direction of the observer
Gibbon	Carpenter (1940)	Breaking off and dropping dead branches in direction of observer
Howler	Carpenter (1934)	Breaking off and dropping dead limbs toward observer; also defecation and urination from directly above observer
Red spider	Carpenter (1935)	Breaking off and dropping branches close to observer
Cebus	Kaufmann (1962)	Dropping nuts and debris onto coatis
Baboons	Brehm (1916), Hornaday (1922), and other sources of unknown reliability	Geladas meeting Hamadryas and rolling stones down upon them; rolling of rocks toward human intruders
Macaques	Kinnaman (1902), quoting another source Hingston (1920) Joléaud (1933) and other sources of unknown reliability	Deliberate tilting-up and rolling of stones down slope; throwing down of pine cones by Japanese monkeys at passers-by
Patas	Boulenger (1937)	Directing "fusillade" of sticks, stones, etc., on river travelers in W. Africa

variation is anticipated as being more rewarding than the consequence of no aiming; in other words, a simple process of operant conditioning is at work, whereby the "aimed" variation is reinforced over the "unaimed."

The objections to such a formulation stem mainly from the lack of information as to the frequency and variability of "directed" performances in these animals. Nevertheless, the learning postulated is of so elementary a kind that all it requires is a very slight modification in the agonistic behavior repertoire apparently characteristic of the species in such circumstances. It is not easy to imagine simpler learning performances, given the usual threat-gesture system of monkeys, for no new act is involved.

For all other species of New and Old World monkeys, only a single, very brief statement about the behavior of a *Cebus capucinus* group on Barro Cororado Island has added to our knowledge. During his two-year study of coatis, Kaufmann (1962) on one occasion saw the monkeys chase some coatis from a tree, then go on to drop nuts and debris from a *Schellea* palm onto them. The coatis ignored the shower except to pounce on and eat the ripe nuts that were included. This observation is of particular interest in view of the reputation of *Cebus* in laboratory experiments and because it is the first by a naturalist of behavior of this type involving nonhuman intruders.

Among the apes, Wallace's observations (1902) on the orang-utan and Schaller's confirmation and elaboration of them (1961) suggest a similar pattern. One of Schaller's observations was as follows:

> A female with a large infant spent 15 minutes throwing a total of about 30 branches varying in size from twigs to limbs 10 feet long and 3 inches in diameter. Considerable effort was expended at times in tearing off the larger branches. Limbs were thrown in three ways: (a) she merely held the branch at her side and dropped it limply; (b) she looked down at me and swung the branch like a large pendulum, and at the peak of the arc closest to me she released it: (c) she lifted branches either as high as her chest or above her head with one hand and hurled them down forcefully. Whatever interpretation is given this behavior, there is no doubt that it induced me to jump nimbly at times and that it kept me effectively away from beneath the tree. [p. 82]

Wallace's account concerned the throwing down of branches and of the fruits of the Durian tree by an adult female with young ones near her; and he supposed that the ape's parental instinct may have been specially aroused. However, the essential features of the situations in which this and the resulting behavior occur are similar to those in the Red spider monkey account, namely disturbance by a human intruder eliciting agitation and redirection of aggression onto the most readily available objects, and an effective directing of the objects toward the observer.

The explanation already proposed seems to need no revision to include the orang-utan data or any other data of similar performances in free-ranging monkeys or apes. This does not imply that such displays always or even usually have a "direction." Schaller's (1963) full account of the mountain gorillas' repertoire of gestures in such circumstances does not suggest that branches or leaves are, in the physical sense, aimed at the observer. The amount and kind of learning involved in "aiming" are such that many other mammals below the primates might achieve this behavior very readily *if* they had happened to evolve the sort of manipulatory and agonistic repertoire which seems to be a general simian characteristic. To underline this point, we may briefly consider the agonistic and the feeding repertoire of baboons in the wild (Hall 1962a and b). First, baboons frequently turn over stones when searching for food. Second, they may pull violently back and forward on tree branches or rocks while staring at and otherwise threatening an observer. Third, they may hit away, with a swift underarm movement, a noxious or unfamiliar small object or living organism as a sequel to, or component of, a startle behavior sequence. These three aspects of their behavior readily dispose these animals to the simple instrumental act involved in tipping a rock toward an intruder. There would be no mystery if it were shown that baboons or chimpanzees, for example, throw sand, stones or sticks, toward a predator on the same horizontal plane. All that is necessary is that the hitting-away movement be combined with the most elementary of feeding acts, that of grasping some object in the hand and "aiming" it in the same way that a threat-gesture or movement is usually directed *toward* an adversary. Because the use of objects as missiles has tended to be confused with the use, and even fashioning, of objects as offensive weapons, the complexity of the behavior involved seems to have been greatly exaggerated.

Linking behavior of this kind with that observed to occur spontaneously in captivity adds very little to the overall picture. Many reports are available of agonistic scooping/throwing in captivity (Kortlandt and Kooij, 1963), but all that need be added as commentary is that horizontal aiming is an extension of the threat-display, involving nothing more than the coordination of two acts basic to the repertoire. Brandishing of a stick and using it to beat another animal, as described by Cooper and Harlow (1961) in an individual *Cebus fatuellus* and in several chimpanzees, is an interesting elaboration of threat-display against other animals, but the significance of such performances must again be regarded first in their functional context, and only later against the supposed evolutionary background. The kind of brandishing action reported is very similar to that which baboons (Hall 1963a) and other monkeys and apes may engage in throwing a sack or a stick over a food-object.

We are not primarily concerned here with sifting through the varied kinds of evidence and deciding as to their reliability and accuracy. It is not yet possible to make valid comparisons of the various species or for example, of terrestrial monkeys and anthropoid apes, of Old World or of New World types, and the like, with respect to their "ability" to engage in this kind of instrumental behavior. Chimpanzee, capuchin, and baboon may turn out to demonstrate this propensity more readily and more flexibly than other nonhuman primates, but it is all too easy to fit the inadequate observational evidence into whatever evolutionary model one chooses — as Kortlandt and Kooij (1963) have done. It is simply the interaction of the processes of learning with the components and sequences of the naturally practiced behavior repertoire that requires a clear and straightforward analysis. The key to the instrumental learning successes of many types shown in the wild and in captivity by these animals is the exploratory-manipulatory tendency, of a quite general kind, which makes it easy for transfer or generalization to take place from one kind of situation to another, and over a wide range of objects or stimuli. Although we can thus simplify the behavioral analysis in such a way as to show that performances of the kind reported are readily to be expected in these animals, it still remains necessary to consider very carefully the kinds of environmental conditions which elicit or inhibit or just fail to elicit these performances.

TOOL-USING IN EXTENSION OF
THE FEEDING REPERTOIRE

The use of an object as a means of obtaining food which the animal cannot reach or which if within its reach, the animal cannot obtain directly is, contrary to the preceding class of performance, reported in birds in several instances, occasionally and rather uncertainly in marine invertebrates, and once only, with two other insufficiently substantiated instances, in subprimate mammals. For monkeys and apes, there is an extensive experimental literature, many observations on animals in captivity, and extremely few field data that provide evidence for analysis. The data will merely be sampled, as in the previous section, to illustrate points that seem significant for the whole comparative picture. Inevitably, this means paying most attention to the areas where most reliable knowledge is available.

The case of the crab, *Melia tessellata*, and actinian "commensalism," described by Duerden and others, is a curious example of the use of a living organism as a tool to aid the feeding of another. Although Duerden says the crabs do not restrict themselves to one species of anemone and may also, as already noted, hold them forward as a kind of defensive aid, the performance need not be classed as more "intelligent" than other sorts of behavioral adaptation to ecological need in which no tool or accessory is involved.

In birds, there are two sorts of performance which have been much discussed, namely, the string-pulling achievements of *Parus* and other passerines, and the use of a cactus-spine or twig as an extention of the bill to probe out insects or larvae in the so-called Galapagos woodpecker-finch, *Cactospiza pallida*. The former type of behavior clearly has some parallel in the probable factors involved here and in similar performances of primates. There may be an "inherited tendency" to pull upon and manipulate with beak and foot grasses, hair, bents, and other long flexible materials, in the course of nestbuilding or perhaps in obtaining certain sorts of food. This factor and practice can be supposed to account for the ease with which some of these birds seem immediately to tackle the task of pulling in a string on the end of which a bait is attached. We may note that the direct pulling-in of a string or stick to the end of which the food-object is attached seems to be a task requiring very little modification of existing repertoire other than trial-and-error application.

The tool-using performances of the woodpecker-finch are usually considered a remarkable example of behavioral adaptation to fit it into the special ecological circumstances of the Galapagos Islands bird population. According to Lack (1947, 1953), this primarily insectivorous finch resembles a woodpecker in that it climbs up and down vertical trunks and branches in search of its food. But whereas the woodpecker, having excavated in a branch with its beak, inserts its long tongue into the crack to get the insect out, the finch has evolved the alternative method of picking up a cactus spine or twig, holding it lengthwise in its beak and poking it up the crack, dropping the twig to seize the insect in its beak as it emerges. It has been seen to reject a twig if it proved too short or too pliable, and sometimes the bird carries a spine or twig about with it, poking it into cracks or crannies as it searches one tree after another. Bowman (1961) added further observations on this behavior. He saw it most frequently in the dry season in the arid zone, where almost every bird of the species was seen carrying a cactus spine in its bill. He also reported two cases of what appeared to be attempts of the bird to adjust the size and shape of its probe to fit the cranny or crack in which it was searching. First,

> One such bird was holding a spine about six inches long. Only about two inches of the spine protruded from the tip of the bill, the remainder passed along one side of the face and neck. Apparently the bird realized that the stick was excessively long, for it made an unsuccessful attempt to twist off approximately three inches of the spine by holding it with the feet. [p. 33]

Second, he quotes an observation made by Mr. Kastdalen in 1956:

> I was looking at a finch the other day, and he convinced me that the stick habit is intelligent and not instinctive. One of them was working in a hole . . . which seemed to be full of bugs, so he had to drop its stick several times to catch the bugs. Each

time it went for a new stick, but after a few times it came with a forked stick, and tried to get it into the hole a couple of times, but in vain. Then he saw what was wrong and turned the stick around and broke it off at the fork, and started working. [p. 33]

Ignoring the terminological points about the bird's "realizing" what it was doing and the distinction between "intelligent" and "instinctive," it is evident that something definable as "tool-making," that is, an attempting to work upon the tool-object, is here involved. However, it is likely that nothing more worthy of note is involved in such an attempt than what is routine in nest-constructing activities.

While it is indeed remarkable that this finch should have evolved a behavioral adaptation supposedly more appropriate at the primate level of evolution, the chief significance of such a performance, in the comparative behavior framework, is perhaps to emphasize the fact that *tool-using as such*, and even tool-making, taken outside of the total behavioral context in which it occurs, is not a criterion of adaptability that should be assigned any special weight. If in rare cases a species of crab or bird evolves a behavioral, rather than a physical, adaptation to deal with some ecological condition, this may be interesting evidence of the versatility of evolutionary processes but involves no more complex type of *learning* than, one may suppose, the sort of trial-and-error adjustments which these "remarkable" species have in common with other crabs and other birds.

Among subprimate mammals, we have already cited Williams' (1950) report of elephants using sticks to scratch their bodies, and he also describes how "Many young elephants develop the naughty habit of plugging up the wooden bell they wear hung around their necks with good stodgy mud or clay so that the clappers cannot ring, in order to steal silently into a grove of cultivated bananas at night" (p. 78). While the performances of elephants in captivity indicate that their potential in tool-using is probably greater than that of any other nonprimate animal, there is no systematic evidence of the variety of their performances in the wild. It can merely be noted in passing, however, that the way in which they pull down or push over trees to get at foliage otherwise beyond their reach is an "instrumental act" at least on a par for behavioral complexity with patterned string or string-pulling performances. It is also, for the elephant, a much more economical way of feeding than would be, say, its attempt to knock off fruit or leaves by brandishing a stick in its trunk.

Apart from elephants, another class of mammal that may be found to use tools as a feeding aid in the wild are bears. The readiness with which they stand on hindlegs and use their paws in manipulations would predispose them to develop such skills where need arises, and Harington (1962) interestingly reviews the evidence that polar bears dislodge or pick up and cast down blocks of ice onto the heads of sleeping walruses. The only subprimate mammal for which there are reliable reports is the sea otter, *Enhydra lutris*. Studies made of its feeding habits show that in the Aleutians as well as in California, mollusks form a substantial part of the diet. In California, abalones are also commonly brought up and eaten, but it is not known whether rocks are used to aid in the process of removing these large shellfish from their sites. Fisher (1939) was the first to give a detailed account of this animal's use of a stone as a tool:

> It is a not uncommon thing to hear a sharp clicking sound and then to locate its point of origin . . . This sound is always made by an otter that is trying to crack open something with a very hard stonelike shell. The object that the otter has in its paws is too small to see — possibly it is some mollusk. The object is held with both paws and with full arm action from well over the head it is brought down hard on a piece of rock that rests on the otter's chest. These pieces of stone are brought to the surface at the same time as the food. It may take several severe blows before the object is cracked enough for the otter to get the food out. These rocks are not small but appear to be almost as large as the large abalones. When the otters roll over they hold both the rock and the food on their chests. This clicking sound is so distinct that it can be heard for some distance above the noise of the waters. [p. 28]

Murie (1940) confirmed this observation on the California animals, and Hall and Schaller (1964) have obtained quantitative data on this performance; they reported that it is usually mussels that are banged against the rock anvil, although occasionally other animals, such as spiny lobsters, may be pounded in this way. Krear (personal communication), who spent from late July until mid-December 1957 on Amchitka in the western Aleutians, watching sea otters most of the time, observed only one young animal traveling with its mother that used a rock as a tool: "The immature was observed on three occasions to bring rocks to the surface, and on these he would pound and crack his food items, most of which were little blue mussels." It is probable that the mussels in the Aleutians did not require tool-use of the sort so frequently seen off the California coast, but that the propensity for such performances is readily available, as is strongly indicated by Kenyon's account (1959) of how an adult otter, captured in the Aleutians, used rocks as anvils on which to pound clams.

The sea otter data suggest very little at present as to the origin, variability, and other characteristics of this behavior. So far as is known, no developmental observations are available, other than the one instance quoted. It is also likely that the pup acquires the habit by observing the behavior of its mother, for it swims for many weeks very close to her, takes food from her chest, and is occasionally offered food by her (Hall and

Schaller, in press). It is thus highly probable that the pup must learn its discriminations of food objects and of behavior appropriate to deal with them by observing the corresponding behavior in the mother. The fundamental dependency relationship is such that "following," both perceptually and in the locomotor and manipulatory senses, is necessary for the pup's survival. This is generally true of mammals and is mentioned here only because it may help to explain the origin of the habit.

Considering now the nonhuman primates, detailed evidence from field studies indicates that only one, the chimpanzee, uses tools; this it does in reference to a probably minor feeding behavior, probing termites out of holes with twigs (Morris-Goodall 1962). Beatty (1951) reported that chimpanzees in Liberia break open palm nuts by hammering them with rocks, and Merfield and Miller (1956) described how chimpanzees poke long twigs into the entrance holes of the ground nests of bees and withdraw the twigs coated with honey. The distance at which this observation was made was 50 yards, using binoculars. Pitman (1931) mentioned seeing a free-living gorilla using a stick to obtain fruit otherwise out of its reach, but Schaller (1963) had no record of such behavior in 12 months of field study.

This lack of evidence of tool-using comes as a surprise to the many investigators familiar with the ease with which other species of great ape and several species of monkey learn spontaneously in captivity, as well as with progressive training procedures, to use sticks, sacks, boxes, or even live rats (Klüver, 1937) to haul in food objects otherwise out of reach. *Cebus capucinus* and perhaps other *Cebus* species appear to be particularly adept in this respect (Klüver 1933; Bierens de Haan 1931), while individuals of the *Papio ursinus* species (Bolwig 196; Hall 1962a) show a similar kind of aptitude. The surprise of the laboratory investigators is due to the apparent discrepancy between the *potential* that these animals have for such performances when given situations designed to elicit them in captivity and their failure to make use of the potential as an aid in increasing their dietary repertoire in the wild. Two of the main factors accounting for this discrepancy are: (1) Systematic field evidence is still far too scanty for us to know how great the discrepancy is; for example, very little is known of the details of the feeding habits of free-ranging *Cebus*. (2) The discrepancy is not a behaviorally significant one but is rather due to a misconception as to the degree of transfer or generalization involved when the wild-born animal is given the usual run of instrumentation tasks in captivity. This point requires a brief elaboration.

If we take as an example the natural feeding behavior of the baboon and the more or less continuous processes of exploration and manipulation of objects that go with it, some of which have already been mentioned, we find that the animal is practicing, either in play or in actual feeding, a variety of skills which are readily generalized in the experimental situation. The young ones carry sticks or branches in their mouths or in one hand and do not use them in feeding. All of them at some time or other break dead branches from bushes in searching for food, as when, for example, they are searching for larvae or ants' nests (Hall 1962a). They push over slabs of rock, and they tend to investigate almost any strange manipulable object that lies in their path. They pull upon telegraph wires, open the doors and windows of unoccupied huts and cars, and so on. In short, they show a generalized tendency to fiddle with and try out objects that may or may not be instrumental in obtaining food. These animals appear to have a surplus of exploratory-manipulatory energy for which there may seem to be no immediate ecological need. However, it is perfectly feasible to suppose that it is just this kind of generalized activity which has enabled baboons to be sufficiently adaptable to survive over large areas of Africa in a very wide variety of habitats, for example, allowing them to be omnivorous in some regions (although they are classed as predominantly vegetarian in all areas where the diet has been adequately scheduled, according to Washburn and DeVore [1961] and Hall [1962a]). Thus, given the behavior repertoire the baboon is known to possess, the learning involved in obtaining food that is out of reach would appear to be of a rudimentary kind.

Similar evidence as to the maturation of the necessary manipulatory coordinations (Schiller 1957) and as to the effective role of natural and instrumental practice (Nissen 1931; Birch 1945) has been put forward for the chimpanzee, and there is no need to review it. One comment of Schiller's is particularly appropriate, however, because it indicates how, in chimpanzees and other species, the "emotional" repertoire of gesture may be readily utilized in differing contexts:

> That a chimpanzee breaks off a branch if excited has nothing to do with his desire to get the food [in an experimental situation]. Once he has the stick in his hand, he will use it sooner or later. Such a sequence can easily be reinforced in a couple of trials, then it appears to be a coherent, continuous pattern. [p. 275]

GENERAL EVALUATION

Tool-using performances have tended to be treated as though they represented some kind of behavioral homology at the different levels of organism in which they have been recorded. This view seems to be incorrect, however, because it seems evident that the application of a common term to so varied an assortment of performances has led to the glossing over of fundamental differences in adaptive significance. While the criterion of tool-using is no longer used by anthropologists to signalize a supposedly critical stage in the transition of ape to human, it is still not unreasonably inferred that tool-using was an important behavioral adaptation somewhere in primate evolution, and that the *making* of tools derived from a prevalence in tool-using far in excess of that now discernible in any living nonhuman primate (Washburn 1950). For anthropologists, behavioral evidence of living nonhuman primates in the wild is thus of interest to the extent that it indicates "transitional" ingredients of essentially hominid characteristics such as the carnivorous tendency and tool-using (Oakley 1951).

In the general framework of animal evolution, we have seen that instances definable as tool-using occur in highly specialized ecological settings, as in the woodpecker-finch, crab-actinian commensalism, and probably the *Ammophila*. These are basically behavioral adaptations that are probably produced by trial-and-error learning, like that commonly found in almost all living organisms. These adaptations do not appear to give their possessors any selective advantage over other species which have evolved alternative forms of adaptation. Rather, they simply enable their possessors to survive at a certain population level in their ecological niches. In other words, such performances are only worthy of special note because of their entirely superficial, indeed one might almost say fortuitous, resemblance to human tool-using. The case of the string-pulling performances of some passerines is of the same order. While one allows that birds of the *Parus* genus, as an example, show a certain aptitude in this kind of problem, as in others, such as pecking open milk bottle tops, no one, but for the human analogy, would probably be disposed on this ground to give this species a specially high rating for adaptability. As others have clearly indicated (Thorpe 1956; Tinbergen 1960), birds may evolve certain rather restricted propensities enabling them to learn through what one might call a special aptitude. The natural practice of food-seeking and nest-construction may fit into the scheme. A performance classifiable as tool-using may in fact be less significant as an adaptability indicator than one which cannot strictly be so considered, such as the performances of thrushes, gulls, or crows in breaking open hard food-objects.

The observations of the sea otter were reviewed at length to refute the view that its performance indicated that a new process had appeared at the *Mammalian* level of evolution. The apparent uniqueness of this performance and its occurrence in the context of a particular marine ecological situation for which the animal shows other peculiar behavioral and physical adaptations, such as lying on the back when feeding, indicate that there is no reason to judge this animal's performances as of any greater evolutionary significance than those for which other marine mammals, such as seals and dolphins, are noted.

In the evaluation of what is known about the nonhuman primates' performances and potentialities, we have to consider two main types of tool-using: that in the service of agonistic behavior and that in obtaining food. It is in the former category that by far the most evidence is available, suggesting that "instrumental acts" with some degree of direction or purpose are quite a widespread and general characteristic in monkeys and apes, as a straightforward function of fear-threat motivation and manipulatory endowment. And indeed it seems, as the quotation from Schiller indicated, that we have here a behavioral adaptation of a fairly general and simple kind which evolved primarily in the context of agonistic tendencies toward opponents that inhibit direct attack. Associating this with the fact that no such instances have been reliably reported in any other class of animal, one can infer that this is the fundamental behavioral situation from which all other instances of primate tool-using have been derived. There is, in most monkeys at any rate, an arousal of fairly strong agonistic tendencies in any food-to-be-gained situation in which they are frustrated. They tend easily, in such circumstances, to show displacement activities or redirections of aggression (Masserman and Pechtel 1953), and their tool-using attempts often consist of throwing actions which are hardly distinguishable from threat-gestures. It will be only through systematic developmental studies of young primates that we shall be able to trace the course of these performances and to study the relationship between frustration responses and the emergence of tool-use in general.

SUMMARY

Tool-using performances in animals have often been considered important indicators of relative intelligence, but no comparative analysis of their probable origin and place within the total ecological and behavioral setting has been available. The usual definition has tended to emphasize features that performances at different phyletic levels have in common, while glossing over the underlying and even overt differences.

The many examples in the literature are sampled with reference to the use of tools: (1) in agonistic behavior; (2) in extending the feeding habits of a species; and (3) in courtship display (Satin bower-birds), nest-hole construction (Ammophila spp.), and, possibly, body care (elephants).

Examples of the second category include what appear to be special behavioral adaptations that are functionally equivalent to physical extensions or modifications, as in the case of the crab-actinian relationship in Melia tessellata, the Galapagos woodpecker-finch, Cactospiza pallida, and possibly also in the sea otter, Enhydra lutris. To varying degrees, the tool-using adaptation has importance in the life of the species. In the crab and the finch, it seems to involve a basic feeding adjustment, while in the sea otter it is reportedly used only with respect to one major item of food, mollusks, and it may be much more prevalent in the southern limits of distribution than in the north. Among nonhuman primates in the wild, tool-using of this sort is rare, not being known in baboons and macaques, and only reliably reported, among the anthropoid apes, in the chimpanzee which appears to use a food-getting tool to obtain a supplementary rather than a staple item of diet.

Examples of the first category occur only in nonhuman primates. In systematic field studies in the wild, "primitive instrumental acts" of breaking off and casting down branches, twigs, or leaves in the direction of the observer have been reported of howlers and red spider monkeys, gibbons, and orangutans. Gorillas include throwing gestures in their complex and apparently stereotyped displays when disturbed, but no "directing" toward the source of disturbance has been noted. Terrestrial monkeys of the *Macaca* and *Papio* genera have been reported to push or roll stones towards intruders. There are, however, no detailed field observations of this behavior, and, if it occurs, it is probably elicited in groups of monkeys that are highly disturbed and unused to human intrusion and would not be seen under the noninterference conditions in which the field observer usually tries to work.

Controversy over the reliability of the evidence on tool-using, particularly in nonhuman primates, and over the explanation of such instances as are irrefutable, seems to stem from the following: (1) a tendency to overestimate the significance of such performances as indicators of behavioral adaptability, largely because of the urge to discover equivalences to stages in human evolution; (2) a failure to analyze in detail the context and function of such performances. It is suggested that the "primitive instrumental acts" involve only an elementary form of operant conditioning imposed upon the agonistic repertoire of the species, and that "direction" of aim with objects is no more surprising than the fact that threat gestures without objects are normally aimed at an intruder.

The discrepancy, commented upon by laboratory investigators, between the apparent ease with which many monkeys and apes use tools to gain food in captivity situations and their apparent failure to use this propensity to advantage in the wild, has no real significance. Possibly the "primitive instrumental acts" provide the primary emotional bases from which any kind of tool-using arises, the transfer to other situations, such as food-getting, being conditioned by the way in which the animals manipulate objects not directly related to food.

The present evaluation of the comparative data has, as its purpose, the clarification of the confusion caused by inadequacy of behavioral evidence and by the biasing of such evidence to fit some evolutionary scheme. The hypothesis that the "emotional" use of tool objects by monkeys and apes may provide the lead to an understanding of the origins, in phylogeny and ontogeny, of such performances in human beings is suggested by the fact that no comparable agonistic performances are known in any other class of animal. On the other hand, tool-using as a feeding adaptation occurs in several different types of animal but has so far proved very rare in monkeys and apes.

ABSTRACT

Use of an object by animals as a functional extension of their limbs in order to obtain food or to facilitate some other goal seeking activity has quite commonly been reported as an especially significant indicator of intelligence or complex learning ability.

The present review has selected well authenticated examples of tool-using behavior from different types of animal, such as wasps, crabs, birds, subprimate mammals, and nonhuman primates, and examined the context of their occurrence and the apparent complexity of performance involved. These performances have been concerned with: a) attainment of food; b) offensive or defensive use against predators or intruders; c) miscellaneous functions such as self-grooming, courtship, nest-building. Categories (a) and (b) contain by far the most instances, and (c) has very few indeed.

The problem, in attempting a comparative analysis of such instances, is to evaluate the performance within the whole context of the animal's capacities and the way these are expressed in various ecological settings. The evidence cited is primarily from naturalistic studies, that from restrictive settings, such as zoo or laboratory, being adduced only in emphasizing discrepancies. As an example, baboons have, so far, not been seen to demonstrate tool-using in the wild in their food-seeking behavior, but they do so readily when given the opportunity in captivity. They thus have a potential which their natural surroundings perhaps only rarely bring into action, whereas chimpanzees demonstrate their capacity for this kind of performance in diverse ways both in the wild and in captivity.

Certain performances by nonprimate animals, such as the Galapagos woodpecker-finch or the California sea otter, indicate that tool-using of a very effective, though presumably restricted kind can evolve in animals having a narrow habitat range, and in whom, therefore, other significant aspects of adaptability may be missing. Further, from assessing the many instances of category (b) and the very few instances of category (a) in wild monkeys and apes, it was tentatively suggested that the emotional offensive-defensive type of tool-using might have had primacy in evolution over that of food-getting and the other miscellaneous instances. A review of this sort, with a suggestion of this kind, is put forward anyway chiefly as an attempt at clarification which may lead to much further detailed studies, experimental and naturalistic, of the animals in question.

As always in describing complex behavior and in deriving models or inferences from the description, the profusion and confusion of terminology are difficult to sort out neatly or clearly. But the objective of this review will have been achieved if, in deliberately avoiding the use of controversial terms, it has been possible to show the need for a fresh research approach to the comparative study of behavioral adaptability in animals with a view to working out much more satisfactorily than at present the bearing that such evidence may have upon fundamental questions of human evolution.

REFERENCES

Andrew, R. J.
  1962 "Evolution of Intelligence and Vocal Mimicking," *Science* 137:585–89.
Beatty, H.
  1951 "A Note on the Behavior of the Chimpanzee," *Journal of Mammalogy* 32:118.
Bierens De Haan, J. A.
  1931 Werkzeuggebrauch und Werkzeugherstellung bei einem niedern Affen *(Cebus hypoleucus Humb.)*. *Zeitschrift für Physiologie* 13:639–95.
Birch, H. G.
  1954 "The Relation of Previous Experience to Insightful Problemsolving," *Journal of Comparative Psychology* 38:367–83.
Bishop, A.
  1962 "Control of the Hand in Lower Primates," *Annals New York Academy Sciences* 102:316–37.
Bolwig, N.
  1959 "A Study of the Behavior of the Chacma Baboon (*Papio ursinus*)," *Behavior* 14:136–63.
  1961 "An Intelligent Tool-Using Baboon," *South African Journal of Science* 57:147–52.
Boulenger, E. G.
  1937 *Apes and Monkeys.* New York: McBride.
Bowman, R. I.
  1961 "Morphological Differentiation and Adaptation in the Galapagos Finches," *University of California Publications in Zoology* 58:1–326.
Brehm, A. E.
  1916 *Tierleben, Band 4: Saugetiere.* Leipzig und Wien: Bibliographisches Institut.
Carpenter, C. R.
  1934 "A Field Study of the Behavior and Social Relations of Howling Monkeys," *Comparative Psychology Monographs* 10, No. 2.
  1935 "Behavior of Red Spider Monkeys in Panama," *Journal of Mammalology* 16:171–80.

1940 "A Field Study in Siam of the Behavior and Social Relations of the Gibbon," *Comparative Psychology Monographs* 16:38–206.

Chance, M. R. A.
1960 "Kohlers Chimpanzees — How Did They Perform?" *Man* 179:130–35.

Chisholm, A. H.
1954 "The Use by Birds of 'Tools' or 'Instruments,'" *Ibis* 96:380–3.

Cihák, R.
1963 "The Development of the Dorsal Interossei in the Human Hand," *Ceskoslovenská morfologie* 11:199–208.

Cooper, L. R., and H. F. Harlow.
1961 "Note on a Cebus Monkey's Use of a Stick as a Weapon," *Psychological Reports* 8:418.

Dart, R. A.
1960 "The Bone Tool-manufacturing Ability of Australopithecus Prometheus," *American Anthropologist* 62:134–43.

DeVore, I.
1962 The Social Behavior and Organization of Baboon Troops. Unpublished Ph.D. Thesis, University of Chicago, Chicago, Illinois.

Duerden, J. E.
1905 "On the Habits and Reactions of Crabs Bearing Actinians in their Claws," *Proceedings of the Zoological Society of London* 2:494–511.

Fisher, E. M.
1939 "Habits of the Southern Sea Otter," *Journal of Mammalology* 20:21–36.

Forster, A.
1916 Die Mm. contrahentes und interossei manus in der Säugetierreihe und beim Menschen. *Archiv für Anatomie und Entwickelungsgeschichte* 101–378.

Hall, K. R. L.
1962a "Numerical data, maintenance activities, and locomotion in the Wild Chacma Baboon, *Papio Ursinus*," *Proceedings of the Zoological Society of London* 139:181–220.

1962b "Sexual, Derived Social, and Agonistic Behavior Patterns in the Wild Chacma Baboon, *Papio Ursinus*," *Proceedings of the Zoological Society of London* 139:284–327.

1962c "Behaviour of Monkeys to Mirror-images," *Nature* 196:1258–61.

1963 "Variations in the Ecology of the Chacma Baboon, *Papio Ursinus*."

Hall, K. R. L. and George B. Schaller.
1964 "Tool-Using Behavior of the California Sea-Otter," *J. Mammal.* 45:287–298.
Harington, C. R.
1962 "A Bear Fable?" *The Beaver* No. 4 (Winter): 4–7.
Hewes, G. W.
1961 "Food Transport and the Origin of Hominid Bipedalism," *American Anthropologist* 63:687–710.
Hill, W. C. O.
1960 *Primates.* Vol. 4. Cebidae, Part A. Edinburgh: University Press.
Hingston, R. W. G.
1920 *A Naturalist in Himalaya.* Boston: Small.
Hornaday, W. T.
1922 *The Minds and Manners of Wild Animals.* New York: Scribner.
Imanishi, K.
1960 "Social Organization of Subhuman Primates in Their Natural Habitat," *Current Anthropology* 1:393–407.
Joléaud, L.
1933 Études de géographie zoologique sur la Berbérie. Les Primates: le Magot. Congrès International de Géographie, Paris 1931. Comptes rendus. Vol. II, part 2, pp. 851–63.
Kaufmann, J. H.
1962 "Ecology and Social Behavior of the Coati, *Nasua Narica,* on Barro Colorado Island, Panama," *University of California Publications in Zoology* 60:95–222.
Kawamura, S.
1959 "The Process of Subculture Propagation among Japanese Macaques," *Journal of Primatology, Primates* (Japan Monkey Centre) 2 (No. 1):43–60.
Kenyon, K. W.
1959 "The Sea Otter," *Annual Report of the Smithsonian Institute, 1958.* Washington, D.C., The Smithsonian Institute, pp. 399–407.
Kinnaman, A. J.
1902 "Mental Life of Two *Macacus Rhesus* Monkeys in Captivity. II," *American Journal of Psychology* 13:173–218.
Klüver, H.
1933 *Behavior Mechanisms in Monkeys.* Chicago: University of Chicago Press.
1937 "Re-examination of Implement-Using Behavior in a *Cebus* Monkey after an Interval of Three Years," *Acta Psychologica* 2:347–97.

Kortlandt, A. and M. Kooij.
1963 "Protohominid Behaviour in Primates" (Preliminary Communication). *Symposium, Zoological Society of London* 10:61–88.

Kummer, H.
1957 Soziales Verhalten einer Mantelparian-Gruppe. *Biehandlung Schweizerisch Zeitschrift Psychologie* 33:1–92.

Lack, D.
1947 *Darwin's Finches.* Cambridge: Cambridge University Press.
1953 "Darwin's Finches," *Scientific American* (April) 188:66–72.

Marshall, A. J.
1960 "Bower-Birds," *Endeavor* 19:202–08.

Masserman, J. H. and C. Pechtel.
1953 "Neuroses in Monkeys," *Proceedings of the New York Academy of Science* 56:253–65.

McDougall, W.
1923 *Outline of Psychology.* New York: Scribner.

Merfield, F. G. and H. Miller
1956 *Gorilla Hunter.* New York: Farrar.

Morgan, C. L.
1900 *Animal Behaviour.* London: E. Arnold.

Morris, D.
1962 *The Biology of Art.* New York: Alfred A. Knopf.

Murie, O. J.
1940 "Notes on the Sea-Otter," *Journal of Mammalology* 21:119–31.

Napier, J. R.
1960 "Studies of the Hands in Living Primates," *Proceedings Zoological Society London* 134:647–57.
1962 "The Evolution of the Hand," *Scientific American* 207:56–62 (No. 6).
1963 "Early Man and his Environment," *Discovery*, March, 12–18.
1963 "Tooling Up," *Newsweek*, May 27, pp. 98f.

Nissen, H. W.
1931 "A Field Study of the Chimpanzee," *Comparative Psychology Monographs* 8.

Oakley, K. P.
1951 "A Definition of Man," *Science News* 20:69–81.
1961 5th ed. *Man the Toolmaker.* London: British Museum of Natural History.

Peckham, G. W. and E. G. Peckham.
1898 "On the Instincts and Habits of Solitary Wasps," *Wisconsin Geological and Nature History Survey*, II.

Pitman, C. R.
   1931   A *Game Warden among his Charges*. London: Nisbet.
Romanes, G. J.
   1882   *Animal Intelligence*. London: Kegan Paul Trench & Co.
Schaller, G. B.
   1961   "The Orang-utan in Sarawak," *Zoologica* 46:73–82.
   1963   *The Mountain Gorilla: Ecology and Behavior*. Chicago:
         University of Chicago Press.
Schiller, P. H.
   1957   "Innate Motor Action as a Basis of Learning," in *In-
         stinctive Behavior* (Editor C. H. Schiller). New York:
         International University Press.
Thorndike, E. L.
   1898   "Animal Intelligence, an Experimental Study of the
         Associative Processes in Animals," *Psychological Re-
         view, Monograph Supplement* 2, no. 4 (whole no. 8).
Thorpe, W. H.
   1951   "The Learning Abilities of Birds," *Ibis* 93:1–52, 252–
         96.
   1956   *Learning and Instinct in Animals*. London: Methuen.
Tinbergen, N.
   1960   "Behaviour, Systematics, and Natural Selection," in
         Evolution after Darwin (Sol Tax, Editor), vol. I: *The
         Evolution of Life*. Chicago: University of Chicago
         Press.
Vevers, G. M. and Weiner, J. S.
   1963   "Use of a Tool by a Captive Capuchin Monkey *(Cebus
         Fatuellus)*," *Symposium on Primate Biology, Zoo-
         logical Society*, London.
Wallace, A. R.
   1902   10th ed. *The Malay Archipelago*. New York: Mac-
         millan.
Washburn, S. L.
   1950   "The Analysis of Primate Evolution with Particular
         Reference to the Origin of Man," *Cold Spring Harbor
         Symposium on Quantitative Biology* 15:67–78.
Washburn, S. L. and I. DeVore.
   1961   "Social Behavior of Baboons and Early Man," in
         Social Life of Early Man. Viking Fund Publications in
         Anthropology, No. 31, pp. 91–105.
Williams, J. H.
   1950   *Elephant Bill*. New York: Doubleday.
Williston, S. W.
   1892   "Notes on the Habits of Ammophila," *Entomological
         News* 3:85–6.
Zuckerman, S.
   1932   *The Social Life of Monkeys and Apes*. London: Kegan
         Paul.

S. L. WASHBURN
C. S. LANCASTER

"Evolution builds a relationship between biology, psychology and behavior, and therefore, the evolutionary success of hunting exerted a profound effect on human psychology." With this basic tenet the authors proceed to draw upon many lines of evidence to speculate on the characteristics of the stages of Pleistocene hominid development. Human hunting, as practiced during that period and as continuing, modified as it is, to the present, is viewed as a unique way of life among the mammals and as the hallmark of that period of human development. The pre-Homo stage of tool-using and hunting lasted more than four times as long as the genus Homo has existed. It is on this early, prolonged base or way of life that all subsequent human development occurred. The authors point out that less than one per cent of hominid history has been dominated by agriculture, and suggest that grinding, boiling, and developing receptacles for carrying are among the preconditions necessary for the development of agriculture.

The hunter's view is essentially different from that of his nonhuman primate precursors. Interpersonal relationships were substantially more complex for the hunter than for any nonhunting primate. The hunter needed space that was large and complex and the earliest hunters must have controlled vastly more land than that used by any other social group of primate.

Attributes of hunting social life most likely included a high degree of cooperation among males and a division of labor, so that females, in addition to child rearing, performed tasks supplemental to those of males in daily life. A home base or a location to which group members could return with the gains of hunting or gathering, and to which the sick member of the group could go for rest and recuperation, must have been exceedingly important as a locus of social activity.

As for the development of tools, the archeological record documents that it was a very long time after the first stone tools before evidence of technological progress in the forms and production of tools began to show itself. The increments of change were slow. For several million years small gains in skill and technology, probably every minute, must have accumulated that in the longer run had great importance for survival and success of middle and later Pleistocene man.

The social organization of hunting is described briefly and it is suggested that the human family was the result of the reciprocity entailed by a hunting way of living, with an adult male as a continuing member added to the basic social grouping of a mother and her offspring. The latter, a female and her young, is a type of enduring unit that is characteristic of some species of nonhuman primates. What is thought of as a human family was developed slowly and in response to many factors in a hunting existence.

The authors have added these and other speculations concerning the behaviors of early man to the incomplete fossil and archeological record. Their thesis is that to understand the origin and nature of human behavior it is first necessary to investigate man the hunter.

20   The Evolution of Hunting

... In contrast to carnivores, human hunting by males is based on a division of labor and is a social and technical adaptation quite different from that of other mammals. Human hunting is made possible by tools, but it is far more than a technique, or even a variety of techniques. It is a way of life, and the success of this adaptation (in its total social, technical, and psychological dimensions) has dominated the course of human evolution for hundreds of thousands of years. In a very real sense our intellect, interests, emotions, and basic social life — all these are evolutionary products of the success of the hunting adaptation. When anthropologists speak of the unity of mankind, they are stating that the selection pressures of the hunting and gathering way of life were so similar

Reprinted from Richard B. Lee and Irven DeVore, editors, *Man the Hunter* (Chicago: Aldine Publishing Company, 1968); copyright © 1969 by the Wenner-Gren Foundation for Anthropological Research, Inc.

and the result so successful that populations of *Homo sapiens* are still fundamentally the same everywhere. In this essay we are concerned with the general characteristics of man that we believe can be attributed to the hunting way of life.

Perhaps the importance of this way of life in producing man is best shown by the length of time hunting has dominated human history. The genus *Homo*[1] has existed for some 600,000 years, and agriculture has been important only during the last few thousand years. Even 6000 years ago large parts of the world's population were nonagricultural, and the entire evolution of man from the earliest populations of *Homo erectus* to existing races took place during the period in which man was a hunter. The common factors that dominated human evolution and produced *Homo sapiens* were preagricultural. Agricultural ways of life have dominated less than 1 percent of human history, and there is no evidence of major biological changes during that period of time. The kind of minor biological changes that occurred and which are used to characterize modern races were not common to *Homo sapiens*. The origin of all common characteristics must be sought in preagricultural times. Probably all experts would agree that hunting was a part of the social adaptation of all populations of the genus *Homo*, and many would regard *Australopithecus*[2] as a still earlier hominid who was already a hunter, although possibly much less efficient than the later forms. If this is true, and if the Pleistocene period had a duration of three million years, then pre-*Homo erectus* human tool using and hunting lasted for at least four times as long as the duration of the genus *Homo* (J. Lancaster, in press). No matter how the earlier times may ultimately be interpreted, the observation of more hunting among apes than was previously suspected (Goodall 1965) and increasing evidence for hunting *Australopithecus* strengthens the position that less than 1 percent of human history has been dominated by agriculture. It is for this reason that the consideration of hunting is so important for the understanding of human evolution.

When hunting and the way of life of successive populations of the genus *Homo* are considered, it is important to remember that there must have been both technical and biological progress during this vast period of time. Although the locomotor system appears to have changed very little in the last 500,000 years, the brain did increase in size, and the form of the face changed. But for present purposes it is particularly necessary to direct attention to the cultural changes that occurred in the last ten or fifteen thousand years before agriculture. There is no convenient term for this period of time, traditionally spoken of as the end of the Upper Paleolithic

[1] The term *Homo* includes Java, Pekin, Maur, and later forms.
[2] Using the term to include both the small *A. africanus* and *A. robustus* large forms, Simpson (1966) briefly and clearly discusses the taxonomy of these forms and of the fragments called Homo.

and the Mesolithic, but Binford and Binford (1966) have rightly emphasized its importance.

During most of human history water must have been a major physical and psychological barrier and the inability to cope with water is shown in the archeological record by the absence of remains of fish, shellfish, or any object that required going deeply into water or the use of boats. There is no evidence that the resources of river and sea were utilized until this late preagricultural period, and, since the consumption of shellfish in particular leaves huge middens, the negative evidence is impressive. It is likely that the basic problem in utilization of resources from sea or river was that man cannot swim naturally but to do so must learn a difficult skill. In monkeys the normal quadrupedal running motions serve to keep them afloat and moving quite rapidly. A macaque, for example, does not have to learn any new motor habit in order to swim. But the locomotor patterns of gibbons and apes will not keep them above the water surface, and even a narrow, shallow stream is a barrier for the gorilla (Schaller 1963). For early man water was a barrier and a danger, not a resource. (Obviously water was important for drinking, for richer vegetation along rivers and lakeshores, and for concentrating animal life. Here we are referring to water as a barrier prior to swimming and boats, and we stress that, judging from the behavior of contemporary apes, even a small stream may be a major barrier.)

In addition to the conquest of water, there seems to have been great technical progress in this late preagricultural period. In addition to a much wider variety of stone tools of earlier kinds, the archeological record shows bows and arrows, grinding stones, boats, houses of much more advanced types and even villages, sledges drawn by animals and used for transport, and the domestic dog. These facts have two special kinds of significance for this symposium. First, the technology of *all* the living hunters belongs to this late Mesolithic era at the earliest, and many have elements borrowed from agricultural and metal-using peoples. Second, the occasional high densities of hunters mentioned as problems and exceptions at the symposium are based on this very late and modified extension of the hunting and gathering way of life. For example, the way of life of the tribes of the Northwest Coast, with polished stone axes for woodworking, boats, and extensive reliance on products of the river and sea, should be seen as a very late adaptation. Goldschmidt's (1959:185–193) distinction between nomadic and sedentary hunting and gathering societies makes this point in a slightly different way. He shows the social elaboration that comes with the settled groups with larger populations.

The presence of the dog (Zeuner 1963) is a good index of the late preagricultural period, and domestic dogs were used by hunters in Africa, Australia, and the Americas. Among the Eskimo, dogs were used in hunting, for transportation, as food in time of famine, and as watch dogs. With dogs, sleds, boats, metal, and complex technology, Eskimos may be a better example of the extremes to which human adaptation can go than an example of primitive hunting ways. . . . Dogs . . . were of great importance in hunting — for locating, tracking, bringing to bay, and even killing. Lee (1965:131) reports that one Bushman with a trained pack of hunting dogs brought in 75 percent of the meat of a camp. Six other resident hunters lacked hunting packs and accounted for only 25 percent of the meat. Dogs may be important in hunting even very large animals; in the Amboseli Game Reserve in Kenya one of us saw two small dogs bring a rhinoceros to bay and dodge repeated charges.

With the acquisition of dogs, bows, and boats it is certain that hunting became much more complex in the last few thousand years before agriculture. The antiquity of traps, snares, and poisons is unknown, but it appears that for thousands of years man was able to kill large game close in with spear or axe. As Brues (1959) has shown, this limits the size of the hunters, and there are no very large or very small fossil men. Pygmoid hunters of large game are probably possible only if hunting is with bows, traps, and poison. It is remarkable that nearly all the estimated statures for fossil men fall between 5 feet 2 inches and 5 feet 10 inches. This suggests that strong selection pressures kept human stature within narrow limits for hundreds of thousands of years and that these pressures relaxed a few thousand years ago, allowing the evolution of a much wider range of statures.

The gathering and the preparing of food also seem to have become more complex during the last few thousand years before agriculture. Obviously, gathering by nonhuman primates is limited to things that can be eaten immediately. In contrast, man gathers a wide range of items that he cannot digest without soaking, boiling, grinding, or other special preparation. Seeds may have been a particularly important addition to the human diet because they are abundant and can be stored easily. Since grinding stones appear before agriculture, grinding and boiling may have been the necessary preconditions to the discovery of agriculture. One can easily imagine that people who were grinding seeds would see repeated examples of seeds sprouting or being planted by accident. Grinding and boiling were certainly known to the preagricultural peoples, and this knowledge could spread along an arctic route, setting the stage for a nearly simultaneous discovery of agriculture in both the New World and the Old World. It was not necessary for agriculture itself to spread through the arctic but only the seed-using technology, which could then lead to the discovery of seed planting. If this analysis is at all correct, then the hunting-gathering adaptation of the Indians of California, for example, should be seen as representing the possibilities of this late preagricultural gathering, making possible much higher population densities than would have been the case in pregrinding and preboiling economy.

Whatever the fate of these speculations, we think that the main conclusion, based on the archeological record, ecological considerations, and the ethnology of the surviving hunter-gatherers, will be sustained. In the last few thousand years before agriculture, both hunting and gathering became much more complex. This final adaptation, including the use of products of river and sea and the grinding and cooking of otherwise inedible seeds and nuts, was worldwide, laid the basis for the discovery of agriculture, and was much more effective and diversified than the previously existing hunting and gathering adaptations.

Hunting by members of the genus *Homo* throughout the 600,000 years that the genus has persisted has included the killing of large numbers of big animals. This implies the efficient use of tools, as Birdsell has stressed at the symposium "Man the Hunter" (sponsored by the Wenner-Gren Foundation for Anthropological Research, 1966). The adaptive value of hunting large animals has been shown by Bourlière (1963), who demonstrated that 75 percent of the meat available to human hunters in the eastern Congo was in elephant, buffalo, and hippopotamus. It is some measure of the success of human hunting that when these large species are protected in game reserves (as in the Murchison Falls or Queen Elizabeth Parks in Uganda) they multiply rapidly and destroy the vegetation. Elephants alone can destroy trees more rapidly than they are replaced naturally, as they do in the Masai Amboseli Reserve in Kenya. Since the predators are also protected in reserves, it appears that human hunters have been killing enough large game to maintain the balance of nature for many thousands of years. It is tempting to think that man replaced the saber-toothed cat as the major predator of large game, both controlling the numbers of the game and causing the extinction of Old World saber-tooths. We think that hunting and butchering large animals put a maximum premium on cooperation among males, a behavior that is at an absolute minimum among the nonhuman primates. It is difficult to imagine the killing of creatures such as cave bears, mastodons, mammoths — or *Dinotherium* at a much earlier time — without highly coordinated, cooperative action among males. It may be that the origin of male-male associations lies in the necessities of cooperation in hunting, butchering, and war. Certainly butchering sites, such as those described by Clark Howell in Spain, imply that the organization of the community for hunting large animals goes back for many, many thousands of years. From the biological point of view, the development of such organizations would have been paralleled by selection for an ability to plan and cooperate (or reduction of rage). Because females and juveniles may be involved in hunting small creatures, the social organization of big-game hunting would also lead to an intensification of a sexual division of labor.

It is important to stress, as noted before, that human hunting is a set of ways of life. It involves divisions of labor between male and female, sharing according to custom, cooperation among males, planning, knowledge of many species and large areas, and technical skill. Goldschmidt (1966:87 and following) has stressed the uniqueness and importance of human sharing, both in the family and in the wider society, and Lee (personal communication) emphasizes orderly sharing as fundamental to human hunting society. The importance of seeing human hunting as a whole social pattern is well illustrated by the old idea, recently revived, that the way of life of our ancestors was similar to that of wolves, rather than that of apes or monkeys. But this completely misses the special nature of the human adaptation. Human females do not go out and hunt and then regurgitate to their young when they return. Human young do not stay in dens but are carried by mothers. Male wolves do not kill with tools, butcher, and share with females who have been gathering. In an evolutionary sense the whole human pattern is new, and it is the success of this particularly human way that dominated human evolution and determined the relation of biology and culture for thousands of years. Judging from the archeological record, it is probable that the major features of this human way, possibly even including the beginnings of language, had evolved by the time of *Homo erectus*.[3]

THE WORLD VIEW OF THE HUNTER

Lévi-Strauss urged that we study the world view of hunters, and, perhaps surprisingly, some of the major aspects of world view can be traced from the archeological record. We have already mentioned that boats and the entire complex of fishing, hunting sea mammals, and using shellfish

---

[3] In speculations of this kind, it is well to keep the purpose of the speculation and the limitation of the evidence in mind. Our aim is to understand human evolution. What shaped the course of human evolution was a succession of successful adaptations, both biological and cultural. These may be inferred in part from the direct evidence of the archeological record. But the record is very incomplete. For example, Lee (personal communication) has described, for the Bushmen, how large game may be butchered where it falls and only meat brought back to camp. This kind of behavior means that analysis of bones around living sites is likely to underestimate both the amount and variety of game killed. If there is any evidence that large animals were killed, it is probable that far more were killed than the record shows. Just as the number of human bones gives no indication of the number of human beings, the number of animal bones, although it provides clues to the existence of hunting, gives no direct evidence of how many animals were killed. The Pleistocene way of life can only be known by inference and speculation. Obviously, speculations are based on much surer ground when the last few thousand years are under consideration. Ethnographic information is then directly relevant and the culture bearers are of our own species. As we go farther back in time, there is less evidence, and the biological and cultural difference becomes progressively greater. Yet it was in those remote times that the human way took shape, and it is only through speculation that we may gain some insights into what the life of our ancestors may have been.

was late. With this new orientation wide rivers and seas changed from barriers to pathways and sources of food, and the human attitude toward water must have changed completely. But many hundreds of thousands of years earlier, perhaps with *Australopithecus,* the relation of the hunters to the land must also have changed from an earlier relationship which may be inferred from studies of contemporary monkeys and apes. Social groups of nonhuman primates occupy exceedingly small areas, and the vast majority of animals probably spend their entire lives within less than four or five square miles. Even though they have excellent vision and can see for many miles, especially from tops of trees, they make no effort to explore more than a tiny fraction of the area they see. Even for gorillas the range is only about fifteen square miles (Schaller 1963), and it is of the same order of magnitude for Savanna baboons (DeVore and Hall 1965). When Hall tried to drive a troop of baboons beyond the end of their range, they refused to be driven and doubled back into familiar territory, although they were easy to drive within the range. The known area is a psychological reality, clear in the minds of the animals. Only a small part of even this limited range is used, and exploration is confined to the canopy, lower branches, and bushes, or ground, depending on the biology of the particular species. Napier (1962) has discussed this highly differential use of a single area by several species. In marked contrast, human hunters are familiar with very large areas. In the area studied by Lee (1965) eleven waterholes and 600 square miles supported 248 Bushmen, less than the number of baboons supported by a single waterhole and a few square miles in the Amboseli Reserve in Kenya. The most minor hunting expedition covers an area larger than most nonhuman primates would cover in a lifetime. Interest in a large area is human. The small ranges of monkeys and apes restrict the opportunities for gathering, hunting, and meeting conspecifics, and limit the kind of predation and the number of diseases. In the wide area, hunters and gatherers can take advantage of seasonal foods and only man among the primates can migrate long distances seasonally. In the small area, the population must be carried throughout the year on local resources, and natural selection has been for biology and behavior that efficiently utilize these limited opportunities. But in the wide area selection is for the knowledge that enables the group to utilize seasonal and occasional food sources. Gathering over a wide and diversified area implies a greater knowledge of flora and fauna, knowledge of the annual cycle, and a different attitude toward group movements. Clearly one of the great advantages of slow maturation is that learning covers a series of years, and the meaning of events in these years becomes a part of the individual's knowledge. With rapid maturation and no language the chances that any member of the group will know the appropriate behavior for rare events is greatly reduced.

Moving over long distances creates problems of carrying food and water. Lee (1965:124) has pointed out that the sharing of food even in one locality implies that food is carried, and there is no use in gathering quantities of fruit or nuts unless they can be moved. If women are to gather while men hunt, the results of the labors of both sexes must be carried back to some agreed-upon location. Meat can be carried away easily, but the development of some sort of receptacles for carrying vegetable products may have been one of the most fundamental advances in human evolution. Without a way of carrying, the advantages of a large area are greatly reduced, and sharing implies that a person carries much more than one can use. However that may be, the whole human pattern of gathering and hunting to share is unique to man. In its small range a monkey gathers only what it itself needs to eat at that moment, and the whole complex of economic reciprocity that dominates so much of human life is unique to man. Wherever archeological evidence can suggest the beginnings of movement over large ranges, cooperation, and sharing, it is dating the origin of some of the most fundamental aspects of human behavior, of the human world view. We believe that hunting large animals may demand all these aspects of human behavior which separate man so sharply from the other primates. If this is so, then the human way appears to be as old as *Homo erectus*.

The price that man pays for his high mobility is well illustrated by the problems of living in the African savanna. Man is not adapted to this environment in the same sense that baboon or vervet monkeys are. Man needs much more water, and without preparation and cooking he can only eat a limited number of the foods on which the local primates thrive. Unless there have been major physiological changes, the diet of our ancestors must have been far more like that of chimpanzees than like that of a savanna-adapted species. Further, man cannot survive the diseases of the African savanna without lying down and being cared for. Even when sick, the locally adapted animals are usually able to keep moving with their troop; and the importance to their survival of a home base has been stressed elsewhere (DeVore and Washburn 1963). Also, man becomes liable to new diseases and parasites by eating meat, and it is of interest that the products of the sea, which we believe were the last class of foods added to human diet, are widely regarded as indigestible and carry diseases to which man is particularly susceptible. Although many humans die of disease and injury, those who do not, almost without exception, owe their lives to others who cared for them when they were unable to hunt or gather, and this uniquely human caring is one of the patterns that builds social bonds in the group and permits the species to occupy almost every environment in the world.

A large territory provides not only a much wider range of possible foods but also a greater variety of potentially useful materials. With tool use this variety takes on meaning, and even the earliest pebble tools show selection in size, form, and material. When wood ceases to be just something to climb on, hardness, texture, and form become important. Availability of materials is critical to the tool user, and early men must have had a very different interest in their environment from that of monkeys or apes. Thus, the presence of tools in the archeological record is not only an indication of technical progress but also an index of interest in inanimate objects and in a much larger part of the environment than is the case with nonhuman primates.

The tools of the hunters include the earliest beautiful man-made objects, the symmetrical bifaces, especially those of the Acheulian tradition. Just how they were used is still a matter of debate, but, as contemporary attempts to copy them show, their manufacture is technically difficult, taking lots of time and practice and a high degree of skill. The symmetry of these tools may indicate that they were swung with great speed and force, presumably attached to some sort of handle. A tool that is moved slowly does not have to be symmetrical, but balance becomes important when an object is swung rapidly or thrown with speed. Irregularities will lead to deviations in the course of the blow or the trajectory of flight. An axe or spear to be used with speed and power is subject to very different technical limitations from those of scrapers or digging sticks, and it may well be that it was the attempt to produce efficient high-speed weapons that first produced beautiful, symmetrical objects.

When the selective advantage of a finely worked point over an irregular one is considered, it must be remembered that a small difference might give a very large advantage. A population in which hunters hit the games 5 percent more frequently, more accurately, or at greater distance would bring back much more meat. There must have been strong selection for greater skill in manufacture and use, and it is no accident that the bones of small-brained men (*Australopithecus*) are never found with beautiful, symmetrical tools. If the brains of contemporary apes and men are compared, the areas associated with hand skills (both in cerebellum and cortex) are at least three times as large in man. Clearly, the success of tools has exerted a great influence on the evolution of the brain and has created the skills that make art possible. The evolution of the capacity to appreciate the product must evolve along with the skills of manufacture and use, and the biological capacities that the individual inherits must be developed in play and practiced in games. In this way the beautiful, symmetrical tool becomes a symbol of a level of human intellectual achievement, representing far more than just the tool itself.

In a small group like the hunting band, which is devoted to one or two major cooperative activities, the necessity for long practice in developing skills to a very high level restricts the number of useful arts and social organization is relatively simple. Where there is little division of labor all men learn the same activities, such as skill in the hunt or in war. In sports we take it for granted that one person will not achieve a very high level of performance in more than a limited set of skills. This limitation is in part biological, but it is important socially as well because great proficiency in a skill necessitates practice. In warfare a wide variety of weapons is useful only if there are enough men so that there can be division of labor and different groups can practice different skills. Handedness, a feature that separates man from ape, is a part of this biology of skill. To be ambidextrous might seem ideal, but in fact the highest level of skill is attained by concentrating both biological ability and practice primarily on one hand.

Hunting changed man's relationship to other animals and his view of what is natural. The human notion that it is normal for animals to flee and the whole concept of animals being wild, is the result of man's habit of hunting. In game reserves many different kinds of animals soon learn not to fear man, and they no longer flee. Woodburn took a Hadza into the Nairobi Park, and the Hadza was amazed and excited, because although he had hunted all his life, he had never seen such a quantity and variety of animals close at hand. His whole previous view of animals was the result of his having been their enemy, and they had reacted to him as the most destructive carnivore. In the park, the Hadza hunter saw for the first time the peace of the herbivorous world. Prior to hunting, the relationship of our ancestors to other animals must have been very much like that of the other noncarnivores. They could have moved close among the other species, fed beside them, and shared the same waterholes. But with the origin of human hunting the peaceful relationship was destroyed, and for at least half a million years man has been the enemy of even the largest mammals. In this way the whole human view of what is normal and natural in the relation of man to animals is a product of hunting, and the world of flight and fear is the result of the efficiency of the hunters.

Behind this human view that the flight of animals from man is natural lie some aspects of human psychology. Men enjoy hunting and killing, and these activities are continued as sports even when they are no longer economically necessary. If a behavior is important to the survival of a species (as hunting was for man throughout most of human history), then it must be both easily learned and pleasurable (Hamburg 1963). Part of the motivation for hunting is the immediate pleasure it gives the hunter, and the human killer can no more afford to be sorry for the game than a cat for its intended victim. Evolution builds a relation between biology, psychology, and behavior, and, therefore, the evolutionary success of hunting exerted a profound effect on human psychology. Perhaps, this is most easily shown by the extent of the efforts devoted to maintain killing as a sport. In former times royalty and nobility maintained parks where they could enjoy the sport of killing, and today the United States government spends many millions of dollars to supply game for hunters. Many people dislike the notion that man is naturally aggressive, that he naturally enjoys the destruction of other creatures. Yet we all know people who use the lightest fishing tackle to prolong the fish's futile struggle, to maximize the personal sense of mastery and skill. And until recently war was viewed in much the same way as hunting. Other human beings were simply the most dangerous game, and war has been far too important in human history for it to be other than pleasurable for the males involved. It is only recently, with the entire change in the nature and conditions of war, that this institution has been challenged, that the wisdom of war as a normal part of national policy or as an approved road to personal social glory has been questioned.

Human killing differs from killing by carnivorous mammals in that the victims are frequently of the same species as the killer. In carnivores there are submission gestures or sounds that normally stop a fatal attack (Lorenz 1966). But in man there are no effective submission gestures. It was the Roman emperor who might raise his thumb; the victim could make no sound or gesture that might restrain the victor or move the crowd to pity. The lack of biological controls over killing conspecifics is a character of human killing that separates this behavior sharply from that of other carnivorous mammals. This difference may be interpreted in a variety of ways. It may be that human hunting is so recent from an evolutionary point of view that there was not enough time for controls to evolve. Or it may be that killing other humans was a part of the adaptation from the beginning, and our sharp separation of war from hunting is due to the recent development of these institutions. Or it may be simply that in most human behavior stimulus and response are not tightly bound. Whatever the origin of this behavior, it has had profound effects on human evolution, and almost every human society has regarded killing members of certain other human societies as desirable (Freeman 1964). Certainly this has been a major factor in man's view of the world, and every folklore contains tales of culture heroes whose fame is based on the human enemies they destroyed.

The extent to which the biological bases for killing have been incorporated into human psychology may be measured by the ease with which boys can be interested in hunting, fishing, fighting, and games of war. It is not that these behaviors are inevitable, but they are easily learned, satisfying, and have been socially rewarded in most cultures. The skills for killing and the pleasures of killing are normally developed in play, and the patterns of play prepare the children for their adult roles. At the conference Woodburn's excellent motion pictures showed Hadza boys killing small mammals, and Laughlin described how Aleuts train boys from early childhood so that they would be able to throw harpoons with accuracy and power while seated in kayaks. The whole youth of the hunter is dominated by practice and appreciation of the skills of the adult males, and the pleasure of the games motivates the practice that is necessary to develop the skills of weaponry. Even in monkeys rougher play and play fighting are largely the activities of the males, and the young females explore less and show a greater interest in infants at an early age. These basic biological differences are reinforced in man by a division of labor which makes adult sex roles differ far more in humans than they do in nonhuman primates. Again, hunting must be seen as a whole pattern of activities, a wide variety of ways of life, the psychobiological roots of which are reinforced by play and by a clear identification with adult roles. Hunting is more than a part of the economic system, and the animal bones in Choukoutien are evidence of the patterns of play and pleasure of our ancestors.

THE SOCIAL ORGANIZATION OF HUMAN HUNTING

The success of the human hunting and gathering way of life lay in its adaptability. It permitted a single species to occupy most of the earth with a minimum of biological adaptation to local conditions. The occupation of Australia and the New World was probably late, but even so there is no evidence that any other primate species occupied more than a fraction of the area of *Homo erectus*. Obviously this adaptability makes any detailed reconstruction impossible, and we are not looking for stages in the traditional evolutionary sense. However, using both the knowledge of the contemporary primates and the archeological record, certain important general conditions of our evolution may be reconstructed. For example, the extent of the distribution of the species noted above is remarkable and gives the strongest sort of indirect evidence for the adaptability of the way of life, even half a million years ago. Likewise, all evidence suggests that the local group was small. Twenty to fifty individuals is suggested by Goldschmidt (1959:187). Such a group size is common in nonhuman primates, and so we can say with some assurance that the number did not increase greatly until after agriculture. This means that the number of adult males who might cooperate in hunting or war was very limited, and this sets limits to the kinds of social organizations that were possible. Probably one of the great adaptive advantages of language was that it permits the planning of cooperation between local groups, temporary division of groups, and the transmission of information over a much wider area than that occupied by any one group.

Within the group of the nonhuman primates the mother and her young may form a subgroup that continues even after the young are fully grown (Yamada 1963; Sade 1965 and 1966). This grouping affects dominance, grooming and resting patterns, and, along with dominance, is one of the factors giving order to the social relations in the group. The group is not a horde in the 19th century sense, but it is ordered by positive affectionate habits and by the strength of personal dominance. Both these principles continue into human society, and dominance based on personal achievement must have been particularly powerful in small groups living dangerous physical lives. The mother-young group certainly continued and the bonds must have been intensified by the prolongation of infancy. But in human society economic reciprocity is added, and this created a wholly new set of interpersonal bonds.

When males hunt and females gather the results are shared and given to the young, and the habitual sharing between a male, a female, and their offspring becomes the basis for the human family. According to this view the human family is the result of the reciprocity of hunting, the addition of a male to the mother-plus-young social group of the monkeys and apes.

A clue to the adaptive advantage and evolutionary origin of our psychological tabu on incest is provided by this view of the family. Incest prohibitions are reported universally among humans and these always operate to limit sexual activity involving subadults within the nuclear family. Taking the nuclear family as the unit of account, incest prohibitions tend to keep the birth rate in line with economic productivity. If in creating what we call the family the addition of a male is important in economic terms, then the male who is added must be able to fulfill the role of a socially responsible provider. In the case of the hunter this necessitates a degree of skill in hunting and a social maturity that is attained some years after puberty. As a young man grows up this necessary delay in his assumption of the role of provider for a female and her young is paralleled by a tabu which prevents him from prematurely adding unsupported members to the family. Brother-sister mating could result in an infant while the brother was still years away from effective social maturity. Father-daughter incest could also produce a baby without adding a productive male to the family. This would be quite different from the taking of a second wife which, if permitted, occurs only when the male has shown he is already able to provide for and maintain more than one female.

To see how radically hunting changed the economic situation it is necessary to remember that in monkeys and apes an individual simply eats what it needs. After an infant is weaned, it is on its own economically and is not dependent on adults. This means that adult males never have economic responsibility for any other animal, and adult females do only when they are nursing. In such a system there is no economic gain in delaying any kind of social relationship. But when hunting makes females and young dependent on the success of male skills, there is a great gain to the family members in establishing behaviors which prevent the addition of infants, unless these can be supported.

These considerations in no way alter the importance of the incest tabu as a deterrent to role conflict in the family and as the necessary precondition to all other rules of exogamy. A set of behaviors is more likely to persist and be widespread if it serves many uses, and the rule of parsimony is completely wrong when applied to the explanation of social situations. However, these considerations do alter the emphasis and the conditions of the discussion of incest. In the first place a mother-son sexual avoidance may be present in some species of monkeys (Sade 1966), and this extremely strong tabu among humans requires a different explanation from the one we have offered for brother-sister and father-daughter incest prohibitions. In this case the role conflict argument may be paramount. Second, the central consideration is that incest produces pregnancies, and the most fundamental adaptive value of the tabu is the provision of situations in which infants are more likely to survive. In the reviews of the incest tabu by Aberle and associates (1963) and Mair (1965) the biological advantages of the tabu in controlling the production of infants are not adequately considered, and we find the treatment by Service (1962) closest to our own. Slater (1959) misunderstood the demographic factors, and incest is most likely in small groups in which the majority of males die young but a few live on into middle age.

That family organization may be attributed to the hunting way of life is supported by ethnography. Since the same economic and social problems as those under hunting continue under agriculture, the institution continued. The data on the behavior of contemporary monkeys and apes also show why this institution was not necessary in a society in which each individual gets its own food.[4] Obviously, the origin of the custom cannot be dated, and we cannot prove *Homo erectus* had a family organized in the human way. But it can be shown that the conditions that make the family adaptive existed at the time of *Homo erectus*. The evidence of hunting is clear in the archeological record. A further suggestion that the human kind of family is old comes from physiology; the loss of estrus is essential to the human family organization, and it is unlikely that this physiology, which is universal in contemporary mankind, evolved recently.

If the local group is looked upon as a source of male-female pairs (an experienced hunter-provider and a female who gathers and who cares for the

[4] The advantage of considering both the social group and the facilitating biology is shown by considering the "family" in the gibbon. The social group consists of an adult male, an adult female, and their young. But this group is maintained by extreme territorial behavior in which no adult male tolerates another, by aggressive females with large canine teeth, and by very low sex drive in the males. The male-female group is the whole society. (Carpenter 1940, reprinted in 1964; Ellefson, 1967.) The gibbon group is based on a different biology from that of the human family and has none of its reciprocal economic functions. Although the kind of social life seen in chimpanzees lacks a family organization, to change it into that of a man would require far less evolution than would be required in the case of the gibbon.

young), then it is apparent that a small group cannot produce pairs regularly, since chance determines whether a particular child is a male or female. If the number maturing in a given year or two is small, then there may be too many males or females (either males with no mates or females with no providers). (The problem of excess females may not seem serious today or in agricultural societies, but among hunters it was recognized and was regarded as so severe that female infanticide was often practiced.) How grave the problem of imbalance can become is shown by the following hypothetical example. In a society of approximately 40 individuals there might be 9 couples. With infants born at the rate of about one in 3 years, this would give 3 infants per year, but only approximately one of these 3 would survive to become fully adult. The net production in the example would be one child per year in a population of 40. And because the sex of the child is randomly determined, the odds that all the children would be male for a three year period are 1 in 8. Likewise the odds for all surviving children being female for a three year period are 1 in 8. In this example the chances of all surviving children being of one sex are 1 in 4, and smaller departures from a 50/50 sex ratio would be very common.

In monkeys, because the economic unit is the individual (not a pair), a surplus of females causes no problem. Surplus males may increase fighting in the group or males may migrate to other groups.

For humans the problem of imbalance in sex ratios may be met by exogamy, which permits mates to be obtained from a much wider social field. The orderly pairing of hunter males with females requires a much larger group than can be supported locally by hunting and gathering, and this problem is solved by reciprocal relations among several local groups. It takes something on the order of 100 pairs to produce enough children so that the sex ratio is near enough to fifty-fifty for social life to proceed smoothly, and this requires a population of approximately 500 people. With smaller numbers there will be constant random fluctuations in the sex ratio large enough to cause social problems. This argument shows the importance of a sizable linguistic community, one large enough to cover an area in which many people may find suitable mates and make alliances of many kinds. It does not mean either that the large community or that exogamy does not have many other functions, as outlined by Mair (1965). As indicated earlier, the more factors that favor a custom, the more likely it is to be geographically widespread and long lasting. What the argument does stress is that the finding of mates and the production of babies under the particular conditions of human hunting and gathering favor both incest tabus and exogamy for basic demographic reasons.

Assumptions behind the argument are that social customs are adaptive, as Tax (1937) has argued, and that nothing is more crucial for evolutionary success than the orderly production of the number of infants that can be supported. This argument also presumes that, at least under extreme conditions, these necessities and reasons are obvious to the people involved, as infanticide attests. The impossibility of finding suitable mates must have been a common experience for hunters trying to exist in very small groups, and the initial advantages of exogamy, kinship, and alliance with other such groups may at first have amounted to no more than, as Whiting said at the conference, a mother suggesting to her son that he might find a suitable mate in the group where her brother was located.

If customs are adaptive and if humans are necessarily opportunistic, it might be expected that social rules would be particularly labile under the conditions of small hunting and gathering societies. At the conference Murdock pointed out the high frequency of bilateral kinship systems among hunters, and the experts on Australia all seemed to believe that the Australian systems had been described in much too static terms. Under hunting conditions systems that allow for exceptions and local adaptation make sense and surely political dominance and status must have been largely achieved.

CONCLUSION

While stressing the success of the hunting and gathering way of life with its great diversity of local forms and while emphasizing the way it influenced human evolution, we must also take into account its limitations. There is no indication that this way of life could support large communities of more than a few million people in the whole world. To call the hunters "affluent" is to give a very special definition to the word. During much of the year many monkeys can obtain enough food in only three or four hours of gathering each day, and under normal conditions baboons have plenty of time to build the Taj Mahal. The restriction on population, however, is the lean season or the atypical year, and, as Sahlins recognized, building by the hunters and the accumulation of gains was limited by motivation and technical knowledge, not by time. Where monkeys are fed, population rises, and Koford (1966) estimates the rate of increase on an island at 16 percent per year.

After agriculture human populations increased dramatically in spite of disease, war, and slowly changing customs. Even with fully human (*Homo sapiens*) biology, language, technical sophistication, cooperation, art, the support of kinship, the control of custom and political power, and the solace of religion — in spite of this whole web of culture and biology — the local group in the Mesolithic was no larger than that of baboons. Regardless of statements made . . . on the case with which hunters obtain food some of the time, it is still true that food was the primary factor in limiting early human populations, as is shown by the events subsequent to agriculture.

The agricultural revolution, continuing into the industrial and scientific revolutions, is now freeing man from the conditions and restraints of 99 percent of his history, but the biology of our species was created in that long gathering and hunting period. To assert the biological unity of mankind is to affirm the importance of the hunting way of life. It is to claim that, however much conditions and customs may have varied locally, the main selection pressures that forged the species were the same. The biology, psychology, and customs that separate us from the apes — all these we owe to the hunters of time past. And, although the record is incomplete and speculation looms larger than fact, for those who would understand the origin and nature of human behavior there is no choice but to try to understand "Man the Hunter."

REFERENCES

Aberle, D. F., *et al.*
  1963 "The Incest Taboo and the Mating Patterns of Animals," *American Anthropologist* 65:253–264.
Binford, L. R. and S. R. Binford
  1966 "The Predatory Revolution: A Consideration of the Evidence for a New Subsistence Level," *American Anthropologist* 68:508–512.
Bourlière, F.
  1963 "Observations on the Ecology of Some Large African Mammals," in *African Ecology and Human Evolution* (F. C. Howell and F. Bourlière, eds.). Viking Fund Publications in Anthropology, Number 36, pp. 43–53.
Brues, A.
  1959 "The Spearman and the Archer," *American Anthropologist* 61:457–469.
Carpenter, C. R.
  1940 "A Field Study in Siam of the Behavior and Social Relations of the Gibbon," *Hylobates lar. Comparative Psychology Monographs* 16:1–212.
  1964 *Naturalistic Behavior of Nonhuman Primates.* University Park: Pennsylvania State University Press.
DeVore, I. and K. R. L. Hall
  1965 "Baboon Ecology," in *Primate Behavior: Field Studies of Monkeys and Apes* (I. DeVore, ed.). New York: Holt, Rinehart and Winston, Inc., pp. 20–52.
DeVore, I. and S. L. Washburn
  1963 "Baboon Ecology and Human Evolution," in *African Ecology and Human Evolution* (F. C. Howell and F. Bourlière, eds.). Viking Fund Publications in Anthropology, Number 36, pp. 335–367.

Ellefson, J. O.
  1967   "A Natural History of Gibbons in the Malay Peninsula
          (*Hylobates lar*)." Unpublished Doctoral Dissertation.
          Berkeley: University of California.
Freeman, D.
  1964   "Human Aggression in Anthropological Perspective,"
          in *The Natural History of Aggression* (J. D. Carthy
          and F. J. Ebling, eds.). New York: Academic Press,
          Inc., pp. 109–119.
Goldschmidt, W.
  1959   *Man's Way*. New York: Holt, Rinehart and Winston.
  1966   *Comparative Functionalism*. Berkeley: University of
          California Press.
Goodall, J.
  1965   "Chimpanzees of the Gombe Stream Reserve," in
          Primate Behavior: Field Studies of Monkeys and Apes
          (I. DeVore, ed.). New York: Holt, Rinehart and
          Winston, Inc., pp. 425–473.
Hamburg, D. A.
  1963   "Emotions in the Perspective of Human Evolution," in
          Expression of the Emotions in Man (P. H. Knapp,
          ed.). New York: International Universities Press, Inc.,
          pp. 300–317.
Koford, C. B.
  1966   "Population Changes in Rhesus Monkeys: Cayo San-
          tiago, 1960–1964," *Tulane Studies in Zoology* 13:1–7.
Lancaster, J. B.
          "The Evolution of Tool-Using Behavior: Primate
          Field Studies, Fossil Apes and the Archeological Rec-
          ord." (Unpublished manuscript.)
Lee, R. B.
  1965   "Subsistence Ecology of Kung Bushmen." Doctoral
          Dissertation. Berkeley: University of California.
Lorenz, K.
  1966   *On Aggression*. New York: Harcourt, Brace and World,
          Inc.
Mair, L.
  1965   *An Introduction to Social Anthropology*. Oxford:
          Clarendon Press.
Napier, J. R.
  1962   "Monkeys and Their Habitats," *New Scientist* 15:88–
          92.
Sade, D. S.
  1965   "Some Aspects of Parent-Offspring and Sibling Re-
          lations in a Group of Rhesus Monkeys, with a Dis-
          cussion of Grooming," *American Journal of Physical
          Anthropology* 23:1–18.

1966 "Ontogeny of Social Relations in a Group of Free Ranging Rhesus Monkeys (*Macaca mulatta* Zimmerman)." Doctoral Dissertation. Berkeley: University of California.

Schaller, G.
1963 *The Mountain Gorilla: Ecology and Behavior*. Chicago: University of Chicago Press.

Service, E. R.
1962 *Primate Social Organization; An Evolutionary Perspective*. New York: Random House.

Simpson, G. G.
1966 "The Biological Nature of Man," *Science* 152:472–478.

Slater, M. K.
1959 "Ecological Factors in the Origin of Incest," *American Anthropologist* 61:1042–1059.

Tax, S.
1937 "Some Problems of Social Organization," in *Social Anthropology of North American Tribes* (F. Eggan, ed.). Chicago: University of Chicago Press, pp 3–34.

Yamada, M.
1963 "A Study of Blood-Relationship in the Natural Society of the Japanese Macaque," *Primates* 4:43–66.

Zeuner, F. E.
1963 *A History of Domesticated Animals*. New York: Harper and Row, Publishers.